D0461222

NOBEL PRIZE LIBRARY

SACHS

SARTRE

SHAW

SILLANPÄÄ

SULLY-PRUDHOMME

Nobel Prize Library

PUBLISHED UNDER THE SPONSORSHIP OF THE

NOBEL FOUNDATION & THE SWEDISH ACADEMY

Nelly Sachs

Jean-Paul Sartre

George Bernard Shaw

Frans Eemil Sillanpää

René Sully-Prudhomme

ALEXIS GREGORY, *New York*, AND
CRM PUBLISHING, *Del Mar, California*

CONTENTS

Nelly Sachs

1966

"For her outstanding lyrical and dramatic writings, which interpret Israel's destiny with touching strength"

Illustrated by JEAN-MICHEL PERCHE

PRESENTATION ADDRESS

By ANDERS ÖSTERLING

NELLY SACHS, like so many other German-Jewish writers, suffered the fate of exile. Through Swedish intervention she was saved from persecution and the threat of deportation and was brought to this country. She has since then worked in peace as a refugee on Swedish soil, attaining the maturity and authority that are now confirmed by the Nobel Prize. In recent years she has been acclaimed in the German world as a writer of convincing worth and irresistible sincerity. With moving intensity of feeling she has given voice to the worldwide tragedy of the Jewish people, which she has expressed in lyrical laments of painful beauty and in dramatic legends. Her symbolic language boldly combines an inspired modern idiom with echoes of ancient Biblical poetry. Identifying herself totally with the faith and ritual mysticism of her people, Miss Sachs has created a world of imagery which does not shun the terrible truth of the extermination camps and the corpse factories, but which at the same time rises above all hatred of the persecutors, merely revealing a genuine sorrow at man's debasement. Her purely lyrical production is now collected under the title *Fahrt ins Staublose* (Journey to the Beyond, 1961), which comprises six interconnected works written during a twenty-year creative period of increasing concentration. There is also a series of dramatic poems, equally remarkable in their way, under the joint title *Zeichen im Sand* (Signs in the Sand, 1961), the themes of which might have been taken from the dark treasure house of Hassidic mysticism but which here have taken on new vigor and vital meaning. Let it suffice here to mention the mystery play *Eli* (1950) about an eight-year-old boy who is beaten to death by a German soldier in Poland when he blows on his shepherd's pipe to call on Heaven's help when his parents are taken away. The visionary cobbler, Michael, manages to trace the culprit to the next village. The soldier has been seized by remorse and, at the encounter in the forest, he collapses without Michael's having to raise his hand against him. The ending denotes a divine justice which has nothing to do with earthly retribution.

Nelly Sachs's writing is today the most intense artistic expression of the reaction of the Jewish spirit to suffering, and thus it can indeed be said to fulfill the humane purpose underlying Alfred Nobel's will.

Doctor Agnon—According to the wording of the diploma, this year's Nobel Prize for Literature has been awarded to you for your "profoundly distinctive narrative art with motifs from the life of the Jewish people." We should be happy if you would consider this international distinction as a sign that your writing need not be isolated within the boundary of its language and that it has proved to have the power to reach out beyond all confining walls and to arouse mankind's sympathy, understanding, and respect. Through me the Swedish Academy conveys its sincere congratulations, and I now ask you to receive the Prize from the hands of His Majesty the King.

Miss Nelly Sachs—You have lived a long time in our country, first as an obscure stranger and then as an honored guest. Today the Swedish Academy honors your "outstanding lyrical and dramatic writings, which interpret Israel's destiny with touching strength." On an occasion like this it is natural also to recall the invaluable interest you have shown in Swedish literature, a token of friendship which in turn has found a response in the desire of our Swedish writers to translate your work. Offering you the congratulations of the Swedish Academy, I ask you now to receive this year's Nobel Prize for Literature from the hands of His Majesty the King.

ACCEPTANCE SPEECH

By NELLY SACHS

IN THE SUMMER of 1939 a German girl friend of mine went to Sweden to visit Selma Lagerlöf, to ask her to secure a sanctuary for my mother and myself in that country. Since my youth I had been so fortunate as to exchange letters with Selma Lagerlöf, and it is out of her work that my love for her country grew. The painter-prince Eugen and the novelist helped to save me.

In the spring of 1940, after tortuous months, we arrived in Stockholm. The occupation of Denmark and Norway had already taken place. The great novelist was no more. We breathed the air of freedom without knowing the language or any person. Today, after twenty-six years, I think of what my father used to say on every tenth of December, back in my home town, Berlin: "Now they celebrate the Nobel ceremony in Stockholm." Thanks to the choice of the Swedish Academy, I am now in the midst of that ceremony. To me a fairy tale seems to have become reality.

In der Flucht
welch grosser Empfang
unterwegs—

Eingehüllt
in der Winde Tuch
Füsse im Gebet des Sandes
der niemals Amen sagen kann
denn er muss
von der Flosse in den Flügel
und weiter—

Der kranke Schmetterling
weiss bald wieder vom Meer—
Dieser Stein
mit der Inschrift der Fliege
hat sich mir in die Hand gegeben—

An Stelle von Heimat
halte ich die Verwandlungen der Welt—

Fleeing,
what a great reception
on the way—

Wrapped
in the wind's shawl
feet in the prayer of sand
which can never say amen
compelled
from fin to wing
and further—

The sick butterfly
will soon learn again of the sea—
This stone
with the fly's inscription
gave itself into my hand—

I hold instead of a homeland
the metamorphoses of the world—

POEMS

By NELLY SACHS

Translated from the German by Michael Hamburger, Ruth and Matthew Mead, *and* Michael Roloff

---

O the chimneys

And though after my skin worms destroy this body, yet in my flesh shall I see God.—Job, 19:26

O the chimneys
On the ingeniously devised habitations of death
When Israel's body drifted as smoke
Through the air—
Was welcomed by a star, a chimney sweep,
A star that turned black
Or was it a ray of sun?

O the chimneys!
Freedomway for Jeremiah and Job's dust—
Who devised you and laid stone upon stone
The road for refugees of smoke?

O the habitations of death,
Invitingly appointed
For the host who used to be a guest—
O your fingers
Laying the threshold
Like a knife between life and death—

O your chimneys,
O your fingers
And Israel's body as smoke through the air!

MR*

To you that build the new house

"There are stones like souls"—RABBI NACHMAN

When you come to put up your walls anew—
Your stove, your bedstead, table and chair—
Do not hang your tears for those who departed,
Who will not live with you then,
On to the stone.
Nor on the timber—
Else weeping will pierce the sleep,
The brief sleep you have yet to take.

Do not sigh when you bed your sheets,
Else your dreams will mingle
With the sweat of the dead.

Oh, the walls and household utensils
Are responsive as Aeolian harps
Or like a field in which your sorrow grows,
And they sense your kinship with dust.

Build, when the hourglass trickles,
But do not weep away the minutes
Together with the dust
That obscures the light.

MH

---

* The initials after each poem identify the translators listed on page 7.

But who emptied your shoes of sand

But who emptied your shoes of sand
When you had to get up, to die?
The sand which Israel gathered,
Its nomad sand?
Burning Sinai sand,
Mingled with throats of nightingales,
Mingled with wings of butterflies,
Mingled with the hungry dust of serpents;
Mingled with all that fell from the wisdom of Solomon,
Mingled with what is bitter in the mystery of wormwood—

O you fingers
That emptied the deathly shoes of sand.
Tomorrow you will be dust
In the shoes of those to come.

MH

A dead child speaks

My mother held me by my hand.
Then someone raised the knife of parting:
So that it should not strike me,
My mother loosed her hand from mine.
But she lightly touched my thighs once more
And her hand was bleeding—

After that the knife of parting
Cut in two each bite I swallowed—
It rose before me with the sun at dawn

And began to sharpen itself in my eyes—
Wind and water ground in my ear
And every voice of comfort pierced my heart—

As I was led to death
I still felt in the last moment
The unsheathing of the great knife of parting.

RMM

Already embraced by the arm of heavenly solace

Already embraced by the arm of heavenly solace
The insane mother stands
With the tatters of her torn mind
With the charred tinders of her burnt mind
Burying her dead child,
Burying her lost light,
Twisting her hands into urns,
Filling them with the body of her child from the air,
Filling them with his eyes, his hair from the air,
And with his fluttering heart—

Then she kisses the air-born being
And dies!

MR

What secret cravings of the blood

What secret cravings of the blood,
Dreams of madness and earth
A thousand times murdered,
Brought into being the terrible puppeteer?

Him who with foaming mouth
Dreadfully swept away
The round, the circling stage of his deed
With the ash-gray, receding horizon of fear?

O the hills of dust, which as though drawn by an evil moon
The murderers enacted:

Arms up and down,
Legs up and down
And the setting sun of Sinai's people
A red carpet under their feet.

Arms up and down,
Legs up and down
And on the ash-gray receding horizon of fear
Gigantic the constellation of death
That loomed like the clock face of ages.

MH

Chorus of the Rescued

We, the rescued,
From whose hollow bones death had begun to whittle his flutes,
And on whose sinews he had already stroked his bow—
Our bodies continue to lament
With their mutilated music.
We, the rescued,
The nooses wound for our necks still dangle
before us in the blue air—
Hourglasses still fill with our dripping blood.
We, the rescued,
The worms of fear still feed on us.
Our constellation is buried in dust.

We, the rescued
Beg you:
Show us your sun, but gradually.
Lead us from star to star, step by step.
Be gentle when you teach us to live again.
Lest the song of a bird,
Or a pail being filled at the well,
Let our badly sealed pain burst forth again
and carry us away—
We beg you:
Do not show us an angry dog, not yet—
It could be, it could be
That we will dissolve into dust—
Dissolve into dust before your eyes.
For what binds our fabric together?
We whose breath vacated us,
Whose soul fled to Him out of that midnight
Long before our bodies were rescued
Into the ark of the moment.
We, the rescued,
We press your hand
We look into your eye—
But all that binds us together now is leave-taking,
The leave-taking in the dust
Binds us together with you.

MR

Chorus of the Stones

We stones
When someone lifts us
He lifts the Foretime—
When someone lifts us
He lifts the Garden of Eden—

When someone lifts us
He lifts the knowledge of Adam and Eve
And the serpent's dust-eating seduction.

When someone lifts us
He lifts in his hand millions of memories
Which do not dissolve in blood
Like evening.
For we are memorial stones
Embracing all dying.

We are a satchel full of lived life.
Whoever lifts us lifts the hardened graves of earth.
You heads of Jacob,
For you we hide the roots of dreams
And let the airy angels' ladders
Sprout like the tendrils of a bed of bindweed.

When someone touches us
He touches the wailing wall.
Like a diamond your lament cuts our hardness
Until it crumbles and becomes a soft heart—
While you turn to stone.
When someone touches us
He touches the forked ways of midnight
Sounding with birth and death.

When someone throws us—
He throws the Garden of Eden—
The wine of the stars—
The eyes of the lovers and all betrayal—

When someone throws us in anger
He throws aeons of broken hearts
And silken butterflies.

Beware, beware
Of throwing a stone in anger—

Breath once transfused our minglement,
Which grew solid in secret
But can awaken at a kiss.

RMM

Chorus of the Unborn

We the unborn
The yearning has begun to plague us
The shores of blood broaden to receive us
Like dew we sink into love
But still the shadows of time lie like questions
Over our secret.

You who love,
You who yearn,
Listen, you who are sick with parting:
We are those who begin to live in your glances,
In your hands which are searching the blue air—
We are those who smell of morning.
Already your breath is inhaling us,
Drawing us down into your sleep
Into the dreams which are our earth
Where night, our black nurse,
Lets us grow
Until we mirror ourselves in your eyes
Until we speak into your ear.

We are caught
Like butterflies by the sentries of your yearning—
Like birdsong sold to earth—
We who smell of morning,
We future lights for your sorrow.

RMM

The voice of the Holy Land

O my children,
Death has run through your hearts
As through a vineyard—
Painted *Israel* red on all the walls of the world.

What shall be the end of the little holiness
Which still dwells in my sand?
The voices of the dead
Speak through reed pipes of seclusion.

Lay the weapons of revenge in the field
That they grow gentle—
For even iron and grain are akin
In the womb of earth—

But what shall be the end of the little holiness
Which still dwells in my sand?

The child murdered in sleep
Arises; bends down the tree of ages
And pins the white breathing star
That was once called Israel
To its topmost bough.
Spring upright again, says the child,
To where tears mean eternity.

RMM

That the persecuted may not become persecutors

Footsteps—
In which of Echo's grottoes
are you preserved,

you who once prophesied aloud
the coming of death?

Footsteps—
Neither bird-flight, inspection of entrails,
nor Mars sweating blood
confirmed the oracle's message of death—
only footsteps—

Footsteps—
Age-old game of hangman and victim,
Persecutor and persecuted,
Hunter and hunted—

Footsteps
which turn time ravenous
emblazoning the hour with wolves
extinguishing the flight in the fugitive's
blood.

Footsteps
measuring time with screams, groans,
the seeping of blood until it congeals,
heaping up hours of sweaty death—

Steps of hangmen
over the steps of victims,
what black moon pulled with such terror
the sweep-hand in earth's orbit?

Where does your note shrill
in the music of the spheres?

RMM

Why the black answer of hate

Why the black answer of hate
to your existence, Israel?

You stranger
from a star one farther away
than the others.
Sold to this earth
that loneliness might be passed on.

Your origin entangled in weeds—
your stars bartered
for all that belongs to moths and worms,
and yet: fetched away from dreamfilled sandy shores of time
like moonwater into the distance.

In the others' choir
you always sang
one note lower
or one note higher—

you flung yourself into the blood of the evening sun
like one pain seeking the other.
Long is your shadow
and it has become late for you
Israel!

How far your way from the blessing
along the aeon of tears
to the bend of the road
where you turned to ashes

and your enemy with the smoke
of your burned body

engraved your mortal abandonment
on the brow of heaven!

O such a death!
When all helping angels
with bleeding wings
hung tattered
in the barbed wire of time!

Why the black answer of hate
to your existence
Israel?

MR

World, do not ask those snatched from death

World, do not ask those snatched from death
where they are going,
they are always going to their graves.
The pavements of the foreign city
were not laid for the music of fugitive footsteps—
The windows of the houses that reflect a lifetime
of shifting tables heaped with gifts from a picture-book heaven—
were not cut for eyes
which drank terror at its source.
World, a strong iron has cauterized the wrinkle of their smile;
they would like to come to you
because of your beauty,
but for the homeless all ways wither
like cut flowers—

But we have found a friend
in exile: the evening sun.
Blessed by its suffering light

we are bidden to come to it with our sorrow
which walks besides us:
A psalm of night.

RMM

Now Abraham has seized the root of the winds

Now Abraham has seized the root of the winds
for home shall Israel come from the dispersion.

It has gathered wounds and afflictions
in the courtyards of the world,
has bathed all locked doors with its tears.

Its elders, having almost outgrown their earthly garb
and extending their limbs like sea plants,

embalmed in the salt of despair
and the wailing wall night in their arms—
will sleep just a spell longer—

But youth has unfurled its flag of longing,
for a field yearns to be loved by them
and a desert watered

and the house shall be built
to face the sun: God

and evening again has the violet-shy word
that only grows so blue in the homeland:
Good night!

MR

Butterfly

What lovely aftermath
is painted in your dust.
You were led through the flaming
core of earth,
through its stony shell,
webs of farewell in the transient measure.

Butterfly
blessed night of all beings!
The weights of life and death
sink down with your wings
on the rose
which withers with the light ripening homewards.

What lovely aftermath
is painted in your dust.
What royal sign
in the secret of the air.

RMM

Then wrote the scribe of The Sohar

Then wrote the scribe of *The Sohar*
opening the words' mesh of veins
instilling blood from stars
which circled, invisible, and ignited
only by yearning.

The alphabet's corpse rose from the grave,
alphabet angel, ancient crystal,
immured by creation in drops of water
that sang—and through them you saw
glinting lapis, ruby and jacinth,
when stone was still soft
and sown like flowers.

And night, the black tiger,
roared; and there tossed
and bled with sparks
the wound called day.

The light was a month that did not speak,
only an aura intimated the soul-god now.

MR

Fleeing

Fleeing,
what a great reception
on the way—

Wrapped
in the wind's shawl
feet in the prayer of sand
which can never say amen
compelled
from fin to wing
and further—

The sick butterfly
will soon learn again of the sea—
This stone

with the fly's inscription
gave itself into my hand—

I hold instead of a homeland
the metamorphoses of the world—
RMM

Dancer

Dancer
like a bride
you conceive
from blind space
the sprouting longing
of distant days of creation—

With the streets of your body's music
you feed upon the air
there
where the globe of earth
seeks new access
to birth.

Through
night-lava
like
eyelids opening gently
the first cry of the creative volcano
blinks.

In the branches of your limbs
the premonitions
build their twittering nests.

Like a milkmaid
at dusk
your fingertips pull
at the hidden sources
of light
until you, pierced by the
torment of evening,
surrender your eyes
to the moon for her vigil.

Dancer
woman in childbirth
you alone
carry on the hidden navel-string
of your body
the identical god-given jewels
of death and birth.

RMM

You

You
in the night
busy unlearning the world
from far far away
your finger painted the ice grotto
with the singing map of a hidden sea
which assembled its notes in the shell of your ear
bridge-building stones
from Here to There
this precise task
whose completion
is left to the dying.

RMM

Glowing enigmas

This night
I turned the corner into
a dark side street
Then my shadow
lay down in my arm
This tired piece of clothing
wanted to be carried
and the color Nothing addressed me:
You are beyond!

I wash my clothes
Much dying sings in the shift
here and there the counterpoint death
The pursuers have threaded in
together with the hypnosis
and the material absorbs it willingly in sleep—

Those who live on have clutched at time
until gold dust was left on their hands
They sing sun—sun—
midnight the dark eye
has been covered with the shroud—

My love flowed out into your martyrdom
broke through death
We live in resurrection—

When the great terror came
I fell dumb—

Fish with its deathly side
turned upward
air bubbles paid for the grappling breath

All words in flight
to their immortal hiding places
where creative power has to spell
its planetary births
and time loses its knowledge
to the enigmas of light—

Lilies on the equator of anguish
When with your hands
you pronounced the blessing
distances contracted
those akin to the sea
drifted toward the beyond
and dust without memory began to flow—

When your jaw dropped
with the weight of earth—

In my room
where my bed stands
a table a chair
the kitchen stove
the universe kneels as everywhere
to be redeemed
from invisibility—
I draw a line
write down the alphabet
paint on the wall the suicidal words
that make the newborn burgeon at once
I have just fastened the planets to truth
when the earth begins to hammer

night works loose
drops out
dead tooth from the gum—

I saw him step from the house
the fire had singed
but not burned him
He carried a briefcase of sleep
under one arm
heavy inside with letters and figures
a whole arithmetic—
Into his arm was branded:
7337 the ruling number
These numbers had conspired among themselves
The man was a surveyor
Already his feet were rising from the earth
One was waiting for him above
to build a new paradise
"Only wait—you too will soon be at rest—"

They collided in the street
Two destinies on the earth
Two circulations of blood in their arteries
Two that breathed on their way
in this solar system
Over their faces a cloud passed
time had cracked
Remembrance peered in
The far and the near had fused
From past and future
two destinies glittered
and fell apart—

MH

The Seeker

I

From the thundering dance-band
where the notes fly from their black nests
suiciding—
the woman possessed by sorrow
walks the magic triangle of seeking
where fire is plucked apart
and water is given for drowning—
lovers die towards each other
veining the air—

In the eclipse of the sun
the green is condemned to ashes
the birds suffocate in fear
for the unknown is approaching—
stealthily the death-by-light
carved out of night
drags into the sand the history of seeking—

Voyaging to the zenith
where the white laughing-gull sits and waits
she already cools her disintegrating dust

Constellation of the beloved
extinguished by the hangman
the lion fallen from the sky—

She searches she searches
ignites the air with pain
the walls of the desert know of love
which climbs new into the evening
the pre-celebration of death—

She seeks her beloved
does not find him
must re-create the world
calls on the angel
to cut a rib from her body
blows on it with divine breath
white palm leaf in sleep
and the veins drawn dreaming
The seeker in her poverty
takes the crumb of earth in her mouth as farewell
her resurrection continues—

II

You are the prophet of the stars
their secrets travel out of your invisibility
seven-colored light out of a veiled sun
Day and night is already lost with flags of truth
Something new approaches
Volcanic confessions beneath my feet—

III

You are scattered
seed which settles nowhere
how can one search the ways of the wind
or colors and blood
and night the religious fear
premonition—the thread in the labyrinth leads you—

IV

It is an impatience—forest fire crackles in the veins
calls: where are you—with the echo perhaps in heaven
and others sit quiet at a table
drinking milk
outside the lilac in its sad fading
the little brother rides upon the goat—
only her pain tells her he is dead
but perhaps the legend has placed him

amid the constellation of the Southern Cross
there where the ice-princess rises from her frozen grave
her jewelry rattles
he warms her
the ice falls off the gleaming millenniums
no time to gather them
time at the stake goes up in flames
burns down when the birds rip open night—

V

Once they spoke to each other through the distance
two prisoners
the hangman bore the voices strung up
back and forth on the road of madness' longing
Had death ever more lovely gifts to deliver—

VI

Where she stands
is the end of the world
the unknown enters where a wound is
but dreams and visions
madness and the script of lightnings
these fugitives from somewhere else
wait until dying is born
then they speak—

VII

What quarter of the sky have you taken up
to the north the gravestone is green
does the future grow there
your body is a plea in outer space: come
the source seeks its humid fatherland

bent without direction is the victim—

RMM

Chorus of Comforters

We are gardeners who have no flowers.
No herb may be transplanted
From yesterday to tomorrow.
The sage has faded in the cradles—
Rosemary lost its scent facing the new dead—
Even wormwood was only bitter yesterday.
The blossoms of comfort are too small
Not enough for the torment of a child's tear.

New seed may perhaps be gathered
In the heart of a nocturnal singer.
Which of us may comfort?
In the depth of the defile
Between yesterday and tomorrow
The cherub stands
Grinding the lightnings of sorrow with his wings
But his hands hold apart the rocks
Of yesterday and tomorrow
Like the edges of a wound
Which must remain open
That may not yet heal.

The lightnings of sorrow do not allow
The field of forgetting to fall asleep.

Which of us may comfort?

We are gardeners who have no flowers
And stand upon a shining star
And weep.

RMM

We mothers

We mothers,
we gather seed of desire
from oceanic night,
we are gatherers
of scattered goods.

We mothers,
Pacing dreamily
with the constellations,
the floods
of past and future,
leave us alone
with our birth
like an island.

We mothers
who say to death:
blossom in our blood.
We who impel sand to love and bring
a mirroring world to the stars—

We mothers,
who rock in the cradles
the shadowy memories
of creation's day—
the to and fro of each breath
is the melody of our love long.

We mothers
rock into the heart of the world
the melody of peace.

RMM

Land of Israel

Land of Israel,
your bounds once measured out
by your saints surmounting the horizon.
Your morning air enchanted by God's firstborn,
your mountains, your bushes
gone up in the breath of flame
of the terribly close-come mystery.

Land of Israel,
chosen starry place
for the celestial kiss!

Land of Israel,
now when your people seared by dying
move into your valleys
and all echoes call the patriarchs' blessing
for those returning,
proclaiming to them where in the shadowless light
Elijah walked with the yeoman at the plow,
where hyssop grew in the garden
and even by the wall of paradise—
where the small alley ran between here and there
there where He gave and took as neighbor
and death needed no cart for harvest.

Land of Israel,
now when your people
come home from the corners of the world with tear-stained eyes
to write the psalms of David anew in your sand
and that afterwork word *finished*
sings on the evening of its harvest—

perhaps a new Ruth is already standing
in poverty holding her gleanings
at the crossroad of her wandering.

RMM

ELI

A MYSTERY PLAY OF THE SUFFERINGS OF ISRAEL

By NELLY SACHS

Translated from the German by Christopher Holme

CHARACTERS

WASHERWOMAN
BAKER WOMAN
SAMUEL
JOSSELE
GIRLS
BRICKLAYERS
MICHAEL
PEDDLER MENDEL
WOMAN
MAN
KNIFE GRINDER
HUNCHBACK
BLIND GIRL
FIDDLER
YOUNG WOMAN
CROWD OF WORSHIPPERS
MAN WITH A MIRROR
THE DAJAN
BEGGAR
RABBI
OLD WOMAN
OLD MAN
CARPENTER
GARDENER
CREATURE
FARMER
TEACHER
SHOEMAKER
HIS WIFE
POSTMAN
DOCTOR
CHILDREN
VARIOUS VOICES

TIME: *After Martyrdom*

Scene One

Marketplace of a small Polish town, in which a number of survivors of the Jewish people have come together. The houses around about in ruins. Nothing but a fountain in the middle, at which a man is working, cutting and laying pipes

WASHERWOMAN (*carrying a basket full of white linen. Chanting*)

From the laundry, the laundry I come
from washing the garments of death,
from washing the shirt of Eli,
washing out the blood, washing out the sweat,
child-sweat, washing out death.

(*To the pipelayer*)

To you, Samuel, will I bring it,
to the Cattle Lane bring it at evening,
where the bats flutter around in the air
as I flutter the Bible pages
looking for the Song of Lamentation
where it burns and smokes and the stones fall.
Your grandson's shirt will I bring you,
the shirt of Eli.

BAKER WOMAN

How came it, Biddy, that he was struck dumb?

WASHERWOMAN

It was on the morning when they fetched the son,
tore him from bed, from sleep—
as they had torn open the door
to the Shrine of Shrines in the Temple—
forbid, forbid—
thus they tore him from sleep.
Rachel his wife, too, they tore from sleep,
drove her before them through the Cattle Lane,
the Cattle Lane—the widow Rosa sat at the corner, at the window
and told the story of how it happened
until they shut her mouth
with a thorn, because her husband was a gardener.
Eli in his nightshirt ran after his parents,
his pipe in his hand,
the pipe he had played in the fields
to lamb and calf—
and Samuel, the grandfather,
ran after his grandson.

And when Eli saw,
saw with the eyes of an eight-year-old
how they drove his parents
through the Cattle Lane, the Cattle Lane,
he put his pipe to his mouth and blew it.
And he did not blow it
as one who pipes to his cattle or in play,
said the widow Rosa while she was yet alive,
no, he threw back his head
like the stag or the roebuck
before it drinks at the spring.
He pointed the pipe to heaven,
he piped to God, did Eli,
said the widow Rosa while she was yet alive.

BAKER WOMAN

Come aside, Biddy, so that he may not hear,
hear our talk, the dumb one.
Must like a sponge else suck in our words,
can bring nothing forth from his throat,
tied tight with death.

(*They go aside*)

WASHERWOMAN

A soldier marching with the procession
looked around and saw Eli
piping to high heaven,
struck him down dead with his rifle butt.

A young soldier he was, very young still,
said the widow Rosa.
Samuel took up the corpse,
sat down upon a milestone,
and is dumb.

BAKER WOMAN
Was not Michael then at hand
to come to the rescue of Eli?

WASHERWOMAN
Michael was in the house of prayer,
in the burning house of prayer,
he checked the flames,
he saved Jossele,
saved Dajan,
saved Jacob,
but Eli is dead.

BAKER WOMAN (*meditating*)
And would perhaps have come to an end with him,
the moment
when HE forsook us?

WASHERWOMAN
And the widow Rosa added too
that Michael came a minute too late,
a tiny minute,
look, tiny as the eye of my needle
with which I had just been sewing up the torn seam
of Eli's shirt.
Why do you think he came too late,
he whom no enemy detained?
He took one step into the side street,
a single step,
there where the house of Miriam once stood,
and then he turned around—
and Eli was dead.
Then said the widow Rosa:
But Michael has the unbroken vision,
not like ours which sees only fragments—
he has the Baalshem vision,
from one end of the world to another—

(*She approaches the fountain*)

Samuel, will it be ready for the Feast,
for New Year, the fountain?

SAMUEL *nods*

BAKER WOMAN
I'll tell you, Biddy, a secret.
I hear the footsteps!

WASHERWOMAN
What footsteps do you hear, Basia?

BAKER WOMAN
When they fetched Isaac, my husband,
the baker, because he baked the pretzels,
the sugar pretzels with forbidden flour,
when they fetched him from the ovens,
I gave him his overcoat,
because the cold outside was cutting—
they whinnied like horses
whinnying with joy at their oats—
"He'll be back, quicker than he can put it on—
he'll be back!"
He came back, without footsteps!
That's when the footsteps began in my ear!
The heavy footsteps,
the strong footsteps,
they said to the earth:
I'll break you open—
in between, his dragging step,
for he walked little,
breathed heavily in the cold,
at the ovens he stood,
by day and by night—

WASHERWOMAN
Do you hear the footsteps still?

BAKER WOMAN
They live in my ear,
they walk in the daytime
they walk in the nighttime,
whether you speak or I speak,
I hear them always.

WASHERWOMAN
Ask Michael
if he can rid you of the footsteps.
I must ask Michael what he knows.

For he stitches sole to uppers,
he must know more than just how to wander to the grave.
Let me tell you, Basia, I'm a washerwoman,
I've made the lye, I've washed, I've rinsed,
but today at the laundry,
there where the seam was torn on Eli's shirt—
there it looked at me—

BAKER WOMAN

If only I could,
I'd open the seam above there,
made bloody by the sun,
could Isaac's eyes but see me—
I'd say,
caught behind bars I am,
bars made of footsteps,
open the bars,
let me out of the heavy footsteps,
the strong footsteps
which break open the earth—
in between, your dragging step—

WASHERWOMAN

The fountain's running!

BAKER WOMAN

The fountain's running!

(*She cups her hands and drinks*)
Take away the footsteps,
the footsteps from my ear—
the footsteps—footsteps—
(*She falls to the ground*)

Curtain

Scene Two

The same marketplace, seen from a different angle. The fountain plays. At one of the ruined houses an old bricklayer and his apprentice are working. In the background a narrow, ruined alley at the end of which the prayer tent can be seen. Green landscape gleams through everywhere

BRICKLAYER

Jossele, fill the bucket at the fountain,
run for the lime there where they're building,
building outside the gates the new town.
No gates are there any more,
no old town any more.
No house of prayer any more,
only earth enough for the holy ground.

(*To himself*)
This was a house, here, this was a hearth,
there's a saucepan still, burned black.
Here's a colored ribbon,
perhaps it was a cradle bow—
perhaps it was an apron string—
who knows?
Here's a skullcap.
Who wore it?
A young man or an old one or a boy?
Did it guard the Eighteen Benedictions, the silent ones,
from idle thoughts,
from wicked thoughts,
or—who knows?

A WOMAN *in a nightdress hurries up the narrow alley, knocking with her finger on walls and stones*

BRICKLAYER

Esther Weinberg, what're you knocking at?
There's no answer locked in the stone.

JOSSELE (*with the bucket*)

The woman has run out of the infirmary,
now she's picking up stones and throwing them away—

BRICKLAYER

Wants to break out of her prison—

JOSSELE

But what is she doing now?

Opening and shutting her hands like cups
and filling them with air.

STONEMASON'S WIFE (*singing*)
Your right leg
light as a bird—
your left leg
light as a bird—
curls in the south wind—
hearts can shiver like water in the hand—
shiver like water—
Oh . . . Oh . . .

(*She runs off*)

BRICKLAYER
She makes her child out of air—

(*He takes a stone*)
We make graves,
but she has broken out already—
is taking lessons already with HIM—

JOSSELE (*runs after the woman and returns*)
The woman is dead.
Said to a stone: "Here I come,"
struck her brow upon it and died.
This letter was lying beside her.

BRICKLAYER (*reading*)
"Finely veined like your temples was the stone.
Laid it to my cheek before going off to sleep,
felt its depressions,
felt its elevations,
its smooth and jagged places—
blew upon it,
and it breathes like you, Esther . . ."
This is from Gad, her husband,
who slaved himself to death in the quarry,
bearing Israel's burden—

JOSSELE *weeps and sighs*

BRICKLAYER
Don't cry, Jossele.
Let us build the old house anew.
If tears hang on the stonework,
if sighs hang on the woodwork,
if the little children can't sleep,
death has a soft bed.

(*He lays bricks, singing and whistling*)
Master of the world!
Thou, Thou, Thou, Thou!
Master of all stones!
Thou, Thou, Thou, Thou!
Where can I find Thee,
and where can I not find Thee?
Thou, Thou, Thou, Thou!

Curtain

Scene Three

The ruined alley near the marketplace, which can just be seen. The fountain plays. Children come running

OLDER GIRL
The school teacher said
today was the day
of Michael's wedding years ago,
the day they snatched his bride from him
before the blessing of the candles.

YOUNGER GIRL
What shall we play?

OLDER GIRL
Wedding and candle-blessing
and I'll be the bride—

BOY (*seizing her*)
And I'll snatch you away.

OLDER GIRL (*freeing herself*)
No, I don't want that,
I'll find myself a baby to cradle.

JOSSELE
When I went on the ship,
the sea always traveled away with us
like the roll of yarn
when I make it pop up on the thread,
but we didn't reach the white
where it begins.

But in sleep I was there.
When I woke up, someone said:
Many are drowned,
but you are saved.
But often the water still follows me.

YOUNGER GIRL
I sat deep below in the night,
and there was a woman there,
as kind as Sister Leah from the infirmary
and she said: Sleep, I'll watch.
And then there came a wall in my mouth
and I ate a wall.

OLDER GIRL
Was the woman your mother?

YOUNGER GIRL
Mother? what's that?

OLDER GIRL (*pulling a rag out of the rubble*)
Here is linen,
and here's a piece of wood
charred only at one end.
Now I've got a baby,
a baby with black hair,
And now I'll cradle it

(*Singing*)
Once on a time there was a tale—
the tale is not a gay one,
the tale begins with singing
about the king of the Jews.

Once on a time there was a king—
a king there was, he had a queen,
the queen she had a vineyard—
Lyulinka, my child . . .

YOUNGER GIRL
Did you learn that from Becky?

OLDER GIRL
Yes.

(*Singing*)
The vineyard it had a tree,
the tree it had a bough,
the bough it had a little nest—
Lyulinka, my child . . .

JOSSELE
Look, I've found a bone—
who makes himself a pipe of dead men's bones
will never pipe the cattle forth—

OLDER GIRL
Does the water still follow you?

JOSSELE
Yes, sometimes,
but more often it is the hanged Isidor who comes
and says: My friend, a roll of yarn
holds like a rope—

OLDER GIRL
It's late,
let's go to Becky.

JOSSELE
Give me your baby,
I'll throw it on the rubble,
there it can cry.

OLDER GIRL
No, don't do that,
Miriam its name is,
and I'll go into the kitchen,
and ask Becky for a whisk,
that'll do for a head.

(*Singing*)
The nest it had a little bird,
the bird it had a little wing,
the wing it had a little feather—
Lyulinka, my child . . .

(*As they all go off slowly, singing from backstage*)
The king he had to die,
the queen she had to perish,
the tree had to shatter,
the bird fly from its nest . . .

Curtain

SCENE FOUR

MICHAEL'*s cobbler's shop in the only unruined house. Through the window, moonlight and open fields. Shelves on the walls with shoes on them. Table with tools. Bench before the window.* MICHAEL, *tall, thin, with reddish hair. He snatches a pair of shoes and puts them on the window bench. Then he lifts up a shoe, so that it is silhouetted in black against the moonlight. It is a small woman's shoe*

MICHAEL
You trod so lightly,
the grasses rose behind your feet.
Here is the strap you tore,
as you hurried toward me, that time—
quick is love,
the sun as it rises
is slower far.
Miriam—

(*He sinks to the ground, his head between his knees*)
What constellation saw your death?
Was it the moon, the sun, or the night?
with stars, without stars?

A cloud passes across the moon. The room is almost dark. Gliding footsteps are heard. A sigh, then a rough man's voice

MAN'S VOICE
Thou art fair, my love,
were I thy bridegroom
I should be jealous of death,
but thus—

Wild laughter, screams

MICHAEL *lies for a long time motionless. The moon shines again. He raises himself, snatches up a pair of heavy men's shoes*

MICHAEL
Isidor's shoes,
the pawnbroker's shoes,
heavy shoes.
A worm is stuck to the sole,
a trodden worm.
The moon shines on,
just as when it saw your death.

(*He sinks to the ground in the same position as before. Heavy footsteps are heard*)

FIRST VOICE
Don't hang it up,
I've got it in a casket,
of sandalwood the casket is—
was the jewel case of the rich, then poor, Sarah—
good customer she was—

SECOND VOICE
Speak, what about the casket?

FIRST VOICE
Buried it, behind the beech tree,
the only beech tree among the pines—
there's a ring inside,
has a stone, an aquamarine,
has a blue fire, the aquamarine—
the whole Mediterranean is in it—
blue, so blue, when the sun plays—
No—in the pockets nothing rattles, empty—
That's the night wind,
rattling silver in the leaves—

SECOND VOICE
Rattle on then with the night wind, you—

MICHAEL *lies motionless. He gets up again, snatches a pair of child's shoes and lifts them above his head. The morning sun begins to redden the sky*

MICHAEL
Shoes,
trodden over on the inside,
lamb's wool sticking to them—
Eli—

(*He sinks into the same position as before. The rending notes of a pipe are heard*)

Curtain

Scene Five

Room of a ruined building. SAMUEL *sits on a bed of boards. On his lap is Eli's death shirt. A candle flickers.* MICHAEL *enters*

MICHAEL
Samuel,
I pray you to help me find what I am seeking,
I seek the hand,
I seek the eyes,
I seek the mouth,
I seek the piece of skin,
into which the corruption of this earth has entered,
I seek Eli's murderer.
I seek the dust
which since Cain has mingled
with every murderer's dust and waited,
meanwhile has formed birds perhaps—
and then murderers.
Perhaps it formed the mandrakes
for which Rachel gave up a night to Leah—
Perhaps it encased Sammael's exhalations of hate—
To think
that this dust may have touched the prayer book of Luria,
when it lay hidden,
till its letters spouted flames—
to think—
Oh, what dust is it that I bring you here on my shoes.

(*He takes off his shoes*)
Samuel, let me ask your dumbness,
Was he tall?

SAMUEL *shakes his head*

MICHAEL
Was he shorter than I and taller than you?

SAMUEL *nods*

MICHAEL
His hair, was it fair?

SAMUEL *nods*

MICHAEL
His eyes, black, blue?

SAMUEL *shakes his head*

MICHAEL
Gray?

SAMUEL *nods*

MICHAEL
His color, red-cheeked, healthy?

SAMUEL *shakes his head*

MICHAEL
Pale then?

SAMUEL *nods*

MICHAEL (*sobbing*)
How many millions of men has the earth?
Murderers like Cain.
Crumbled mandrakes,
nightingale dust,
Dust of prayer books,
from which letters spring out like flames.

SAMUEL *hands* MICHAEL *a shepherd's pipe.* MICHAEL *breathes into it. A weak note is heard. He points to the death shirt, on which the form of a man's head is silhouetted*

Look, oh look,
the candle throws the shadow—
or your dumbness speaks:
Very young still,
the nose is broad,
its nostrils quiver with blood lust,
the eyes have the pupils of a wolf—
The mouth is small as a child's—

The face disappears

Thus faces are compounded in dreams—
water poured from the invisible—
It is gone
and burns in my eyes.
Until I find him
it will get between me and everything on this earth,

It will hang in the air—
In the bread I eat
this nightmare dust will be my food.
In the apple I eat
the murderer's face will lurk—
Samuel,
Your speech has already reached
where all dust is at an end.
Beyond the Word this thing was compounded.

(*He backs to the door, where he puts on his shoes*)

Curtain

SCENE SIX

Open side of the marketplace, giving on to the fields. The splashing of the fountain is heard. On a sandy path in plowland, PEDDLER MENDEL *stands and cries his wares, surrounded by onlookers*

MENDEL
Bargain offer! Amazing opportunity!
It is my privilege to show you:
Apron material, washable, colorfast, with flower designs,
with flower designs,
Stockings of wool, stockings of silk, straight from Paris.
Elastic, look, you can stretch it
from here to kingdom come, and back it springs—
direct from America.
From England I have lavender for headaches
and peppermint for a bad digestion—
But this linen now from Russia—
not now for the dead, no longer,
not for the feet pointing toward the door—
no, for the lovely bride, for baby too—

WOMAN (*to her husband*)
Look here,
what a holiday dress that'd make for me,
Just now with the New Year coming in.

MAN
We live in the poorhouse,
you have neither table nor chair,
what do you want with such stuff?

WOMAN
Why, look now,
the little Sterntal woman
has a better husband than I,
he's bought her the fine scarf already.

MAN
Where you now stand, it ran with blood—
We are saved

WOMAN
and ought to have joy in our safety.

MAN (*to the* PEDDLER)
You're spoiling the women all over again.
This love of finery
will bring even mourning crepe out in pleats and flounces.

MENDEL
I have no wife,
but if I had one, I'd vie with Solomon.
He who praises the virtuous wife
praises her attire as well—

MAN
Very well, measure me a length of the stuff.

KNIFE GRINDER
Scissors to grind,
Knives to grind,
Sickles for the new crop—

ANOTHER WOMAN
I wish he'd be off
and do his grinding away from here—
The noise of knives grinding
Is more than a body can stand—

KNIFE GRINDER
Next time you eat

you'll need a knife—
Next time you harvest
you'll need a knife—
When next you dress
two knives you'll need.

(*He grinds on*)

OTHER WOMAN
A lot it matters to you—
or don't you feel it? that your grinding
carves up the world in pieces.

KNIFE GRINDER
I hate nobody,
want to give no offense—
I grind because it's my trade—

OTHER WOMAN
So it's his trade,
as it's mine to weep—
and another's to die.

Two teenage girls go across

ONE GIRL (*speaking to the* PEDDLER)
Peddler, I want to buy a hank of woolen yarn.

(*To her companion*)
Let me lay the hank around your wrists.
You hold them still while I wind
and it's like saying goodbye.
Me they held fast by the wrists
and took my mother away—
and the goodbye went from her to me—
from me to her,
till it was at an end—

They walk on. A FIDDLER *has come and starts to play. They all begin to dance*

HUNCHBACK
What longing in the bones—
the old Adam ferments in the notes,
the new man has his first rib already.

BLIND GIRL *comes with hands stretched before her, holding twigs and sticks. She is barefoot and dressed in rags*

GIRL (*coming to a halt in front of the* FIDDLER)
There's a twitching under my foot.
The pavement of our longing must be here at an end.
There go all my journeys.

(*She throws down the sticks*)
Always, when my feet got a new wound
a journey was at an end
like a clock that strikes.
I wanted to see my love once more
but then they took away my eyes—
from that time on, I counted midnight.
Now I am but a tear removed from my love,
and the last wound has opened in my foot—

(*She sinks to the ground and is taken away*)

HUNCHBACK
She's brought with her only the skeleton of her journeys—
The flesh is all consumed with longing—
She wanted to see her love once more—
but the Devil
shies from the mirror of love in a human look
and shattered it—

TWO CHILDREN (*collect the twigs and sing*)
We've got sticks,
we've got journeys,
we've got bones,
ei, ei, ei—

MENDEL
This one stick
I could use to tie up my bundle,
the others you can keep.

FIDDLER *plays on, and everybody dances*

HUNCHBACK
Don't dance so heavily

knocking at the walls of sleep—
it could flood you,
too many young hearts inside them—
there'll be love dust—
Who knows how that grain will taste—
who knows?

YOUNG WOMAN (*with a child on her arm, to the* HUNCHBACK)
Don't stare at my child like that!
God preserve it from the evil eye—

HUNCHBACK
Forbid that I should scorch it with my look.
I only wonder
how you were able to bear it
in these times—

YOUNG WOMAN
In a hole in the earth I bore it,
in a hole I suckled it—
Death took its father,
me he did not take,
saw the milk in my breasts
and did not take me.

HUNCHBACK (*repeating her words*)
And did not take you—

YOUNG WOMAN
Forgive me if I offended you.
But God preserve me,
I thought at first
you were a living piece
of Israel's misfortune.

HUNCHBACK (*pointing to his hump*)
You saw the satchel
in which the scapegoat carries its people's misfortune.

YOUNG WOMAN
To me it seems
a hundred or more years have passed
since I sat in my hole—
I can't bear the light any more—
I only blink—
To me these seem not human beings,
mounds of earth I see dancing—
night can preserve no names.
Whatever barks, whatever sings
I've long forgotten—

HUNCHBACK (*pointing to the long shadows thrown by the* PEDDLER)
It's a late hour already in Israel.

All the dancers throw long shadows. Their bodies are as if blotted out by the glare of the evening sun. Only the YOUNG WOMAN *with her child stands out clearly in the light*

Curtain

SCENE SEVEN

Marketplace as at the beginning. In the background the narrow alley ending in the prayer tent. A CROWD OF WORSHIPERS *is gathering for the Festival Service*

FIRST WORSHIPER
Here is the place
where baker Isaac of the shuffling gait
was struck down because of a sugar pretzel.
His shop sign was an iron pretzel,
on it the children's eyes
had fastened with longing,
and eaten their fill of it—
One child fell dead,
had eaten enough.
Thought Isaac,
I'll bake a sugar pretzel,
then another and once again,
so that they'll not eat themselves to death
with their eyes on the iron pretzel.
One pretzel he baked, no more.
The iron pretzel glowed
as in the baker's oven fire,
until a man of war took it away,
melted it down for the next death.

A MAN *with a looking glass in his hand passes by, looking into it*

MAN

There, where you carried your children—
I believe we were seven in number—
there your body collapsed on to the grave gaping below,
your withered breasts hung over it in mourning.
O my mother,
your murderer held a mirror before you
so that you might have comic death—
Mother, you looked at yourself
until your jaw sagged on to your breast—
but the great Angel spread his wings over you!
Through the barbed wire of the times
he came hasting to you
with torn wings—
for iron and steel have grown rampant, Mother,
building primeval forests in the air—
murderer's brains have grown rampant—
vines of premeditated anguish sprouting from them.
Mirror, mirror,
echo from the forest of the dead—
victims and hangmen,
victims and hangmen
played with their breath upon you the dying game.
Mother,
one day there'll be a constellation called Mirror.

(*He passes on*)

SECOND WORSHIPER (*to* THIRD WORSHIPER)

Is he still saying kaddish into the mirror?

THIRD WORSHIPER

Yes. Holy Baalshem,
last sheaf-carrier of Israel's strength,
weaker your people has become and weaker,
a swimmer
whom only death brings to land.

THE DAJAN

But I tell you:
Many a one of you has had the potent faith,
behind the curtain of night
has forced down
the great tranquilizers life and death.

(*Pointing to a house wrecked by gunfire*)

Not with such weapons alone was the battle fought,
I tell you:
Battlefields there are—battlefields
which the inventors of daylight murder
have never dreamed of.
Many a prayer
Has hung with flaming wings before the cannon's mouth,
many a prayer
has burned up the night like a sheet of paper!
Sun, moon, and stars have been arrayed by Israel's prayer
along the potent strings of faith—
diamonds and carbuncles
about the dying throat of her people
O! O!—

HUNCHBACK

They say,
because of my jerking shoulders
they hate me—

KNIFE GRINDER

They say,
because of my perpetual smile
they hate me—

MENDEL

They say,
because of this heap of stone
which was once my house
they hate me—

BEGGAR *with a feather in his hat*

When I turn the hat over
it's a grave for money,
or I put it on,

and it's something
which has to do with flying.
What are riches in a Jew
but an ice pit around a frozen tear!—

THE DAJAN
I see,
see the beginning of your jerking shoulders, Simon—
when with Abraham you dug the well of the "Seven Oaths"
in Beersheba—
I see,
I see the beginning of your smile, Aman—
on Horeb planted in the seventy elders,
to sprout again
sprout in the wandering dust of the lip.
Stones are stones—
Earth of Paradise in them, but in greed destroyed.
But they do not know the beginning.
not the eternal beginning—
and that's why they hate us—

ALL THE BYSTANDERS
That's why they hate us—

THE DAJAN (*shouting*)
Eli, because of you,
to know your beginning—

(He collapses)

Curtain

Scene Eight

The same. THE WORSHIPERS *have disappeared into the prayer tent. Murmurs are heard, then the voice of the* RABBI *pronouncing the Shophar lines*

VOICE OF THE RABBI
Tekiá—

A long note is heard, of a single pitch

VOICE
Shevarim—

Three notes in succession

VOICE
Teruá—

A trilled note

The shadow of the seven-branched candlestick is silhouetted on the tent wall. The tent is opened. The worshipers march out

FIRST WORSHIPER
The air is new—
gone is the smell of burning,
gone is the smell of blood,
gone is the smell of smoke—
the air is new!

SECOND WORSHIPER
In my ear there's a noise
as if someone were pulling
the barb from the wound—
the barb that is sticking in the middle of the earth—
Someone takes the two halves of the earth apart
like an apple,
the two halves of today and yesterday—
takes out the maggot
and joins the casing together again.

THE WORSHIPERS *march across the marketplace*

SEVERAL WORSHIPERS
Happy New Year!
May the moment when He forsook us
be at an end!

OTHERS JOINING THEM
And Israel emptied forth its soul for death—

OTHERS
The horn has sounded to call us home.
He did not forget us.
On the palms of both hands engraved
has He His people!

Everyone has gone off, the marketplace is empty. AN OLD WOMAN *comes and sits on the edge of the fountain*

OLD WOMAN

Isn't he coming yet, the Rabbi?
Still not here yet, the Rabbi—

(*She gets up and goes to meet him, weeping*)

There comes the Rabbi!
A cake I baked
in the oven out there in the fields—
the other women said:
That's a fine cake you've baked,
your holiday cake. I said,
It's for the Rabbi, the cake.
I took three measures of flour,
as Sarah did when she baked for the angels,
the angels
when they came to Abraham at evening—

RABBI

There's nothing in the scripture
about their coming at evening—

OLD WOMAN

Always the angels come at evening.
And the water at the spring
has a mouth that speaks.

RABBI

Why are you crying, Grandma?

OLD WOMAN

Have I not a right to cry?
The rats have eaten the cake,
the cake for the Rabbi.

RABBI

New flour will be given you
and we'll eat the cake together—

OLD WOMAN

Can't bake any more,
can't eat any more,
can only weep.

(*Weeping more violently*)

RABBI

Do you live in the house with the old people, Grandma?

OLD WOMAN

I live in the third cellar
on the marketplace.

RABBI

Why don't you live with the old people?

OLD WOMAN

Because I must live
there where I live.
Yehudi was born there,
Natel was born there,
Taubel was born there—
their cry is still in the place,
and Taubel's dance is in the place—
Michael gave me a pair of shoes
because the grave-earth had entered into the old ones,
Yehudi's earth,
Taubel's earth,
Natel's earth.
They're shoes from Rabbi Sassow,
they're Tsaddick shoes,
holy shoes, holy dancing shoes.

(*She laces them up tighter*)

Taubel's dancing is in them.
Look!

(*She begins to dance*)

Curtain

SCENE NINE

Marketplace at the fountain. THE GIRLS *fill the jugs and hand them to the dusty bricklayers as they pass, building the new town*

BRICKLAYER (*to a girl*)

Thanks for the drink,
I am going now to build the new town.

GIRL

Cement this in too.
It's got the Holy Words in it,

given to me by my love,
and I wore them on this chain about my neck.

BRICKLAYER
How can one part with such a gift?

GIRL
Short my life will be,
but the walls,
they must hold.

SECOND BRICKLAYER (*to another girl*)
Let us wed in spring,
for it is written:
Marry in winter
while the chrysalis lives on its dreams,
and your dream will shatter
before spring comes.
But when it flies,
then God himself will open brooks and buds—

THIRD BRICKLAYER (*drinking thirstily*)
Always Israel was thirsty.
What people can ever have drunk at so many springs?
But now, thirst upon thirst,
all deserts together have worked at this our thirst.

A CARPENTER *with a door passes across the stage.* THE BEGGAR *with the feather in his hat enters*

BEGGAR
That is a door.
A door is a knife
and parts the world in two halves.
If I stand in front and knock on it
because I'm a beggar,
then perhaps it'll be opened to me
and the smell of roast meat
and the smell of soaked clothes stream out.
It is the smell of human homes.
He who has a fine beggar's nose
can smell tears too
or built-in well-being.
But the housewife says:
"No, it's too early in the day,"
and "No" says the closing door.
At the next door I come too late,
all I get is a glimpse
of a bed thrown open,
and the door shuts,
sad as an evening blessing.
Carpenter, hang no doors,
they are the knives
which cut the world apart.

CARPENTER
Man, collect your feather wits,
doors are for the cold and for burglars.
And since cold too is a burglar,
things are right as they are.

BEGGAR (*going up to the door and knocking*)
Here is Israel, door of the world,
Door of the world, open!

CARPENTER
It is well made,
it does not move,
but behind it,
the swallows migrate.

BEGGAR (*throwing himself on the sand before the door*)
There's your threshold!

TROOP OF YOUNG BRICKLAYERS
We build, we build
the new town, the new town,
the new town!
We bake, we bake
The bricks of the new town!

THE DAJAN
And Abraham raised his hovel
again and again
and set it in direction toward Him.

FIRST BRICKLAYER
Moses baked bricks,
David baked bricks,
now we bake bricks,
we the survivors!
His thornbush in the desert
are we, we, we!

SECOND BRICKLAYER
We bake!
and this here is our candle!

(*He stamps the earth with his foot*)

THIRD BRICKLAYER
We have new miracles!
Our desert too had quails and manna,
for a time I lived on snow,
ate clouds and sky—

CARPENTER
What do you say to the secret of a potato peeling
washed up at my feet by the flood of hate?
That was my Ark.
If I now say "God,"
you know where the strength comes from.

GARDENER *with an apple tree*
For a new Adam,
for a new Eve.

ALL (*singing*)
We bake, we bake,
to build the new house—

THE DAJAN
I fear you don't trench deep enough,
those foundations will only bear the easygoing.

(*Drinking at the fountain*)
The new Pentateuch, I tell you, the new Pentateuch
is written in mildew, the mildew of fear
on the walls of the death cellars.

FIRST BRICKLAYER
Anguish of worms on the fishhook,
anguish of fish over the worm,
Anguish of beetles under my foot—
enough of the gravedigger's spade!

(*To* THE DAJAN)
Save your hay of memories for next winter—
here is fresh grass.

(*He wreathes a girl with grasses*)
Dust worshipers we are.
As long as the dust bears such fruit,
so long will we grub in its furrows
and make paradises of dust
with the apples
which like grim forebodings smell of departure—

GARDENER *with apple tree*
This comes from the alien earth.
The patriarchal dust is missing,
has nourished the holy citron—
Rachel of the well-deep eyes nourished it—
David, the shepherd of lambs.
My fingers crook themselves,
to sink its roots in alien earth—

FIRST BRICKLAYER
Perhaps the air will turn
into a new plant habitat,
in virtue of new inventions—
citron in the air,
home in the air.

ALL (*singing*)
We bake, we bake—

THE DAJAN (*to himself*)
I saw one who gnawed his own flesh
filling himself out to one side like the moon
and thinning down toward the other world—
I saw a child smile
before it was thrown on to the flames—
Where is that now?
My God, where is that now?

Curtain

SCENE TEN

Country road. Uprooted or burned trees on either side. Fields churned up by warfare. Rank weeds flowering over them. KNIFE GRINDER *and* PEDDLER MENDEL *walking together, the latter with his stock on a handcart*

KNIFE GRINDER (*pointing back along the road*)
They're all on edge a bit there, Brother Mendel.

MENDEL
He who sits in the dark
lights himself a dream—
He who loses his bride
embraces the air—
He whose garment was touched by death
so that he cried out
has thoughts eating at him like worms—
A good thing I had hidden my stock
under the stonework.
Business wasn't bad today—

KNIFE GRINDER
What did that man mean
when he picked out the one whose shoulder jerks
and you others?

MENDEL
How should I know?
Once I saw a dowser,
his wand jumped up
whenever a spring was found.
So the Dajan seeks everywhere
the spring of hate
which was given to Israel to drink.
But even though I knew better than I do,
you from another tribe,
how could I explain to you?

KNIFE GRINDER
Brother, why do you speak such words!
When we lay in the hayloft,
in the Pole Yarislav's hayloft,
Then we were both one!
Eyes only, to espy the enemy,
ears only, to listen for creaking steps—
hair on the head
to rise to heaven in damp terror—
there came to us *one* sleep,
one hunger, *one* awakening,
came the yellow-eyed owl
who collects twigs
when she smells death—
looked into the loft window,
cried out like a hangman's daughter,
if he had had one:
Tuwoo!

MENDEL
You made a gurgling sound in your dream
like a drowning man—

KNIFE GRINDER
You spoke much about a light
that had set fire to your stock—

MENDEL
Do you hear the crickets, Brother?

KNIFE GRINDER
No.

MENDEL
Pity.
It is the brightest sound in this world,
not every ear can catch it.
But did you see one?

KNIFE GRINDER
No—

MENDEL
Worse the pity.
They sit where the invisible begins.
They're beggars already at the gates of Paradise,
said Grandmother to us children.
But once a cricket was sitting
on a roll of rose-pink satin ribbon—

KNIFE GRINDER (*to a stray dog which runs past*)
Here, here, comrade.
With your four paws
you can accompany my two.
If Mendel has his cricket,
I'll have my dog.
When I grind, he'll bark—

There'll be two for the wind to stroke,
two to hunger and stand outside,
with the earth under our paws.
When sun, moon, and stars enter his pupils—
and a whole world too.
O you warm, walking grain of earth
with two mirrors—

AN OLD BEGGAR MAN *comes to meet them*

MENDEL
Who are you, Grandpa?

OLD MAN
I am not nor am I Grandpa!

MENDEL
You are not, yet you speak!
Where do you come from?

OLD MAN (*pointing to the grinding wheel*)
Are you a knife grinder?

KNIFE GRINDER
Yes.

OLD MAN
So you know the truth.

KNIFE GRINDER
Why do you answer as in a question game?

OLD MAN
For the reason that there's fire in the stone,
and therefore life,
and in the knife death—
Therefore day by day you grind life with death.
That's where I come from.

KNIFE GRINDER
Alive out of death?

OLD MAN
From there where the murderers sowed my people in the earth.
O may its seed be full of stars!

KNIFE GRINDER
By you?

OLD MAN
I was only half sown,
lying already in the grave,
knew already how the warmth leaves the flesh—
how motion leaves the bones—
heard already the language of the bones when corruption sets in—
language of the blood when it congeals—
language of the dust
striving anew after love—

KNIFE GRINDER
But how were you saved?

MENDEL
Had you a ring,
a fine pearl to sell,
paid for your life with a secret glint?

OLD MAN
You wretched sacks,
stuffed with questions and quarreling.
What do you know of it,
when the bodies become empty
whispering like sea shells,
oh, when they rise on the white-flecked waves
of eternity?

KNIFE GRINDER
But tell us, how were you saved?

OLD MAN
We had fled,
Amschel, brown Yehudi, and I,
Three nations were taken captive
three languages taken captive,
hands taken captive
to be made to dig their own graves,
to grasp their own death.
Bodies were slaughtered
and the remains poured out on the ground.
How many thousands of millions of miles of anguish from HIM!

MENDEL *and* KNIFE GRINDER
But you, you?

OLD MAN
The soldier
who filled in the earth over us
and buried us—
blessings be on him—
he saw by the lantern light,
for it was night,
that they had not slaughtered me enough
and that my eyes were opening—
and he fetched me out
and hid me—

KNIFE GRINDER
Very hard to believe.

MENDEL
There's no telling,
speak on.

OLD MAN
That soldier that morning—
so he told me later—
had had a letter from his mother.
Blessings be on her!
For that reason he was not intoxicated like the rest
and he saw the blinking of my eyes.
The mother wrote:
"Really I meant to put this letter with the socks,
the home-knitted ones.
But my longing gave me no peace—"
blessings be on it!
"And I am writing today
without waiting till they are finished.
But your suit, the blue one,
has been brushed and hung out to air
because of the moth powder.
So it won't smell of it
when you come."
But it didn't happen
that she was able to post the letter at once,
for she fell ill during the night.
And a neighbor came—
blessings be on her!—
asked how she was—
but really all she wanted was an onion—
a small one to cook with her potatoes,
for her own were finished.
Ah, that she ate potatoes
and not turnips—
Blessed be all onions!—
and she was given an onion
and took the letter to the post
and the soldier got it on that morning
and did not get intoxicated like the others—
and saw the blinking of my eyes—

KNIFE GRINDER
How many onionskins came together there
to save you!
And what more will sprout
from your onion luck?

OLD MAN
I'm going to the Rabbi in the grave town.
My body will hold out no longer,
sand has touched the sand—
yet now it is the *one* death I die,
the other, which resides in a hangman's hand muscles
like a skeleton key in the burglar's fist,
that I don't need any more,
I have the right key!

KNIFE GRINDER *and* MENDEL *resume their walking*

MENDEL
I am pleased, I am pleased!

KNIFE GRINDER
What pleases you, Brother?

MENDEL
I am pleased
that I gave Michael a pair of laces
for his walking shoes.
If he reaches Paradise
he'll have my laces on his feet.
The death-shirt of Eli too was of my linen—

KNIFE GRINDER
Why was it good,
that you gave the shoemaker the laces,
and why should he die,
young as he is?

MENDEL (*as if telling him a secret*)
I don't know,
but good it is in any case.
He may be one of the Thirty-six
on whose deeds the world rests—
one who follows the course of the waters
and hears the turning of the earth—
one for whom the vein behind the ear
which for us throbs only in the hour of death
throbs every day,
one who wears Israel's walking shoes to the end—

KNIFE GRINDER (*to the dog*)
Here, then, come,
you look as if you were hungry.
The tongue hangs from your throat,
so you are thirsty too—
We'll go into the village,
if a twig of a stork's nest is still left of it,
to a farmer,
if a fingernail of a farmer's still to be found,
look for a sickle,
sharpen it
and cut with it the weeds in the field—
Perhaps we'll find a pool of water too,
in which death has not yet washed his bloody hands—
and then we'll drink—

(*He nods goodbye and walks across the field with the dog*)

MENDEL
Now it's as before.
Saved, but alone.

Curtain

SCENE ELEVEN

Night. A wood. An invisible light source illuminates a fallen chimney and some trees with twisted branches. MICHAEL *in his wandering stops and listens*

VOICE FROM THE CHIMNEY
We stones were the last things to touch Israel's sorrow.
Jeremiah's body in smoke,
Job's body in smoke,
the Lamentations in smoke,
whimpering of little children in smoke,
mothers' cradle songs in smoke,
Israel's way of freedom in smoke—

VOICE OF A STAR
I was the chimney sweep—
my light turned black—

TREE
I am a tree.
I can no longer stand straight.
It hung on me and swung
as though all the world's winds hung and swung on me.

SECOND TREE
Blood pressed on to my roots—
All the birds which nested in my crown
had bloody nests.
Every evening I bleed afresh—
My roots climb from their grave—

FOOTPRINTS IN THE SAND
We filled the last minutes with death.
Grew ripe like apples from the heavy tread of men—
the mothers who touched us were in a hurry,
but the children were as light as spring rains—

VOICE OF THE NIGHT
Here are their last sighs,
I kept them for you,
feel them!
Their abode is in the never aging breezes—
in the breathing of those to come,
inconceivable in the sadness of night—

While MICHAEL *listens, there is seen, scarcely distinguishable from the tree roots,* A CREATURE *sitting on the ground, sewing at a white prayer shawl. Near him a death's head in the grass*

CREATURE
Michael!

MICHAEL (*approaching*)
Hirsch the tailor
in his lifetime looked like that.
You have perishable company with you—

CREATURE
Hirsch am I, the tailor, and my neighbor there
was someone's wife, perhaps my own—
I don't know—for although, there,

(*He points to the* CHIMNEY)
I was employed as Death,
once over the frontier it is hard to find anything again.
One minute past midnight
everything looks the same—
But however that may be,
if I'd listened to my blessed wife
I'd be sitting with the living in America,
among whom I have a brother—
not here among my like.
Look, she said
when it all began,
You're a stag, Hirsch, a stag,
so you must scent it coming
or hasn't the Jewish people
a nose for what's in store?—
the knives are stirring in the drawer,
the scissors of the great tailor are grating,
and the fire in the stove is forming grisly faces
as in the Witch of Endor's cave—
But above all, I feel glances,
glances squinting like the cat's—
Michael, Michael—
you they have not touched,
you they have spared,
and you stood up to them everywhere,
so to speak to windward,
as my one-time customer, the gamekeeper, would have said,
like a game animal
which has lost its scent—
but me they brought to bay
because of my protruding cheekbones
and also because of my legs.
Death, you gave two sickle blades,
they said,
it's quicker that way.
Unless you send your people up in smoke,
unless you burn your own flesh and blood
we'll unscrew your pelvis
and remove your two sickle blades.
And then you'll have better food
than all of us together.
Smoke weighs more heavily in the stomach than bread—

(*He lays the prayer shawl aside. Pointing to the death's head*)
It is too dark, that one there
doesn't shine any more—
And I burned them
and I ate smoke,
and I stoked HIM into the fire.
And I ran into the wood
and there stood raspberry canes,
and I ate raspberries
after I had stoked HIM into the fire,
and I could not die,
because I am Death
but look there—

(*Shouting*)
look there—

CHIMNEY
I am the Camp Commandant.
March, march
go the thoughts out of my head!

Smoke begins to rise and transform itself into transparent shapes. Moon and stars shed a black light. The tree roots are corpses with twisted limbs. THE CREATURE *gets up and throws the prayer shawl high into the smoke*

A GIANT FORM *wraps itself in it and rises singing into the sky*
Hear, O Israel.
He our God,
He the One—

THE CHIMNEY *crumbles*

THE CREATURE *is struck, dying*
Hear, O Israel
He our God,
He the One—

FOOTPRINTS IN THE SAND
Come gathering, gathering, Michael,
a time is there again,
a time which had run out—
gather it up—
gather it up—

MICHAEL *stoops, walking in the footprints*

MICHAEL
He who goes gathering death moments
needs not a basket, but a heart to fill—

Curtain

Scene Twelve

Frontier of the neighboring country. Heath and moorland

MICHAEL
All signposts point downward.
Foxgloves grow here—
no, not gloves but fingers
grow here like weeds,
not like those flowers
with which Miriam filled her little shoe
when she broke the strap:
"The gloved fingers will stroke you,"
she said,
"as you sew it up."
The fingers which grow here
are fingers of men's hands.

VOICES OF THE FINGERS
We are the fingers of the killers.
Each one wears a premeditated death
like a false moonstone.
Look, Michael, like this—

A FINGER (*reaching for* MICHAEL'*s throat*)
My finger's specialty was strangling,
the compression of the windpipe
with a slight turn to the right.

(*Gurgling noise*)

MICHAEL *has sunk to the ground*

VOICE OF THE SECOND KILLER
Your knees, Michael,
your wrists—
do you hear, of glass—
everything is fragile on earth.
A good man's not afraid of dust,
and here's a wineglassful of blood—

MICHAEL
Great death, great death, come—

VOICE OF THE SECOND KILLER
That's out of fashion.
Here are the small dainty deaths—
your neck—
just there where the hair gets downy—

VOICE OF THE THIRD KILLER
In the name of Science—
this injection—
Whoever volunteers turns light-colored
like rotten wood—

LONG BONY FINGER
Don't be afraid.
I want neither to bid good night to your windpipe
nor to be rough to your joints.
I'm only the professorial finger
of the new wisdom.
I want a little conversation with your gray matter—

MICHAEL
Away—

VOICE OF THE PROFESSORIAL FINGER
Job is grown weak,
tired organ-grinder of a once-fresh tune.
The seas have been drawn out into horsepower on one hand
and into tap water on the other.
Their ebb and flow are in the hands of a moon-man.
Michael the shoemaker
sews sole and uppers together
with his waste-product thread—
Shoemaker saint!
Were the fountain pens asleep among you
which should have bought your people free?

VOICE OF THE WILDLY GESTICULATING FINGER
I am the conductor's finger
I conducted the music for their good night.

March music is heard
Old the world had to become
before the hate
which bloodily sought
to solve the Jew puzzle
hit on the notion
of banishing it from the world with music—

The music becomes weaker. THE FINGERS, *held by a giant finger on strings, dance their respective activities.* THE PROFESSORIAL FINGER taps MICHAEL *on the head. The Earth falls like a black apple*

MICHAEL (*shouting*)
Is that star lost?

ECHO
Lost!

MICHAEL'S VOICE
Hear me . . .

Curtain

Scene Thirteen

Open field. MICHAEL *lying on the ground, gets up.* A FARMER *with a cow on a halter approaches*

MICHAEL
The finger last pointed in this direction,
murderers betray the murderer in the end.
How peaceful in daylight this spot looks.
The crickets sing,
a jay calls its mate.
The cow has the primeval face
of a creature just stroked by its Creator's hand.
As everywhere, the farmer is tasting out the secret of the wheat grain.

(*To the* FARMER)
A good evening to you,
would there be a shoemaker's in this neighborhood?

FARMER
You come from over there, across the frontier?
You've death on your brow—

MICHAEL
How can you tell?

FARMER
When a man has something shining between the eyes,
big as a snowflake—

MICHAEL
May be
that the death of my people shines in me.

FARMER
A Pole are you or even—a Jew?

MICHAEL
On this earth I am both.

FARMER
That is much!

There beyond the big meadow
is the way to the village.
Next door to the inn garden
is the shoemaker's shop.

A CHILD *has joined them.* MICHAEL *pulls out his shepherd's pipe and plays*

CHILD
If I'd a pipe like that
I'd be piping day and night,
I'd be piping in my sleep—

MICHAEL
It's from a dead child—

FARMER (*repeating*)
From a dead child—

MICHAEL
From a boy
who was murdered—

FARMER
Who was murdered—

MICHAEL
As his parents were being driven to their death
he ran after in his shirt—

FARMER
After in his shirt—

MICHAEL
On this pipe he piped to God for help—

FARMER
Piped to God for help—

MICHAEL
Then a soldier struck him dead—

FARMER
Then a soldier struck him dead—

MICHAEL *plays his pipe. Children, calves, sheep, and foals come frisking to it.* THE MOTHERS *lift up their babies. Some* MEN, *sickle in hand, lower their heads*

Curtain

Scene Fourteen

House of the village schoolteacher. In the garden stand the SCHOOLTEACHER *and his* SON *looking up into the great linden tree.* BOYS *are practicing stone-throwing at a scarecrow, made of old bits of war gear and metal parts, in the plowed field*

BOY (*after throwing*)
That sounded as if someone had cried out.

CHILD
Yes, it was Isidor the peddler's voice
as we drove him out of the village.
Oy, he said, oy,
and there he lay in the ditch.

BOY
And reached out for his cap,
look, like this, with his hand turned inward,
just as he used to do when weighing things—
and Hans called out:
"Has the evening sun caught your cap?"
and gave him another to remember us by—

SCHOOLTEACHER
There hangs the bee swarm.
Hark to the music it makes.
There'll be honey,
never has the linden tree flowered so well,
what luck
that it was spared by men's wars.

BOY
How nice it smells here, Father, O!
And then the honey on our bread, O!

MOTHER (*from the house*)
I'll just pick the lettuce
and chop the chervil for the soup,
dinner will soon be ready.

Why don't you get out your butterfly net, Hans?
Look at all those moths on the thyme—

BOY (*picking up a stone*)
Just a minute!

SCHOOLTEACHER
Leave the scarecrow alone,
too much corpse smell in the field,
the crows get more and more—

BOY (*pointing at* MICHAEL)
No, there I'll throw it.

SCHOOLTEACHER
Don't do that!

BOY
Why yesterday and not today?

SCHOOLTEACHER
Although I teach arithmetic,
that's a mathematical puzzle I can't solve—

MICHAEL *walks past*

BOY (*to himself*)
Yesterday I'd have sent the stone after him,
it'd have fallen near the manure pit, I expect,
after first tripping two feet.
Today it stays in my hand,
but I'll throw it into the pond,
to give something a fright at least—

Curtain

Scene Fifteen

Shoemaker's shop in frontier village

SHOEMAKER
No, not like that, no truly!
Only—perhaps you are for us
like shoes of former times, of long ago.
They fitted nobody,
good leather, but unsuited—
not for our climate,
for the deserts perhaps,
for the Holy Land perhaps,
for those markets perhaps
where the Isidors hawk their wares differently from us—
but of course as things went with you then—
no, that we didn't want—
not like that—

MICHAEL
Since Abraham wandered forth from Ur
we have spent our efforts
to build our house toward HIM
as others build facing the sun—
True, many turned themselves in the opposite direction—
Old shepherds let the star clocks strike unheeded
and slept like Isidor the pawnbroker with crooked fingers—
But there was a boy—
Master, the sole cries out in my hand,
it reeks of death—

SHOEMAKER
May be so,
for a dying steer stretched out its paws
and then—

A MAN *enters, holding a small child by the hand*
Are my shoes ready?

SHOEMAKER
My assistant's just working on them—

MICHAEL
This sole can't be patched,
it's torn up the middle.

MAN
Make me a new sole then—

CHILD
Father, this is the man
who had the pipe.
There it is on the flowerpot.
O let me play it!

MAN
You don't play strangers' pipes.

CHILD (*crying*)
The pipe—

MAN
She's crying
because she wants her mother.
She always wants something:
One day it's the blackbird
which used to come for scraps
and disappeared,
another it's the old sheepdog
which ran across the rails
and was run over—

MICHAEL (*aloud*)
Everything begins with wanting.
Even this here—

(*He lets earth from the flowerpot trickle through his hands*)

And these here—

(*He points to the hides from which the shoes are cut*)

CHILD
The pipe—

MAN
I'll buy you a pipe.
When you've got it,
all the children will follow you
and give you their toys—

CHILD
No, *this* pipe,
then the cows'll come and the little calves.

THE MAN *takes the child by the hand, and as they go out*

SHOEMAKER'S WIFE (*at the door*)
I want something too.
Farmer, when'll you have a roast to spare?
With me it's the mouth
that does the wanting.
What kind of want is that?

Curtain

SCENE SIXTEEN

A farmhouse bedroom

CHILD *asleep*

MAN
Teeth everywhere,
do you hear how it rattles?
Hollow tooth where oats should be.
Black horse climbing,
shaking its mane,
and showing its teeth.
The calves drink with their teeth
and fleck the udders with blood—
the rye-stalks bitten off—teeth without rats—
Do you hear it, Wife,
here in the room,
there, there!

(*She points to the wall*)
Teeth where bricks should be—
Wife, the bricklayer must to the gallows—

WIFE
Be quiet now,
the child's asleep,
the fever's very high!

MAN
Now it's rattling,
the whole house rattles—
(*His teeth chatter*)

CHILD (*in a dream*)
All the trees go walking
all the trees go walking
lift up their root-feet and walk
when I pipe—

MAN (*singing*)
All the shades go walking,
come, dear hearse-cloth,
cover up the white moon-tooth for me.
Wasn't it a milk-tooth
which dropped from his mouth with the pipe—
Wife, wife,

the milk has teeth,
teeth—

A knock on the window

MAN (*opening the window*)
Who's there?

BAKER
Baker Hans.
Here's a sugar pretzel for little Annie.
The iron pretzel,
my good shop-sign from the Jew baker in Poland,
has turned red.
They're whispering already.
The dead children don't touch the pretzel crumbs
I scatter for them into the night,
and drag the malt away.
Lately they sat like a swarm of wasps on the shop counter.
The squint-eyed child stamped its feet on the wood,
as if to warm itself,
then it climbed bolt upright to the ceiling
and hung there like flypaper.
In the morning it fell off.
The flies had eaten it up.

MAN (*rattling the windowpane, which is lit up by the moon*)
Look, that's how you did with the squint-eyed one—
Here's the pretzel,
there's the pretzel,
till it had ceased to squint.
Now it's squinting your day away,
as mine is chewed by the milk-tooth.

BAKER
They say
you once killed a holy child?

MAN
Stuff and nonsense!
All children are holy.

POSTMAN (*coming on*)
Why do you quarrel for first place in child murder?

BAKER
Sorter of cry-baby parcels!
Did no sender
write "Fragile" on them?

POSTMAN
My orders were
to heed the addressee,
not the sender.

DOCTOR (*coming out of the bedroom*)
Your child—

WIFE (*coming on*)
The child is dead!

Curtain

Scene Seventeen

Country road. On either side, thick pine forest. MICHAEL *walking. Behind a pine tree,* THE MAN *is standing*

MICHAEL
A look has pierced my back,
I am held fast.

They look at one another

MAN
If he hadn't thrown his head back
I shouldn't have struck him down,
the milk-tooth wouldn't have fallen out with the pipe.
But—that was contrary to Order—
to throw the head back—
that had to be corrected.
And where did he pipe to?
A secret signal?
A signal through the air—
beyond all control—
Help, shoemaker,
the milk-tooth is growing out of the earth—
beginning to gnaw at me—
right through my shoe—
my feet are crumbling—
becoming earth—

(*Shrieking*)
Where's the Order in all this, the
World Order—
I am alive,
I am not dead—
not hung—
not burned—
not thrown live into the earth——

(*At the top of his voice*)
It's a mistake, a mistake,
I'm crumbling, crumbling—
I'm a stump—
sitting on the sand
that a moment ago was my flesh—

The air has opened out into circles. In the first circle appears THE EMBRYO *in its mother's womb, with the primal light on its brow*

VOICE
Child with the light of God,
read in the hands of the murderer—

MAN
My hands, my hands—
don't leave me, O my hands—

(*His hands crumble off*)

The horizon opens out as the greatest of the circles. A BLEEDING MOUTH *appears like a setting sun*

VOICE
Open,
dumb mouth of Samuel!

VOICE OF SAMUEL
Eli!

The mother's womb dissolves in smoke. The primal light fastens on to MICHAEL'*s brow*

MICHAEL
Crumbling one!
His eyes become holes—
the light seeks out other mirrors.
I see through the holes—
glasses for the sun's eclipse—
into your skull
which frames that world
which you as commanded have packed
inside it,
as in a soldier's knapsack—
There it lies—twitching,
an insect star with wings torn off—
In it stirs a hand
that stole a lightning bolt—
A raven consumes a human leg—
lightning consumes the raven—
I see nothing more—

VOICE
Footprints of Israel,
gather yourselves together!
Last earthly moments of Israel,
gather yourselves together!
Last moments of suffering,
gather yourselves together!

MICHAEL
Under my feet it jumps up.
From my hands it plunges down.
My heart pours something out—

VOICE
Your shoes are worn to pieces—come!

MICHAEL *is gathered up and vanishes*

FINAL CURTAIN

Postscript to ELI

This mystery play has as its leading figure Michael, a young shoemaker. In Hassidic mysticism he is one of the secret Servants of God who, thirty-six in number (and quite unaware of it themselves), carry the invisible universe. According to the prophet Isaiah, the Lord puts the arrow he has used back in its quiver so that it may remain in darkness. Thus Michael feels, darkly, the inner call to seek the murderer of the child Eli, the child who raised to heaven the shepherd's pipe with which he used to call the cattle together—"like the stag or roebuck before it drinks at the spring"—to pipe to

God, as his parents were being taken away to their death. A young soldier, believing this to be a secret signal (symbol of unbelief), struck the boy dead.

Michael goes his quiet way through this legend made of truth, sees in the shadow thrown by a light on Eli's death shirt the face of the murderer, and in transcendental fashion experiences once more during his travels the bloody events of our forsaken age. The murderer, when Michael finally sees him face to face, crumbles to dust before the divine light shining from Michael's countenance (picture of remorse).

In this world of night, where a secret equilibrium seems to reign, the victim is always innocence. The child Eli and the child of the murderer both die, victims of evil.

This mystery play was the outcome of a terrible experience of the Hitler time at the height of its smoke and flame, and was written down in a few nights after my flight to Sweden.

The shepherd's pipe raised in desperation by a child to God—attempted outbreak of the human in the face of horror.

The soldier: "If he hadn't thrown his head back, I shouldn't have struck him down . . ."

That was a sign beyond all control—could be a secret signal.

No more trust in good on earth.

Written in a rhythm which must make the Hassidic mystical fervor visible also in mime to the performer—the encounter with the divine radiance which accompanies each of our everyday words. Always designed to raise the unutterable to a transcendental level, so as to make it bearable and in this night of nights to give a hint of the holy darkness in which quiver and arrow are hidden.

THE LIFE AND WORKS OF NELLY SACHS

By HARRY ZOHN

WHEN Nelly Sachs was awarded her share of the Nobel Prize for Literature on December 10, 1966, a date that coincided with her seventy-fifth birthday, international prominence came almost overnight to a poetess who had been living and working in relative obscurity. Until then she had been known and her full stature recognized only by those able to read her work in the original German. Fellow poets and critics like Ingeborg Bachmann, Ilse Aichinger, Hans Magnus Enzensberger, Beda Allemann, Paul Celan, and Walter A. Berendsohn paid tribute to her long before her work was widely disseminated. Enzensberger called her work "the only poetic testimony which can hold its own next to the speechless horror of documentary reports," and Kurt Pinthus described it as "the presumably final expression in the German language of the ancestral sequence of six thousand years which began with the psalmists and the prophets."

What is perhaps the most characteristic and most poignant comment made on the work of Nelly Sachs is contained in an open letter written her a few years ago by the German-Jewish poetess Hilde Domin, who, like Miss Sachs, had tasted the bitter bread of exile. Miss Domin speaks of a nightmarish memory: those postwar pictures of concentration camps showing piles of corpses, with the dead resembling horribly twisted puppets. Not until fifteen years later, when Hilde Domin began reading the poetry of Nelly Sachs, were those dead buried for her and only then did they enter the memories we normally have of the departed. Through her painfully beautiful allegorical and metaphorical variations on her one basic theme, the Holocaust, Nelly Sachs has given voice to the millions who are all too often recalled only in the form of cold, merciless seven-digit figures, and she has planted "lilies on the equator of anguish."

In this sense the writings of Nelly Sachs must have provided a great catharsis for thousands of readers—survivors of the Nazi horror as well as those who can empathize only on the basis of historical and poetic accounts. The transmutation of her personal tragedy into a poetic vision was also therapy for the poetess herself. For years a psychic malady sent her in and out of sanatoriums, and only the tangible evidences of recognition and warm expressions of kinship and friendship that reached her in the last decade of her life enabled her to keep the past down and the demons at bay. "Death gave me my language," Nelly Sachs once said, and her statement, "Writing is my mute outcry—I only wrote because I had to free myself," stamps her as a soul sister of Franz Kafka.

Miss Sachs, who described her work as "a sheaf of lightning on an acre of paper," regarded herself as the vessel of a higher idea: she did not seek to become the poetess of the Holocaust; the subject sought her out. "The terrible experiences which brought me to the verge of death and darkness were my teacher. My metaphors are my wounds; only in this way can my work be understood." Some of the metaphors that recur in her poetry are star, dust, sand (symbolizing the past, the inexorable passing of time as in an hourglass), and butterfly (signifying transcendence and re-creation). The basic configuration of her work is the relationship between the pursuers and the pursued, the murderers and the murdered, the age-old drama involving executioners and their victims. But Nelly Sachs's later work goes far beyond its point of departure. The agony of the Nazi victims is viewed as but a phase in the millennial travail of the Jewish people, in the ongoing history of human suffering everywhere. This history, from Abraham's anguish to Auschwitz and Hiroshima, is projected into the visionary realm of a "landscape of screams": the leitmotifs of flight and transformation are projected into a chiliastic future not bound by time or space.

Nelly (Leonie) Sachs was born in Berlin on December 10, 1891, as the only child of William Sachs, a well-to-do industrialist, and Margarethe Karger Sachs. Her father was a music lover and an amateur pianist, and the artistic home environment instilled in the child a love of literature and a desire to become a dancer. In the large garden of her home in the fashionable Tiergarten district, the delicate girl played with a pet fawn and read Novalis, Hölderlin, Dostoevsky, Stifter, and other writers. Her education was for the most part a private one. At the age of seventeen she started writing, producing mostly atmospheric, slightly melancholy, neo-Romantic poetry in traditional, rhymed forms, including some sonnets, but also puppet plays with a fairy-tale flavor. Stefan Zweig, the sensitive and helpful mentor of so many budding writers, early recognized the worth of Nelly Sachs's efforts, and despite the fact that they were not in the mainstream of the Expressionism current at that time, he discerned a certain ecstatic quality in her poetry. Yet there was little or nothing in her early work to indicate the future flowering of her genius that was brought about by the ordeal of her people.

In 1921 Nelly Sachs published a 124-page volume entitled *Legenden und Erzählungen* (Legends and Stories). Since Nelly Sachs had grown up in an assimilationist environment, in a Christian intellectual world tinged with mysticism, it is not surprising that some of these legends are downright Christological, one of them being called *"Das Christusbild"* (The Icon). As a young writer Nelly Sachs was rooted in the thought world of German Romanticism, which means the Catholic Middle Ages, and of German mysticism, particularly that of Jakob Böhme, the seventeenth-century thinker. She was especially influenced by Böhme's insight that the godhead, and indeed all things, are characterized by an antithesis, the harmony and opposition of light and darkness, good and evil, gentleness and ferocity, love and hate. In succeeding years some of her verse appeared in newspapers like the *Vossische Zeitung* and the *Berliner Tageblatt,* but a collection of her poetry which Leo Hirsch, the editor of the latter paper, prepared for the prestigious Insel-Verlag could no longer be published. Between 1933 and 1938 the poetess was still able to publish in *Die Jugend, Der Morgen,* and other Jewish papers and periodicals. But she remained largely unknown. After 1933 much of her work was lost, and the poetess herself later refused to acknowledge her earlier work and to have it republished.

Nelly Sachs became interested in the common roots of Judaism and Christianity, and in the *Zohar,* the "Book of Splendor," the great cabalistic work dating from the late thirteenth century, she found many insights similar to Böhme's. Under the influence of Martin Buber she read the Old Testament, particularly the Psalms. Jewish mysticism, specifically Hasidism, became another marked influence on her work.

Following the death of her father in 1930, the poetess was caught up in the tragedy of German Jewry, seeing friends and relatives carried off to their doom. In 1940 she and her ailing mother were saved from being sent to a forced labor camp and worse by the opportunity to emigrate to Sweden through the good offices of Selma Lagerlöf, Dr. Einar Salln, and Prince Eugene of the Swedish Royal Court who had been alerted to the plight of the two women by a courageous German lady named Gudrun Harlan Dähnert.

Nelly Sachs had long read, and been inspired by, the great Swedish writer Selma Lagerlöf; she had corresponded with her since she was fifteen and inscribed her volume of stories to this "shining example." By an irony of fate, Selma Lagerlöf died a few months before her friends were able to reach Stockholm.

At first Nelly Sachs was busy learning Swedish, achieving such competence in that language that she was able to make a modest living by translating Swedish poetry into German, publishing several highly praised volumes of translations from Johannes Edfelt (who in turn translated her work into Swedish), Gunnar Ekelöf, Erik Lindegren, and others. Above all, she devoted most of her time to taking care of her mother, who died in 1950 at the age of seventy-eight.

During the years in which she tended her mother, the victims of the Holocaust were ever-present in the conversations, the memories, the dreams and nightmares of the two women. Nelly Sachs evoked them at night and gave voice to their unspeakable anguish. Although she had occasion to associate with young Swedish writers, the poetess lived in relative cultural isolation until the 1960s, lacking contact with contemporary German literature and its practitioners, even with the living language.

Stipends and prizes eased her life materially in her last years, and her seventieth birthday was marked by the publication of her collected poetry under the title *Fahrt ins Staublose* (Journey into a Dustless Realm, 1961).

In 1960 she had gone to her native country for the first time in twenty years to receive the Droste-Hülshoff Prize. The award bears the name of the foremost poetess of nineteenth-century Germany and indicates the tradition in which Nelly Sachs is rooted and her rank, together with Else Lasker-Schüler and Gertrud Kolmar, as one of the foremost German-Jewish poetesses of our century.

In October 1965, she went to Frankfurt am Main to receive, in historic St. Paul's Church, the Peace Prize of the German Book Trade. She was the first female recipient of a prize previously awarded to such illustrious men as Albert Schweitzer, Martin Buber, Thornton Wilder, Paul Tillich, and Max Tau. The citation which accompanied the Peace Prize includes the following passage: "The poetic works of Nelly Sachs are a testimony to Jewish destiny in times that were inhuman, and they represent a reconciliation. Her lyrics and plays are works in the German language at its best; they are works of forgiveness, of deliverance, of peace."

In her original small, two-room apartment at Bergsundstrand 23, overlooking Lake Mälar, which was decorated in her favorite colors, royal blue and pale pink, the tiny, frail woman was a gracious hostess to an ever-growing circle of friends and admirers until her death on May 2, 1970. Her will provided that about one-half of the Nobel Prize money and all proceeds from her books should go toward the care of homeless children, irrespective of race or religion.

Nelly Sachs's poetry is not easy of access, being ecstatic, mystical, and visionary in quality. Reflecting her concept of an "invisible universe," it has cosmic pretensions and an intricate symbolism born of a desire to go to the roots of our age and of the human condition. Through her poetry she attempted to make the inscrutable happenings of our time transparent and meaningful. Although almost her entire work consists of unrhymed, free-flowing, rhythmically structured verse, Nelly Sachs wrote with the careful craftsmanship of a Hölderlin, a Novalis, or a Rilke. There is something age-old and timeless about her highly imagistic language, an exquisite, occasionally idiosyncratic German harking back to mysticism and Romanticism, flavored with the Hebrew Scriptures (which Nelly Sachs could read only in German translation), and replete with images drawn from Jewish mysticism. An entirely undogmatic religiosity may be discerned in her work. The figures of the Old Testament which she invokes are mythical representatives of basic religious experiences. Neither the Old Testament God of vengeance nor the New Testament concept of God as the living father shapes her work. As in Hasidism, her God is both transcendent and immanent. Christ is viewed as the supreme incarnation of human suffering, and the poetess longs for a return of earthly things to the supernatural realm.

With volume after volume published since the end of World War II, Nelly Sachs has disproved Theodor Wiesengrund-Adorno's dictum that after Auschwitz it is no longer possible to create a poem. Writing to her cousin Manfred George in 1946, Nelly Sachs expressed the hope that after the war Jewish artists would heed the voice of their blood, so that the age-old springs might flow again. As for herself—"I shall not cease to follow the fiery and starry road of our people, step by step, and to bear witness with my poor talents."

Her first collection of poetry after the creative caesura of 1933—

When the great terror came
I fell dumb

—appeared in East Berlin in 1947 under the title *In den Wohnungen des Todes* (In the Habitations of Death). Together with the play *Eli. Ein Mysterienspiel vom Leiden Israels* (Eli. A Mystery Play About the Sufferings of Israel, 1943), it is the fountainhead of her future work. This volume, dedicated "to my dead brothers and sisters," contains not only such striking poems as "O the Chimneys" and "A Dead Child Speaks," but also cycles entitled "Prayers for the Dead Fiancé," "Choruses after Midnight" and rhymed "Epitaphs Written on Air" (for a peddler, a lady painter, a dancer, a Spinoza scholar, a feeble-minded woman, a rock collector, a puppet player, etc., all identified by their initials). The motif of flight and pursuit, the symbol of the hunter and his quarry are at the center of her poetic thought, and for their expression she favored the cyclic form.

Miss Sachs's next volume, *Sternver-*

dunkelung (Eclipse of the Stars, 1949), dedicated to the memory of her father, contains poems expressing an unquenchable faith in the indestructibility of the people of Israel and the significance of its mission. Poems like "Now Abraham Has Seized the Root of the Winds" and "In the Land of Israel" are expressive of the poetess's pride in, and hopes for, the newly founded state of Israel.

Nelly Sachs felt that in our time millions have died false deaths, manmade, machine-produced, mass deaths. In one of her most striking poems in *Sternverdunkelung* she describes a Golem Death; he becomes the navel of the world, his skeleton spreads its arms to bestow a false blessing.

Und niemand weiss weiter (And No One Knows How To Go On) appeared in 1957 and *Flucht und Verwandlung* (Flight and Metamorphosis) the following year. A volume issued in 1965, *Späte Gedichte* (Late Poems), includes Nelly Sachs's extended poetic sequence *Glühende Rätsel* (Glowing Riddles). The poetess made a recording of some of these lyrical fragments—in the manner of a private incantation, as it were, her rendition being gentle yet insistent, evocative and hortatory. This is curiously compressed, enigmatic, elliptic poetry, poems with a new kind of conciseness that have penetrated to the mystic border region where language touches silence and reduces everything earthly to its barest substance. *Die Suchende,* a short poetic cycle written in the summer of 1966, was issued on the occasion of Nelly Sachs's seventy-fifth birthday, and now her longtime publishers, Suhrkamp Verlag, have introduced a volume of *Letzte Gedichte* (Last Poems).

Nelly Sachs's collected dramatic works, issued in 1962 under the title *Zeichen im Sand* (Signs in the Sand), consist of fourteen dramas—brief experimental plays, cultic plays, dramatic happenings, playlets, and scenic studies. The poetess apparently began to express in these *"szenische Dichtungen"* what she could no longer express in verse. Reality coalesces with vision and the word spills over into pantomime and the dance. She envisaged a new kind of ballet in which there would be a symbiosis between words and gestures, expression and statement, and where words would be uttered —breathed forth, as it were—and illuminated, enhanced through rhythm and movement. In general, these bold scenic studies defy staging. The direction for one of them is "This scene must be sought on the human retina." Of another Nelly Sachs has said that in it "the eternal game between hunter and quarry, hangman and victim is played on the deepest plane." The drama is permeated by this terrible question of mankind: "Why does it take evil to create a saint, a martyr?"

The play *Eli* was written with great excitement and visionary fervor in a few nights in 1943, after Nelly Sachs had received crushing news about unspeakable atrocities in Nazi Europe. It deals with the cosmic aftermath of the Holocaust and takes place in a destroyed Polish ghetto among the few survivors of the carnage who live very self-consciously on the sites of past horrors and try to do some physical and psychic rebuilding. The past and the present, the dead and the living, the actual and the symbolic commingle. In seventeen loosely connected scenes the tragedy of an eight-year-old shepherd boy during the war is presented through flashbacks and is interwoven with the legend of the *Lamed Vovniks,* the Thirty-Six Just Men, those who support the "invisible universe," who have the gift of unbroken vision and of seeking cosmic connections, who forever restore the balance between destructive and curative forces in the world, who are destined to wear out Israel's wandering shoes. One of these elect is Michael, and he is, appropriately enough, a shoemaker, plying the same trade as Jakob Böhme. The boy Eli, who has raised his shepherd's flute heavenward in his anguish, has been murdered in his nightshirt by a member of the German occupation forces. Michael's search for the murderer actually provides the only continuity of action in the play. When Michael has tracked this soldier down, vengeance is not for him; seared by the radiance of Michael's Baal Shem-like glance and gnawed at by Eli's tooth, the German breaks down and literally disintegrates, whereupon Michael, his earthly mission completed, goes to his reward.

In her notes on this play, Nelly Sachs says: "In this world of night, where a secret equilibrium seems to reign, the victim is always innocence." She is intent upon lifting the unutterable onto a transcendent plane, "so as to make it bearable and in this night of nights to give a hint of the holy darkness in which quiver and arrow are hidden." In language replete with Hasidic-mystical fervor, with her syntax sometimes suggesting Yiddish cadences, Nelly Sachs has written a play rich in allusion and full of woe and wonder, one that brings into play the techniques of mime, music, and the dance. Both before and after its German stage premiere in 1962, *Eli* was presented over the radio in Germany, Sweden, and England, and an operatic version by Walter Steffens has been performed in Dortmund.

Nelly Sachs's poetic and dramatic work, so reflective of her empathy with her martyred people and with suffering humanity everywhere, are not so much accusations as plaints of someone who has faith in the illuminating and curative power of poetry, of the word as such. As she invokes the memory of the martyred, the poetess mourns the degradation of man. She is concerned that after this trial by fire the world might continue on its accustomed course and cheat the time of sorrow out of its hard-won meaning.

Peoples of the earth
Do not destroy the universe of words
let not the knife of hatred lacerate
the sound born together with the first
breath.

"To those building the new house" her advice is: "Build, but do not weep away the minutes . . ." She would remind her coreligionists that hate and revenge cannot be the building stones of anything new and that Jewish chosenness also involves the burden, and perhaps the privilege, of having to endure more than others.

There is a passage in the *Zohar* which says that "there are places in the heavens above us which open up only to the voice of song." Such a voice was that of Nelly Sachs.

Harry Zohn is professor of Germanic languages and literature at Brandeis University.

THE 1966 PRIZE

By KJELL STRÖMBERG

NELLY SACHS shared the 1966 Nobel Prize for Literature with the Israeli writer S. Y. Agnon. She received her half of the Prize, 150,000 Swedish crowns worth about $50,000, "for her outstanding lyrical and dramatic writings, which interpret Israel's destiny with touching strength," according to the Swedish Academy's short account of the reasons for the award. The Prize was a particularly welcome present as December 10 coincided with her seventy-fifth birthday.

In Sweden, where she had come to live in 1940, Nelly Sachs gradually built up a fairly good position for herself in the small world of letters, not only through her own writing, which was first published in East Berlin and then in Western Germany, but also mainly through her masterly translations of some famous Swedish poets, Erik Lindegren, Gunnar Ekelöf, and Johannes Edfelt. All three were either actual or future members of the Swedish Academy, and they loyally repaid their moral debt by translating a number of her poems in their turn. Olof Lagercrantz, the literary editor of Sweden's biggest newspaper, *Dagens Nyheter,* devoted a whole series of articles to her work, which was later published in one volume called *Creation Continues.* Coming as it did at the right moment, this book helped to pave the way toward Nelly Sachs's award.

It was not, however, until 1963 that the candidacy of Nelly Sachs was put forward in earnest. A report on her work was written for the Academy by her great friend, Johannes Edfelt, a lyric poet and translator and an essayist who specialized in German literature, who was at that time president of the Swedish P. E. N. Club. He refrains from any direct recommendation, but his whole report expresses unqualified admiration. He describes how the rootless immigrant Nelly Sachs reached her maturity and her authority as a lyric and dramatic poet on Swedish soil, and he ends with these words: "In the free rhythm of her verse she renews the German poetic tradition belonging to the great names such as Hölderlin, Novalis and Rilke . . . It is thanks to this that she has been able to make the tragedy of the Jewish people her own tragedy, and to penetrate so deeply into the human condition of the refugee."

The Swedish Academy was apparently not entirely convinced by this opinion from a future colleague, and so it also sought the advice of two German literary historians, Professor Walter A. Berendsohn of Hamburg University, who had been living in Stockholm for a long time, and Walter Jens of Tübingen University. Berendsohn declared that, without any doubt, Nelly Sachs was "one of the most important figures in the living literature of the present time," and in awarding her the Nobel Prize the Swedish Academy "would also be paying deserved tribute to the Jewish people, who had been so sorely tried, and whose very existence was still threatened." Jens went still further: "I know of no one else among living writers, when all is said and done, who is more worthy to receive the Nobel Prize than Nelly Sachs. This Jewess has, in her second homeland and writing in German, restored its ancient distinction to the language of her persecutors."

Nelly Sachs was somewhat alarmed by the crowd of friends and journalists who swarmed into her tiny apartment after the announcement of the award to congratulate her and to hear what she had to say. She hoped that at last her dream of many years would come true, to visit Israel. When asked whether she had any other plans, the laureate replied that she was particularly looking forward to giving material help, with her Prize money, to the very dear friend who had made it possible for her to find a refuge in Sweden, and who was now living under difficult conditions in Dresden.

Nelly Sachs bravely faced the photographers, although she was obviously unused to this kind of appearance. Her smile expressed a strange mixture of happiness and sorrow as, standing at her window overlooking one of Stockholm's numerous canals, she briefly sketched her self-portrait with touching grace and humility: "I feel myself to be, solely and exclusively, a human being. When one has lived through so many horrors, one cannot look on oneself as belonging to any particular nation. Of course, I am a Swedish citizen, but my language is German, and it is that which links me with other human beings." She spoke of her visit to Germany the previous year and said: "At first I felt that going back there was very difficult; but then I met some young writers who seemed very different from the older generations."

For the official ceremony, Nelly Sachs wore a long dress of midnight blue velvet. After Agnon's long speech in Hebrew, Nelly Sachs's short statement, delivered in German, in a weak voice which trembled with emotion but was perfectly audible, gave the impression of fresh spring water bubbling into the desert.

Translation by Camilla Sykes.

Jean-Paul Sartre

1964

"For his work which, rich in ideas and filled with the spirit of freedom and the quest for truth, has exerted a far-reaching influence on our age"

ANNOUNCEMENT

By ANDERS ÖSTERLING

MEMBER
OF THE SWEDISH ACADEMY

THIS YEAR the Nobel Prize for Literature has been granted by the Swedish Academy to the French writer Jean-Paul Sartre "for his work which, rich in ideas and filled with the spirit of freedom and the quest for truth, has exerted a far-reaching influence on our age."

It will be recalled that the laureate has made it known that he did not wish to accept the Prize. The fact that he has declined this distinction does not in the least modify the validity of the award. Under the circumstances, however, the Academy can only state that the presentation of the Prize cannot take place.

In a public announcement, printed in *Le Figaro* of October 23, 1964, Mr. Sartre expressed his regret that his refusal of the Prize had given rise to scandal, and wished it to be known that, unaware of the irrevocability of the Swedish Academy's decisions, he had sought by letter to prevent their choice falling upon him. In this letter, he specified that his refusal was not meant to slight the Swedish Academy but was rather based on personal and objective reasons of his own.

As to personal reasons, Mr. Sartre pointed out that due to his conception of the writer's task he had always declined official honors and thus his present act was not unprecedented. He had similarly refused membership in the Legion of Honor and had not desired to enter the Collège de France, and he would refuse the Lenin Prize if it were offered to him. He stated that for a writer to accept such an honor would be to associate his personal commitments with the awarding institution;

and above all, a writer should not allow himself to be turned into an institution.

Among his objective reasons, Mr. Sartre listed his belief that interchange between East and West must take place between men and between cultures without the intervention of institutions. Furthermore, since the conferment of past Prizes did not, in his opinion, represent equally writers of all ideologies and nations, he felt that his acceptance might be undesirably and unjustly interpreted.

Mr. Sartre closed his remarks with a message of affection for the Swedish public.

[*Publisher's Note:* At the request of M. Sartre, none of his works are reprinted in the Nobel Prize Library.]

George Bernard Shaw

1925

"For his work which is marked by both idealism and humanity, its stimulating satire often being infused with a singular poetic beauty"

Illustrated by CHARLES MOZLEY

PRESENTATION ADDRESS

By PER HALLSTRÖM

CHAIRMAN OF THE NOBEL COMMITTEE
OF THE SWEDISH ACADEMY

GEORGE BERNARD SHAW showed in the novels of his youth the same conception of the world and the same attitude to social problems that he has maintained ever since. This provides a better defense for him than anything else against the repeated accusations of lack of honesty and of acting as a professional buffoon at the court of democracy. From the very beginning his convictions have been so firm that it seems as if the general process of development, without having any substantial influence on himself, has carried him along to the tribune from which he now speaks. His ideas were those of a somewhat abstract logical radicalism; hence they were far from new, but they received from him a new definiteness and brilliance. In him these ideas combined with a ready wit, a complete absence of respect for any kind of convention, and the merriest humor—all gathered together in an extravagance which has scarcely ever before appeared in literature.

What puzzled people most was his rollicking gaiety: they were ready to believe that the whole thing was a game and a desire to startle. This was so far from being true that Shaw himself has been able to declare with a greater justice that his careless attitude was a mere stratagem: he had to fool people into laughing so they should not hit upon the idea of hanging him. But we know very well that he would hardly have been frightened out of his outspokenness by anything that might have happened, and that he chose his weapons just as much because they suited him as because they were the most effective. He wielded them with the certitude of genius, which rested on an absolutely quiet conscience and a faithful conviction.

Early he became a prophet of revolutionary doctrines, quite varied in their value, in the spheres of esthetics and sociology, and he soon won for himself a notable position as a debater, a popular speaker, and a journalist. He set his mark on the English theater as a champion of Ibsen and as an opponent of superficial tradition, both English and Parisian. His own dramatic production began quite late, at the age of thirty-six, in order to help satisfy the demands that he had aroused. He wrote his plays with instinctive sureness, based on the certainty that he had a great deal to say.

In this casual manner he came to create what is to some extent a new kind of dramatic art, which must be judged according to its own special principles. Its novelty does not lie so much in structure and form; from his wide-awake and trained knowledge of the theater, he promptly and quite simply obtains any scenic effect he feels necessary for his ends. But the directness with which he puts his ideas into practice is entirely his own; and so too are the bellicosity, the mobility, and the multiplicity of his ideas.

In France he has been called the Molière of the twentieth century; and there is some truth in the parallel, for Shaw himself believes that he was following classical tendencies in dramatic art. By classicism he means the rigorously rational and dialectical bent of mind and the opposition to everything that could be called romanticism.

He began with what he calls *Plays Unpleasant* (1898), so named because they brought the spectator face to face with unpleasant facts and cheated him of the thoughtless entertainment or sentimental edification that he expected from the stage. These plays dwell on serious abuses—the exploitation and prostitution of poor people, while those who perpetrate these abuses manage to retain their respectability.

It is characteristic of Shaw that his orthodox socialistic severity toward the community is combined with a great freedom from prejudice and a genuine psychological insight when he deals with the individual sinner. Even in these early pieces one of his finest qualities, his humanity, is fully and clearly marked.

Plays Pleasant (1898), with which he varied his program, have on the whole the same purport but are lighter in tone. With one of these he gained his first great success. This was *Arms and the Man,* an attempt to demonstrate the flimsiness of military and heroic romance, in contrast to the sober and prosaic work of peace. Its pacifist tendency won from the audience a more ready approbation than the author had generally received. In *Candida,* a kind of *Doll's House* with a happy ending, he created the work which for a long time was his most poetical one. This was due chiefly to the fact that in this play the strong superior woman, which for him—for reasons unknown to us—has become the normal type, has here been given a richer, warmer, and more gentle soul than elsewhere.

In *Man and Superman* (1903) he took his revenge by proclaiming that woman, because of her resolute and undisguisedly practical nature, is destined to be the superman whose coming has been so long prophesied with such earnest yearning. The jest is amusing, but its creator seems to regard it more or less seriously, even if one takes into account his spirit of opposition to the earlier English worship of the gentle female saint.

His next great drama of ideas, *Major Barbara* (1905), has a deeper significance. It discusses the problem of whether evil ought to be conquered by the inner way, the spirit of joyful and religious sacrifice; or by the outer way, the eradication of poverty, the real foundation of all social defects. Shaw's heroine, one of his most remarkable female characters, ends in a compromise between the power of money and that of the Salvation Army. The process of thought is here carried out with great force, and naturally with a great deal of paradox. The drama is not entirely consistent, but it reveals a surprisingly fresh and clear conception of the joy and poetry of the life of practical faith. Shaw the rationalist here shows himself more liberal and more chivalrous than is customary with the type.

Time does not permit us to hint at the course of his further campaign even in his more outstanding works: suffice it to say that without a trace of opportunism he turns his weapons against everything that he conceives as prejudice in whatever camp it may be found. His boldest assault would seem to be in *Heartbreak House* (1919), where he sought to embody—always in the light of the comic spirit—every kind of perversity, artificiality, and morbidity that flourishes in a state of advanced civilization, playing with vital values, the hardening of the conscience, and the ossification of the heart, under a frivolous preoccupation with art and science, politics, money-hunting, and erotic philandering. But, whether owing to the excessive wealth of the material or to the difficulty of treating it gaily, the piece has sunk into a mere museum of eccentricities with the ghostlike appearance of a shadowy symbolism.

In *Back to Methuselah* (1921) he achieved an introductory essay that was even more brilliant than usual, but his dramatic presentation of the thesis, that man must have his natural age doubled many times over in order to acquire enough sense to manage his world, furnished but little hope and little joy. It looked as if the writer of the play had hypertrophied his wealth of ideas to the great injury of his power of organic creation.

But then came *Saint Joan* (1923), which showed this man of surprises at the height of his power as a poet. This it did especially on the stage, where all that was most valuable and central in the play was thrown into due relief and revealed its real weight, even against the parts that might evoke opposition. Shaw had not been happy in his previous essays in historical drama; and this was natural enough, as he happened to combine with his abundant and quick intelligence a decided lack of historical imagination and sense of historical reality. His world lacked one dimension, that of time, which according to the newest theories is not without significance for space. This led to an unfortunate lack of respect for all that had once been and to a tendency to represent everything as diametrically opposite to what ordinary mortals had previously believed or said.

In *Saint Joan* his good head still cherishes the same opinion on the whole, but his good heart has found in his heroine a fixed point in the realm of the unsubstantial, from which it has been able to give flesh and blood to the visions of the imagination. With doubtful correctness he has simplified her image, but he has also made uncommonly fresh and living the lines that remain, and he has endowed *Saint Joan* with the power of directly holding the multitude. This imaginative work stands more or less alone as a revelation of heroism in an age hardly favorable to genuine heroism. The mere fact that it did not fail makes it highly remarkable; and the fact that it was able to make a triumphal progress all around the world is in this case evidence of considerable artistic worth.

If from this point we look back on Shaw's best works, we find it easier in many places, beneath all his sportiveness and defiance, to discern something of the same idealism that has found expression in the heroic figure of Saint Joan. His criticism of society and his perspective of its course of development may have appeared too nakedly logical, too hastily thought out, too unorganically simplified; but his struggle against traditional conceptions that rest on no solid basis and against traditional feelings that are either spurious or only half-genuine, have borne witness to the loftiness of his aims. Still more striking is his humanity; and the virtues to which he has paid homage in his unemotional way—spiritual freedom, honesty, courage, and clearness of thought—have had so very few stout champions in our times.

What I have said has given a mere glimpse of Shaw's life work, and scarcely anything has been said about his famous prefaces—or rather treatises—accompanying most of the plays. Great parts of them are insurpassable in their clarity, their quickness, and their brillance. The plays themselves have given him the position of one of the most fascinating dramatic authors of our day, while his prefaces have given him the rank of the Voltaire of our time—if we think only of the best of Voltaire. From the point of view of a pure and simple style they would seem to provide a supreme, and in its way classic, expression of the thought and polemics of an age highly journalistic in tone, and, even more important, they strengthen Shaw's distinguished position in English literature.

There was no formal Acceptance Speech by Shaw.

MAN AND SUPERMAN

A COMEDY AND A PHILOSOPHY

By GEORGE BERNARD SHAW

ACT I

ROEBUCK RAMSDEN *is in his study, opening the morning's letters. The study, handsomely and solidly furnished, proclaims the man of means. Not a speck of dust is visible: it is clear that there are at least two housemaids and a parlormaid downstairs, and a housekeeper upstairs who does not let them spare elbow-grease. Even the top of* ROEBUCK*'s head is polished: on a sunshiny day he could heliograph his orders to distant camps by merely nodding. In no other respect, however, does he suggest the military man. It is in active civil life that men get his broad air of importance, his dignified expectation of deference, his determinate mouth disarmed and refined since the hour of his success by the withdrawal of opposition and the concession of comfort and precedence and power. He is more than a highly respectable man: he is marked out as a president of highly respectable men, a chairman among directors, an alderman among councilors, a mayor among aldermen. Four tufts of iron-gray hair, which will soon be as white as isinglass, and are in other respects not at all unlike it, grow in two symmetrical pairs above his ears and at the angles of his spreading jaws. He wears a black frock coat, a white waistcoat (it is bright spring weather), and trousers, neither black nor perceptibly blue, of one of those indefinitely mixed hues which the modern clothier has produced to harmonize with the religions of respectable men. He has not been out of doors yet today; so he still wears his slippers, his boots being ready for him on the hearthrug. Surmising that he has no valet, and seeing that he has no secretary with a shorthand notebook and a typewriter, one meditates on how little our great burgess domesticity has been disturbed by new fashions and methods, or by the enterprise of the railway and hotel companies which sell you a Saturday to Monday of life at Folkestone as a real gentleman for two guineas, first-class fares both ways included.*

How old is ROEBUCK*? The question is important on the threshold of a drama of ideas; for under such circumstances everything depends on whether his adolescence belonged to the sixties or to the eighties. He was born, as a matter of fact, in 1839, and was a Unitarian and Free Trader from his boyhood, and an Evolutionist from the publication of the* Origin of Species. *Consequently he has always classed himself as an advanced thinker and fearlessly outspoken reformer.*

Sitting at his writing table, he has on his right the windows giving on Portland Place. Through these, as through a proscenium, the curious spectator may contemplate his profile as well as the blinds will permit. On his left is the inner wall, with a stately bookcase, and the door not quite in the middle, but somewhat farther from him. Against the wall opposite him are two busts on pillars: one, to his left, of John Bright; the other, to his right, of Mr. Herbert Spencer. Between them hang an engraved portrait of Richard Cobden; enlarged photographs of Martineau, Huxley, and George Eliot; autotypes of allegories by Mr. G. F. Watts (for Roebuck believes in the fine arts with all the earnestness of a man who does not understand them), and an impression of Dupont's engraving of Delaroche's Beaux Arts hemicycle, representing the great men of all ages. On the wall behind him, above the mantelshelf, is a family portrait of impenetrable obscurity.

A chair stands near the writing table for the convenience of business visitors. Two other chairs are against the wall between the busts.

A PARLORMAID *enters with a visitor's card.* ROEBUCK *takes it, and nods, pleased. Evidently a welcome caller.*

RAMSDEN. Show him up.

(*The* PARLORMAID *goes out and returns with the visitor.*)

THE MAID. Mr. Robinson.

(MR. ROBINSON *is really an uncommonly nice looking young fellow. He must, one thinks, be the jeune premier; for it is not in reason to suppose that a second such attractive male figure should appear in one story. The slim, shapely frame, the elegant suit of new mourning, the small head and regular features, the pretty little moustache, the frank clear eyes, the wholesome bloom on the youthful complexion, the well brushed glossy hair, not curly, but of fine texture and good dark color, the arch of good nature in the eyebrows, the erect forehead and neatly pointed chin, all announce the man who will love and suffer later on. And that he will not do so without sympathy is guaranteed by an engaging sincerity and eager modest serviceableness which stamp him as a man of amiable nature. The moment he appears,* RAMSDEN*'s face expands into fatherly liking and welcome, an expression which drops into one of decorous grief as the young man approaches him with sorrow in his face as well as in his black clothes.* RAMSDEN *seems to know the nature of the bereavement. As the visitor advances silently to the writing table, the old man rises and shakes his hand across it without a word: a long, affectionate shake which tells the story of a recent sorrow common to both.*)

RAMSDEN (*concluding the handshake and cheering up*). Well, well, Octavius, it's the common lot. We must all face it some day. Sit down.

(OCTAVIUS *takes the visitor's chair.* RAMSDEN *replaces himself in his own.*)

OCTAVIUS. Yes: we must face it, Mr. Ramsden. But I owed him a great deal. He did everything for me that my father could have done if he had lived.

RAMSDEN. He had no son of his own, you see.

OCTAVIUS. But he had daughters; and yet he was as good to my sister as to me. And his death was so sudden! I always intended to thank him—to let him know that I had not taken all his care of me as a matter of course, as any boy takes his father's care. But I waited for an opportunity; and now he is dead—dropped without a moment's warning. He will never know what I felt. (*He takes out his handkerchief and cries unaffectedly.*)

RAMSDEN. How do we know that, Octavius? He may know it: we cannot tell. Come! don't grieve. (OCTAVIUS *masters himself and puts up his handkerchief.*) That's right. Now let me tell you something to console you. The last time I saw him—it was in this very room—he said to me: "Tavy is a generous lad and the soul of honor; and when I see how little consideration other men get from their sons, I realize how much better than a son he's been to me." There! Doesn't that do you good?

OCTAVIUS. Mr. Ramsden: he used to say to me that he had met only one man in the world who was the soul of honor, and that was Roebuck Ramsden.

RAMSDEN. Oh, that was his partiality: we were very old friends, you know. But there was something else he used to say about you. I wonder whether I ought to tell you or not!

OCTAVIUS. You know best.

RAMSDEN. It was something about his daughter.

OCTAVIUS (*eagerly*). About Ann! Oh, do tell me that, Mr. Ramsden.

RAMSDEN. Well, he said he was glad, after all, you were not his son, because he thought that someday Annie and you—(OCTAVIUS *blushes vividly.*) Well, perhaps I shouldn't have told you. But he was in earnest.

OCTAVIUS. Oh, if only I thought I had a chance! You know, Mr. Ramsden, I don't care about money or about what people call position; and I can't bring myself to take an interest in the business of struggling for them. Well, Ann has a most exquisite nature; but she is so accustomed to be in the thick of that sort of thing that she thinks a man's character incomplete if he is not ambitious. She knows that if she married me she would have to reason herself out of being ashamed of me for not being a big success of some kind.

RAMSDEN (*getting up and planting himself with his back to the fireplace*). Nonsense, my boy, nonsense! You're too modest. What does she know about the real value of men at her age? (*More seriously.*) Besides, she's a wonderfully dutiful girl. Her father's wish would be sacred to her. Do you know that since she grew up to years of discretion, I don't believe she has ever once given her own wish as a reason for doing anything or not doing it. It's always "Father wishes me to," or "Mother wouldn't like it." It's really almost a fault in her. I have often told her she must learn to think for herself.

OCTAVIUS (*shaking his head*). I couldn't ask her to marry me because her father wished it, Mr. Ramsden.

RAMSDEN. Well, perhaps not. No: of course not. I see that. No: you certainly couldn't. But when you win her on your own merits, it will be a great happiness to her to fulfill her father's desire as well as her own. Eh? Come! you'll ask her, won't you?

OCTAVIUS (*with sad gaiety*). At all events I promise you I shall never ask anyone else.

RAMSDEN. Oh, you shan't need to. She'll accept you, my boy—although (*here he suddenly becomes very serious indeed*) you have one great drawback.

OCTAVIUS (*anxiously*). What drawback is that, Mr. Ramsden? I should rather say which of my many drawbacks?

RAMSDEN. I'll tell you, Octavius (*He takes from the table a book bound in red cloth.*) I have in my hand a copy of the most infamous, the most scandalous, the most mischievous, the most blackguardly book that ever escaped burning at the hands of the common hangman. I have not read it: I would not soil my mind with such filth; but I have read what the papers say of it. The title is quite enough for me. (*He reads it.*) The Revolutionist's Handbook and Pocket Companion. By John Tanner, M.I.R.C., Member of the Idle Rich Class.

OCTAVIUS (*smiling*). But Jack—

RAMSDEN (*testily*). For goodness' sake, don't call him Jack under my roof. (*He throws the book violently down on the table. Then, somewhat relieved, he comes past the table to* OCTAVIUS, *and addresses him at close quarters with impressive gravity.*) Now, Octavius, I know that my dead friend was right when he said you were a generous lad. I know that this man was your schoolfellow, and that you feel bound to stand by him because there was a boyish friendship between you. But I ask you to consider the altered circumstances. You were treated as a son in my friend's house. You lived there; and your friends could not be turned from the door. This man Tanner was in and out there on your account almost from his childhood. He addresses Annie by her Christian name as freely as you do. Well, while her father was alive, that was her father's business, not mine. This man Tanner was only a boy to him: his opinions were something to be laughed at, like a man's hat on a child's head. But now Tanner is a grown man and Annie a grown woman. And her father is gone. We don't as yet know the exact terms of his will; but he often talked it over with me; and I have no more doubt than I have that you're sitting there that the will appoints me Annie's trustee and guardian. (*Forcibly.*) Now I tell you, once for all, I can't and I won't have Annie placed in such a position that she must, out of regard for you, suffer the intimacy of this fellow Tanner. It's not fair; it's not right: it's not kind. What are you going to do about it?

OCTAVIUS. But Ann herself has told Jack that whatever his opinions are, he will always be welcome because he knew her dear father.

RAMSDEN (*out of patience*). That girl's mad about her duty to her parents. (*He starts off like a goaded ox in the direction of John Bright, in whose expression there is no sympathy for him. As he speaks he fumes down to Herbert Spencer, who receives him still more coldly.*) Excuse me, Octavius; but there are limits to social toleration. You know that I am not a bigoted or prejudiced man. You know that I am plain Roebuck Ramsden when other men who have done less have got handles to their names, because I have stood for equality and liberty of conscience while they were truckling to the Church and to the aristocracy. Whitefield and I lost chance after chance through our advanced opinions. But I draw the line at Anarchism and Free Love and that sort of thing. If I am to be Annie's guardian, she will have to learn that she has a duty to me. I won't have it: I will not have it. She must forbid John Tanner the house; and so must you.

(*The* PARLORMAID *returns.*)

OCTAVIUS. But—

RAMSDEN (*calling his attention to the servant*). Ssh! Well?

THE MAID. Mr. Tanner wishes to see you, sir.

RAMSDEN. Mr. Tanner!

OCTAVIUS. Jack!

RAMSDEN. How dare Mr. Tanner call on me! Say I cannot see him.

OCTAVIUS (*hurt*). I am sorry you are turning my friend from your door like that.

THE MAID (*calmly*). He's not at the door, sir. He's upstairs in the drawing room with Miss Ramsden. He came with Mrs. Whitefield and Miss Ann and Miss Robinson, sir.

(RAMSDEN'*s feelings are beyond words.*)

OCTAVIUS (*grinning*). That's very like Jack, Mr. Ramsden. You must see him, even if it's only to turn him out.

RAMSDEN (*hammering out his words with suppressed fury*). Go upstairs and ask Mr. Tanner to be good enough to step down here. (*The* PARLORMAID *goes out; and* RAMSDEN *returns to the fireplace, as to a fortified position.*) I must say that of all the confounded pieces of impertinence—well, if these are Anarchist manners, I hope you like them. And Annie with him! Annie! A—(*He chokes.*)

OCTAVIUS. Yes: that's what surprises me. He's so desperately afraid of Ann. There must be something the matter.

(MR. JOHN TANNER *suddenly opens the door and enters. He is too young to be described simply as a big man with a beard. But it is already plain that middle life will find him in that category. He has still some of the slimness of youth; but youthfulness is not the effect he aims at: his frock coat would befit a prime minister; and a certain high chested carriage of the shoulders, a lofty pose of the head, and the Olympian majesty with which a mane, or rather a huge wisp, of hazel colored hair is thrown back from an imposing brow, suggest Jupiter rather than Apollo. He is prodigiously fluent of speech, restless, excitable (mark the snorting nostril and the restless blue eye, just the thirty-secondth of an inch too wide open), possibly a little mad. He is carefully dressed, not from the vanity that cannot resist finery, but from a sense of the importance of everything he does which leads him to make as much of paying a call as other men do of getting married or laying a foundation stone. A sensitive, susceptible, exaggerative, earnest man: a megalomaniac, who would be lost without a sense of humor.*

Just at present the sense of humor is in abeyance. To say that he is excited is nothing: all his moods are phases of excitement. He is now in the panic-stricken phase; and he walks straight up to RAMSDEN *as if with the fixed intention of shooting him on his own hearthrug. But what he pulls from his breast pocket is not a pistol, but a foolscap document which he thrusts under the indignant nose of* RAMSDEN *as he exclaims*—)

TANNER. Ramsden: do you know what that is?

RAMSDEN (*loftily*). No, sir.

TANNER. It's a copy of Whitefield's will. Ann got it this morning.

RAMSDEN. When you say Ann, you mean, I presume, Miss Whitefield.

TANNER. I mean our Ann, your Ann, Tavy's Ann, and now, Heaven help me, my Ann!

OCTAVIUS (*rising, very pale*). What do you mean?

TANNER. Mean! (*He holds up the will.*) Do you know who is appointed Ann's guardian by this will?

RAMSDEN (*coolly*). I believe I am.

TANNER. You! You and I, man. I! I!! I!!! Both of us! (*He flings the will down on the writing table.*)

RAMSDEN. You! Impossible.

TANNER. It's only too hideously true. (*He throws himself into* OCTAVIUS'*s chair.*) Ramsden: get me out of it somehow. You don't know Ann as well as I do. She'll commit every crime a respectable woman can; and she'll justify every one of them by saying that it was the wish of her guardians. She'll put everything on us; and we shall have no more control over her than a couple of mice over a cat.

OCTAVIUS. Jack: I wish you wouldn't talk like that about Ann.

TANNER. This chap's in love with her: that's another complication. Well, she'll either jilt him and say I didn't approve of him, or marry him and say you ordered her to. I tell you, this is the most staggering blow that has ever fallen on a man of my age and temperament.

RAMSDEN. Let me see that will, sir. (*He goes to the writing table and picks it up.*) I cannot believe that my old friend Whitefield would have shown such a want of confidence in me as to associate me with— (*His countenance falls as he reads.*)

TANNER. It's all my own doing: that's the horrible irony of it. He told me one day that you were to be Ann's guardian; and like a fool I began arguing with him about the folly of leaving a young woman under the control of an old man with obsolete ideas.

RAMSDEN (*stupended*). My ideas obsolete!!!!!!!

TANNER. Totally. I had just finished an essay called Down with Government by the Grayhaired; and I was full of arguments and illustrations. I said the proper thing was to combine the experience of an old hand with the vitality of a young one. Hang me if he didn't take me at my word and alter his will—it's dated only a fortnight after that conversation—appointing me as joint guardian with you!

RAMSDEN (*pale and determined*). I shall refuse to act.

TANNER. What's the good of that? I've been refusing all the way from Richmond; but Ann keeps on saying that of course she's only an orphan; and that she can't expect the people who were glad to come to the house in her father's time to trouble much about her now. That's the latest game. An orphan! It's like hearing an ironclad talk about being at the mercy of the winds and waves.

OCTAVIUS. This is not fair, Jack. She is an orphan. And you ought to stand by her.

TANNER. Stand by her! What danger is she in? She has the law on her side; she has popular sentiment on her side; she has plenty of money and no conscience. All she wants with me is to load up all her moral responsibilities on me, and do as she likes at the expense of my character. I can't control her; and she can compromise me as much as she likes. I might as well be her husband.

RAMSDEN. You can refuse to accept the guardianship. *I* shall certainly refuse to hold it jointly with you.

TANNER. Yes; and what will she say to that? what does she say to it? Just that her father's wishes are sacred to her, and that she shall always look up to me as her guardian whether I care to face the responsibility or not. Refuse! You might as well refuse to accept the embraces of a boa constrictor when once it gets round your neck.

OCTAVIUS. This sort of talk is not kind to me, Jack.

TANNER (*rising and going to* OCTAVIUS *to console him, but still lamenting*). If he wanted a young guardian, why didn't he appoint Tavy?

RAMSDEN. Ah! why indeed?

OCTAVIUS. I will tell you. He sounded me about it; but I refused the trust because I loved her. I had no right to let myself be forced on her as a guardian by her father. He spoke to her about it; and she said I was right. You know I love her, Mr. Ramsden; and Jack knows it too. If Jack loved a woman, I would not compare her to a boa constrictor in his presence, however much I might dislike her. (*He sits down between the busts and turns his face to the wall.*)

RAMSDEN. I do not believe that Whitefield was in his right senses when he made that will. You have admitted that he made it under your influence.

TANNER. You ought to be pretty well obliged to me for my influence. He leaves you two thousand five hundred for your trouble. He leaves Tavy a dowry for his sister and five thousand for himself.

OCTAVIUS (*his tears flowing afresh*). Oh, I can't take it. He was too good to us.

TANNER. You won't get it, my boy, if Ramsden upsets the will.

RAMSDEN. Ha! I see. You have got me in a cleft stick.

TANNER. He leaves me nothing but the charge of Ann's morals, on the ground that I have already more money than is good for me. That shows that he had his wits about him, doesn't it?

RAMSDEN (*grimly*). I admit that.

OCTAVIUS (*rising and coming from his refuge by the wall*). Mr. Ramsden: I think you are prejudiced against Jack. He is a man of honor, and incapable of abusing—

TANNER. Don't, Tavy: you'll make me ill. I am not a man of honor: I am a man struck down by a dead hand. Tavy: you must marry her after all and take her off my hands. And I had set my heart on saving you from her!

OCTAVIUS. Oh, Jack, you talk of saving me from my highest happiness.

TANNER. Yes, a lifetime of happiness. If it were only the first half hour's happiness, Tavy, I would buy it for you with my last penny. But a lifetime of happiness! No man alive could bear it: it would be hell on earth.

RAMSDEN (*violently*). Stuff, sir. Talk sense; or else go and waste someone else's time: I have something better to do than listen to your fooleries. (*He positively kicks his way to his table and resumes his seat.*)

TANNER. You hear him, Tavy! Not an idea in his head later than eighteen-sixty. We can't leave Ann with no other guardian to turn to.

RAMSDEN. I am proud of your contempt for my character and opinions, sir. Your own are set forth in that book, I believe.

TANNER (*eagerly going to the table*). What! You've got my book! What do you think of it?

RAMSDEN. Do you suppose I would read such a book, sir?

TANNER. Then why did you buy it?

RAMSDEN. I did not buy it, sir. It has been sent me by some foolish lady who seems to admire your views. I was about to dispose of it when Octavius interrupted me. I shall do so now, with your permission. (*He throws the book into the waste-paper basket with such vehemence that* TANNER *recoils under the impression that it is being thrown at his head.*)

TANNER. You have no more manners than I have myself. However, that saves ceremony between us. (*He sits down again.*) What do you intend to do about this will?

OCTAVIUS. May I make a suggestion?

RAMSDEN. Certainly, Octavius.

OCTAVIUS. Aren't we forgetting that Ann herself may have some wishes in this matter?

RAMSDEN. I quite intend that Annie's wishes shall be consulted in every reasonable way. But she is only a woman, and a young and inexperienced woman at that.

TANNER. Ramsden: I begin to pity you.

RAMSDEN (*hotly*). I don't want to know how you feel towards me, Mr. Tanner.

TANNER. Ann will do just exactly what she likes. And what's more, she'll force us to advise her to do it; and she'll put the blame on us if it turns out badly. So, as Tavy is longing to see her—

OCTAVIUS (*shyly*). I am not, Jack.

TANNER. You lie, Tavy: you are. So let's have her down from the drawing-room and ask her what she intends us to do. Off with you, Tavy, and fetch her. (TAVY *turns to go.*) And don't be long; for the strained relations between myself and Ramsden will make the interval rather painful. (RAMSDEN *compresses his lips, but says nothing.*)

OCTAVIUS. Never mind him, Mr Ramsden. He's not serious. (*He goes out.*)

RAMSDEN (*very deliberately*). Mr. Tanner: you are the most impudent person I have ever met.

TANNER (*seriously*). I know it, Ramsden. Yet even I cannot wholly conquer shame. We live in an atmosphere of shame. We are ashamed of everything that is real about us; ashamed of ourselves, of our relatives, of our incomes, of our accents, of our opinions, of our experience, just as we are ashamed of our naked skins. Good Lord, my dear Ramsden, we are ashamed to walk, ashamed to ride in an omnibus, ashamed to hire a hansom instead of keeping a carriage, ashamed of keeping one horse instead of two and a groom-gardener instead of a coachman and footman. The more things a man is ashamed of, the more respectable he is. Why, you're ashamed to buy my book, ashamed to read it; the only thing you're not ashamed of is to judge me for it without having read it; and even that only means that you're ashamed to have heterodox opinions. Look at the effect I produce because my fairy godmother withheld from me this gift of shame. I have every possible virtue that a man can have except—

RAMSDEN. I am glad you think so well of yourself.

TANNER. All you mean by that is that you think I ought to be ashamed of talking about my virtues. You don't mean that I haven't got them: you know perfectly well that I am as sober and honest a citizen as yourself, as truthful personally, and much more truthful politically and morally.

RAMSDEN (*touched on his most sensitive point*). I deny that. I will not allow you or any man to treat me as if I were a mere member of the British public. I detest its prejudices; I scorn its narrowness; I demand the right to think for myself. You pose as an advanced man. Let me tell you that I was an advanced man before you were born.

TANNER. I knew it was a long time ago.

RAMSDEN. I am as advanced as ever I was. I defy you to prove that I have ever hauled down the flag. I am more advanced than ever I was. I grow more advanced every day.

TANNER. More advanced in years, Polonius.

RAMSDEN. Polonius! So you are Hamlet, I suppose.

TANNER. No: I am only the most impudent person you've ever met. That's your notion of a thoroughly bad character. When you want to give me a piece of your mind, you ask yourself, as a just and upright man, what is the worst you can fairly say of me. Thief, liar, forger, adulterer, perjurer, glutton, drunkard? Not one of these names fit me. You have to fall back on my deficiency in shame. Well, I admit it. I even congratulate myself; for if I were ashamed of my real self, I should cut as stupid a figure as any of the rest of you. Cultivate a little impudence, Ramsden; and you will become quite a remarkable man.

RAMSDEN. I have no—

TANNER. You have no desire for that sort of notoriety. Bless you, I knew that answer would come as well as I know that a box of matches will come out of an automatic machine when I put a penny in the slot: you would be ashamed to say anything else.

(*The crushing retort for which* RAMSDEN *has been visibly collecting his forces is lost forever; for at this point* OCTAVIUS *returns with* MISS ANN WHITEFIELD *and her* MOTHER; *and* RAMSDEN *springs up and hurries to the door to receive them. Whether* ANN *is good-looking or not depends upon your taste; also and perhaps chiefly on your age and sex. To* OCTAVIUS *she is an enchantingly beautiful woman, in whose presence the world becomes transfigured, and the puny lines of individual consciousness are suddenly made infinite by a mystic memory of the whole life of the race to its beginnings in the east, or even back to the paradise from which it fell. She is to him the reality of romance, the inner good sense of nonsense, the unveiling of his eyes, the freeing of his soul, the abolition of time, place and circumstance, the etherealization of his blood into rapturous rivers of the very water of life itself, the revelation of all the mysteries and the sanctification of all the dogmas. To her*

MOTHER *she is, to put it as moderately as possible, nothing whatever of the kind. Not that* OCTAVIUS'*s admiration is in any way ridiculous or discreditable.* ANN *is a well formed creature, as far as that goes; and she is perfectly ladylike, graceful, and comely, with ensnaring eyes and hair. Besides, instead of making herself an eyesore, like her* MOTHER, *she has devised a mourning costume of black and violet silk which does honor to her late father and reveals the family tradition of brave unconventionality by which* RAMSDEN *sets such store.*

But all this is beside the point as an explanation of ANN'*s charm. Turn up her nose, give a cast to her eye, replace her black and violet confection by the apron and feathers of a flower girl, strike all the aitches out of her speech, and* ANN *would still make men dream. Vitality is as common as humanity; but, like humanity, it sometimes rises to genius; and* ANN *is one of the vital geniuses. Not at all, if you please, an oversexed person: that is a vital defect, not a true excess. She is a perfectly respectable, perfectly self-controlled woman, and looks it; though her pose is fashionably frank and impulsive. She inspires confidence as a person who will do nothing she does not mean to do; also some fear, perhaps, as a woman who will probably do everything she means to do without taking more account of other people than may be necessary and what she calls right. In short, what the weaker of her own sex sometimes call a cat.*

Nothing can be more decorous than her entry and her reception by RAMSDEN, *whom she kisses. The late Mr. Whitefield would be gratified almost to impatience by the long faces of the men (except* TANNER, *who is fidgety), the silent handgrasps, the sympathetic placing of chairs, the sniffing of the widow, and the liquid eye of the daughter, whose heart, apparently, will not let her control her tongue to speech.* RAMSDEN *and* OCTAVIUS *take the two chairs from the wall, and place them for the two ladies; but* ANN *comes to* TANNER *and takes his chair, which he offers with a brusque gesture, subsequently relieving his irritation by sitting down on the corner of the writing table with studied indecorum.* OCTAVIUS *gives* MRS. WHITEFIELD *a chair next* ANN, *and himself takes the vacant one which* RAMSDEN *has placed under the nose of the effigy of Mr. Herbert Spencer.*

MRS. WHITEFIELD, *by the way, is a little woman, whose faded flaxen hair looks like straw on an egg. She has an expression of muddled shrewdness, a squeak of protest in her voice, and an odd air of continually elbowing away some larger person who is crushing her into a corner. One guesses her as one of those women who are conscious of being treated as silly and negligible, and who, without having strength enough to assert themselves effectually, at any rate never submit to their fate. There is a touch of chivalry in* OCTAVIUS'*s scrupulous attention to her, even while his whole soul is absorbed by* ANN.

*(*RAMSDEN *goes solemnly back to his magisterial seat at the writing table, ignoring* TANNER, *and opens the proceedings.)*

RAMSDEN. I am sorry, Annie, to force business on you at a sad time like the present. But your poor dear father's will has raised a very serious question. You have read it, I believe?

*(*ANN *assents with a nod and a catch of her breath, too much affected to speak.)*

I must say I am surprised to find Mr. Tanner named as joint guardian and trustee with myself of you and Rhoda. (*A pause. They all look portentous; but they have nothing to say.* RAMSDEN, *a little ruffled by the lack of any response, continues.*) I don't know that I can consent to act under such conditions. Mr.

Tanner has, I understand, some objection also; but I do not profess to understand its nature: he will no doubt speak for himself. But we are agreed that we can decide nothing until we know your views. I am afraid I shall have to ask you to choose between my sole guardianship and that of Mr. Tanner; for I fear it is impossible for us to undertake a joint arrangement.

ANN (*in a low musical voice*). Mamma—

MRS. WHITEFIELD (*hastily*). Now, Ann, I do beg you not to put it on me. I have no opinion on the subject; and if I had, it would probably not be attended to. I am quite content with whatever you three think best.

(TANNER *turns his head and looks fixedly at* RAMSDEN, *who angrily refuses to receive this mute communication.*)

ANN (*resuming in the same gentle voice, ignoring her mother's bad taste*). Mamma knows that she is not strong enough to bear the whole responsibility for me and Rhoda without some help and advice. Rhoda must have a guardian; and though I am older, I do not think any young unmarried woman should be left quite to her own guidance. I hope you agree with me, Granny?

TANNER (*starting*). Granny! Do you intend to call your guardians Granny?

ANN. Don't be foolish, Jack. Mr. Ramsden has always been Grandpapa Roebuck to me: I am Granny's Annie; and he is Annie's Granny. I christened him so when I first learned to speak.

RAMSDEN (*sarcastically*). I hope you are satisfied, Mr. Tanner. Go on, Annie: I quite agree with you.

ANN. Well, if I am to have a guardian, can I set aside anybody whom my dear father appointed for me?

RAMSDEN (*biting his lip*). You approve of your father's choice, then?

ANN. It is not for me to approve or disapprove. I accept it. My father loved me and knew best what was good for me.

RAMSDEN. Of course I understand your feeling, Annie. It is what I should have expected of you; and it does you credit. But it does not settle the question so completely as you think. Let me put a case to you. Suppose you were to discover that I had been guilty of some disgraceful action—that I was not the man your poor dead father took me for! Would you still consider it right that I should be Rhoda's guardian?

ANN. I can't imagine you doing anything disgraceful, Granny.

TANNER (*to* RAMSDEN). You haven't done anything of the sort, have you?

RAMSDEN (*indignantly*). No, sir.

MRS. WHITEFIELD (*placidly*). Well, then, why suppose it?

ANN. You see, Granny, Mamma would not like me to suppose it.

RAMSDEN (*much perplexed*). You are both so full of natural and affectionate feeling in these family matters that it is very hard to put the situation fairly before you.

TANNER. Besides, my friend, you are not putting the situation fairly before them.

RAMSDEN (*sulkily*). Put it yourself, then.

TANNER. I will. Ann: Ramsden thinks I am not fit to be your guardian; and I quite agree with him. He considers that if your father had read my book, he wouldn't have appointed me. That book is the disgraceful action he has been talking about. He thinks it's your duty for Rhoda's sake to ask him to act alone and to make me withdraw. Say the word; and I will.

ANN. But I haven't read your book, Jack.

TANNER (*diving at the waste-paper basket and fishing the book out for her*). Then read it at once and decide.

RAMSDEN (*vehemently*). If I am to be your guardian, I positively forbid you to read that book, Annie. (*He smites the table with his fist and rises.*)

ANN. Of course not, if you don't wish it. (*She puts the book on the table.*)

TANNER. If one guardian is to forbid you to read the other guardian's book, how are we to settle it? Suppose I order you to read it! What about your duty to me?

ANN (*gently*). I am sure you would never purposely force me into a painful dilemma, Jack.

RAMSDEN (*irritably*). Yes, yes, Annie: this is all very well, and, as I said, quite natural and becoming. But you must make a choice one way or the other. We are as much in a dilemma as you.

ANN. I feel that I am too young, to inexperienced, to decide. My father's wishes are sacred to me.

MRS. WHITEFIELD. If you two men won't carry them out I must say it is rather hard that you should put the responsibility on Ann. It seems to me that people are always putting things on other people in this world.

RAMSDEN. I am sorry you take it in that way.

ANN (*touchingly*). Do you refuse to accept me as your ward, Granny?

RAMSDEN. No: I never said that. I greatly object to act with Mr. Tanner: that's all.

MRS. WHITEFIELD. Why? What's the matter with poor Jack?

TANNER. My views are too advanced for him.

RAMSDEN (*indignantly*). They are not. I deny it.

ANN. Of course not. What nonsense! Nobody is more advanced than Granny. I am sure it is Jack himself who has made all the difficulty. Come, Jack! be kind to me in my sorrow. You don't refuse to accept me as your ward, do you?

TANNER (*gloomily*). No, I let myself in for it; so I suppose I must face it. (*He turns away to the bookcase, and stands there, moodily studying the titles of the volumes.*)

ANN (*rising and expanding with subdued but gushing delight*). Then we are all agreed; and my dear father's will is to be carried out. You don't know what a joy that is to me and to my mother! (*She goes to* RAMSDEN *and presses both his hands, saying:*) And I shall have my dear Granny to help and advise me. (*She casts a glance at* TANNER *over her shoulder.*) And Jack the Giant Killer. (*She goes past her mother to* OCTAVIUS.) And Jack's inseparable friend Ricky-ticky-tavy. (*He blushes and looks inexpressibly foolish.*)

MRS. WHITEFIELD (*rising and shaking her widow's weeds straight*). Now that you are Ann's guardian, Mr. Ramsden, I wish you would speak to her about her habit of giving people nicknames. They can't be expected to like it. (*She moves towards the door.*)

ANN. How can you say such a thing, Mamma! (*Glowing with affectionate remorse.*) Oh, I wonder can you be right! Have I been inconsiderate? (*She turns to* OCTAVIUS, *who is sitting astride his chair with his elbows on the back of it. Putting her hand on his forehead she turns his face up suddenly.*) Do you want to be treated like a grown up man? Must I call you Mr. Robinson in future?

OCTAVIUS (*earnestly*). Oh please call me Ricky-ticky-tavy. "Mr. Robinson" would hurt me cruelly. (*She laughs and pats his cheek with her finger; then comes back to* RAMSDEN.) You know I'm beginning to think that Granny is rather a piece of impertinence. But I never dreamed of its hurting you.

RAMSDEN (*breezily, as he pats her affectionately on the back*). My dear Annie, nonsense. I insist on Granny. I won't answer to any other name than Annie's Granny.

ANN (*gratefully*). You all spoil me, except Jack.

TANNER (*over his shoulder, from the bookcase*). I think you ought to call me Mr. Tanner.

ANN (*gently*). No you don't, Jack. That's like the things you say on purpose to shock people: those who know you pay no attention to them. But, if you like, I'll call you after your famous ancestor Don Juan.

RAMSDEN. Don Juan!

ANN (*innocently*). Oh, is there any harm in it? I didn't know. Then I certainly won't call you that. May I call you Jack until I can think of something else?

TANNER. Oh, for Heaven's sake don't try to invent anything worse. I capitulate. I consent to Jack. I embrace Jack. Here endeth my first and last attempt to assert my authority.

ANN. You see, Mamma, they all really like to have pet names.

MRS. WHITEFIELD. Well, I think you might at least drop them until we are out of mourning.

ANN (*reproachfully, stricken to the soul*). Oh, how could you remind me, mother? (*She hastily leaves the room to conceal her emotion.*)

MRS. WHITEFIELD. Of course. My fault as usual! (*She follows* ANN.)

TANNER (*coming from the bookcase*). Ramsden: we're beaten—smashed—nonentitized, like her mother.

RAMSDEN. Stuff, sir. (*He follows* MRS. WHITEFIELD *out of the room.*)

TANNER (*left alone with* OCTAVIUS, *stares whimsically at him*). Tavy: do you want to count for something in the world?

OCTAVIUS. I want to count for something as a poet: I want to write a great play.

TANNER. With Ann as the heroine?

OCTAVIUS. Yes: I confess it.

TANNER. Take care, Tavy. The play with Ann as the heroine is all right; but if you're not very careful, by Heaven she'll marry you.

OCTAVIUS (*sighing*). No such luck, Jack!

TANNER. Why, man, your head is in the lioness's mouth: you are half swallowed already—in three bites—Bite One, Ricky; Bite Two, Ticky; Bite Three, Tavy; and down you go.

OCTAVIUS. She is the same to everybody, Jack: you know her ways.

TANNER. Yes: she breaks everybody's back with the stroke of her paw; but the question is, which of us will she eat? My own opinion is that she means to eat you.

OCTAVIUS (*rising, pettishly*). It's horrible to talk like that about her when she is upstairs crying for her father. But I do so want her to eat me that I can bear your brutalities because they give me hope.

TANNER. Tavy; that's the devilish side of a woman's fascination: she makes you will your own destruction.

OCTAVIUS. But it's not destruction: it's fulfillment.

TANNER. Yes, of her purpose; and that purpose is neither her happiness nor yours, but Nature's. Vitality in a woman is a blind fury of creation. She sacrifices herself to it: do you think she will hesitate to sacrifice you?

OCTAVIUS. Why, it is just because she is self-sacrificing that she will not sacrifice those she loves.

TANNER. That is the profoundest of mistakes, Tavy. It is the self-sacrificing women that sacrifice others most recklessly. Because they are unselfish, they are kind in little things. Because they have a purpose which is not their own purpose, but that of the whole universe, a man is nothing to them but an instrument of that purpose.

OCTAVIUS. Don't be ungenerous, Jack. They take the tenderest care of us.

TANNER. Yes, as a soldier takes care of his rifle or a musician of his violin. But do they allow us any purpose or freedom of our own? Will they lend us to one another? Can the strongest man escape from them when once he is appropriated? They tremble when we are in danger, and weep when we die; but the tears are not for us, but for a father wasted, a son's breeding thrown away. They accuse us of treating them as a mere means to our pleasure; but how can so feeble and transient a folly as a man's selfish pleasure enslave a woman as the whole purpose of Nature embodied in a woman can enslave a man?

OCTAVIUS. What matter, if the slavery makes us happy?

TANNER. No matter at all if you have no purpose of your own, and are, like most men, a mere breadwinner. But you, Tavy, are an artist: that is, you have a purpose as absorbing and as unscrupulous as a woman's purpose.

OCTAVIUS. Not unscrupulous.

TANNER. Quite unscrupulous. The true artist will let his wife starve, his children go barefoot, his mother drudge for his living at seventy, sooner than work at anything but his art. To women he is half vivisector, half vampire. He gets into intimate relations with them to study them, to strip the mask of convention from them, to surprise their inmost secrets, knowing that they have the power to rouse his deepest creative energies, to rescue him from his cold reason, to make him see visions and dream dreams, to inspire him, as he calls it. He persuades women that they may do this for their own purpose while he really means them to do it for his. He steals the mother's milk and blackens it to make printer's ink to scoff at her and glorify ideal women with. He pretends to spare her the pangs of child-bearing so that he may have for himself the tenderness and fostering that belong of right to her children. Since marriage began, the great artist has been known as a bad husband. But he is worse: he is a child-robber, a blood-sucker, a hypocrite and a cheat. Perish the race and wither a thousand women if only the sacrifice of them enable him to act Hamlet better, to paint a finer picture, to write a deeper poem, a greater play, a profounder philosophy! For mark you, Tavy, the artist's work is to show us ourselves as we really are. Our minds are nothing but this knowledge of ourselves; and he who adds a jot to such knowledge creates new mind as surely as any woman creates new men. In the rage of that creation he is as ruthless as the woman, as dangerous to her as she to him, and as horribly fascinating. Of all human struggles there is none so treacherous and remorseless as the struggle between the artist man and the mother woman. Which shall use up the other? that is the issue between them. And it is all the deadlier because, in your romanticist cant, they love one another.

OCTAVIUS. Even if it were so—and I don't admit it for a moment—it is out of the deadliest struggles that we get the noblest characters.

TANNER. Remember that the next time you meet a grizzly bear or a Bengal tiger, Tavy.

OCTAVIUS. I meant where there is love, Jack.

TANNER. Oh, the tiger will love you. There is no love sincerer than the love of food. I think Ann loves you that way: she patted your cheek as if it were a nicely underdone chop.

OCTAVIUS. You know, Jack, I should have to run away from you if I did not make it a fixed rule not to mind anything you say. You come out with perfectly revolting things sometimes.

(RAMSDEN *returns, followed by* ANN. *They come in quickly, with their former leisurely air of decorous grief changed to one of genuine concern, and, on* RAMS-

DEN'*s part, of worry. He comes between the two men, intending to address* OCTAVIUS, *but pulls himself up abruptly as he sees* TANNER.)

RAMSDEN. I hardly expected to find you still here, Mr. Tanner.

TANNER. Am I in the way? Good morning, fellow guardian. (*He goes towards the door.*)

ANN. Stop, Jack. Granny: he must know, sooner or later.

RAMSDEN. Octavius: I have a very serious piece of news for you. It is of the most private and delicate nature—of the most painful nature too, I am sorry to say. Do you wish Mr. Tanner to be present while I explain?

OCTAVIUS (*turning pale*). I have no secrets from Jack.

RAMSDEN. Before you decide that finally, let me say that the news concerns your sister, and that it is terrible news.

OCTAVIUS. Violet! What has happened? Is she—dead?

RAMSDEN. I am not sure that it is not even worse than that.

OCTAVIUS. Is she badly hurt? Has there been an accident?

RAMSDEN. No: nothing of that sort.

TANNER. Ann: will you have the common humanity to tell us what the matter is?

ANN (*half whispering*). I can't. Violet has done something dreadful. We shall have to get her away somewhere. (*She flutters to the writing table and sits in* RAMSDEN'*s chair, leaving the three men to fight it out between them.*)

OCTAVIUS (*enlightened*). Is that what you meant, Mr. Ramsden?

RAMSDEN. Yes. (*Octavius sinks upon a chair, crushed.*) I am afraid there is no doubt that Violet did not really go to Eastbourne three weeks ago when we thought she was with the Parry Whitefields. And she called on a strange doctor yesterday with a wedding ring on her finger. Mrs. Parry Whitefield met her there by chance; and so the whole thing came out.

OCTAVIUS (*rising with his fists clenched*). Who is the scoundrel?

ANN. She won't tell us.

OCTAVIUS (*collapsing into the chair again*). What a frightful thing!

TANNER (*with angry sarcasm*). Dreadful. Appalling. Worse than death, as Ramsden says. (*He comes to* OCTAVIUS.) What would you not give, Tavy, to turn it into a railway accident, with all her bones broken, or something equally respectable and deserving of sympathy?

OCTAVIUS. Don't be brutal, Jack.

TANNER. Brutal! Good Heavens, man, what are you crying for? Here is a woman whom we all supposed to be making bad water color sketches, practicing Grieg and Brahms, gadding about to concerts and parties, wasting her life and her money. We suddenly learn that she has turned from these sillinesses to the fulfillment of her highest purpose and greatest function—to increase, multiply and replenish the earth. And instead of admiring her courage and rejoicing in her instinct; instead of crowning the completed womanhood and raising the triumphal strain of "Unto us a child is born: unto us a son is given," here you are—you who have been as merry as grigs in your mourning for the dead—all pulling long faces and looking as ashamed and disgraced as if the girl had committed the vilest of crimes.

RAMSDEN (*roaring with rage*). I will not have these abominations uttered in my house. (*He smites the writing table with his fist.*)

TANNER. Look here: if you insult me again I'll take you at your word and leave your house. Ann: where is Violet now?

ANN. Why? Are you going to her?

TANNER. Of course I am going to her. She wants help; she wants money; she wants respect and congratulation; she wants every chance for her child. She does not seem likely to get it from you: she shall from me. Where is she?

ANN. Don't be so headstrong, Jack. She's upstairs.

TANNER. What! Under Ramsden's sacred roof! Go and do your miserable duty, Ramsden. Hunt her out into the street. Cleanse your threshold from her contamination. Vindicate the purity of your English home. I'll go for a cab.

ANN (*alarmed*). Oh, Granny, you mustn't do that.

OCTAVIUS (*broken-heartedly, rising*). I'll take her away, Mr. Ramsden. She had no right to come to your house.

RAMSDEN (*indignantly*). But I am only too anxious to help her. (*Turning on* TANNER.) How dare you, sir, impute such monstrous intentions to me? I protest against it. I am ready to put down my last penny to save her from being driven to run to you for protection.

TANNER (*subsiding*). It's all right, then. He's not going to act up to his principles. It's agreed that we all stand by Violet.

OCTAVIUS. But who is the man? He can make reparation by marrying her; and he shall, or he shall answer for it to me.

RAMSDEN. He shall, Octavius. There you speak like a man.

TANNER. Then you don't think him a scoundrel, after all?

OCTAVIUS. Not a scoundrel! He is a heartless scoundrel.

RAMSDEN. A damned scoundrel. I beg your pardon, Annie; but I can say no less.

TANNER. So we are to marry your sister to a damned scoundrel by way of reforming her character! On my soul, I think you are all mad.

ANN. Don't be absurd, Jack. Of course you are quite right, Tavy; but we don't know who he is: Violet won't tell us.

TANNER. What on earth does it matter who he is? He's done his part; and Violet must do the rest.

RAMSDEN (*beside himself*). Stuff! lunacy! There is a rascal in our midst, a libertine, a villain worse than a murderer; and we are not to learn who he is! In our ignorance we are to shake him by the hand; to introduce him into our homes; to trust our daughters with him; to—to—

ANN (*coaxingly*). There, Granny, don't talk so loud. It's most shocking: we must all admit that; but if Violet won't tell us, what can we do? Nothing. Simply nothing.

RAMSDEN. Hmph! I'm not so sure of that. If any man has paid Violet any special attention, we can easily find that out. If there is any man of notoriously loose principles among us—

TANNER. Ahem!

RAMSDEN (*raising his voice*). Yes sir, I repeat, if there is any man of notoriously loose principles among us—

TANNER. Or any man notoriously lacking in self-control.

RAMSDEN (*aghast*). Do you dare to suggest that *I* am capable of such an act?

TANNER. My dear Ramsden, this is an act of which every man is capable. That is what comes of getting at cross purposes with Nature. The suspicion you have just flung at me clings to us all. It's a sort of mud that sticks to the judge's ermine or the cardinal's robe as fast as to the rags of the tramp. Come, Tavy: don't look so bewildered: it might have been me: it might have been Ramsden; just as it might have been anybody. If it had, what could we do but lie and protest—as Ramsden is going to protest.

RAMSDEN (*choking*). I—I—I—

TANNER. Guilt itself could not stammer more confusedly. And yet you know perfectly well he's innocent, Tavy.

RAMSDEN (*exhausted*). I am glad you admit that, sir. I admit, myself, that there is an element of truth in what you say, grossly as you may distort it to gratify your malicious humor. I hope, Octavius, no suspicion of me is possible in your mind.

OCTAVIUS. Of you! No, not for a moment.

TANNER (*drily*). I think he suspects me just a little.

OCTAVIUS. Jack: you couldn't—you wouldn't—

TANNER. Why not?

OCTAVIUS (*appalled*). Why not!

TANNER. Oh, well, I'll tell you why not. First, you would feel bound to quarrel with me. Second, Violet doesn't like me. Third, if I had the honor of being the father of Violet's child, I should boast of it instead of denying it. So be easy: our friendship is not in danger.

OCTAVIUS. I should have put away the suspicion with horror if only you would think and feel naturally about it. I beg your pardon.

TANNER. My pardon! nonsense! And now let's sit down and have a family council. (*He sits down. The rest follow his example, more or less under protest.*) Violet is going to do the State a service; consequently she must be packed abroad like a criminal until it's over. What's happening upstairs?

ANN. Violet is in the housekeeper's room—by herself, of course.

TANNER. Why not in the drawingroom?

ANN. Don't be absurd, Jack. Miss Ramsden is in the drawingroom with my mother, considering what to do.

TANNER. Oh! the housekeeper's room is the penitentiary, I suppose; and the prisoner is waiting to be brought before her judges. The old cats!

ANN. Oh, Jack!

RAMSDEN. You are at present a guest beneath the roof of one of the old cats, sir. My sister is the mistress of this house.

TANNER. She would put me in the housekeeper's room, too, if she dared, Ramsden. However, I withdraw cats. Cats would have more sense. Ann: as your guardian, I order you to go to Violet at once and be particularly kind to her.

ANN. I have seen her, Jack. And I am sorry to say I am afraid she is going to be rather obstinate about going abroad. I think Tavy ought to speak to her about it.

OCTAVIUS. How can I speak to her about such a thing? (*He breaks down.*)

ANN. Don't break down, Ricky. Try to bear it for all our sakes.

RAMSDEN. Life is not all plays and poems, Octavius. Come! face it like a man.

TANNER (*chafing again*). Poor dear brother! Poor dear friends of the family! Poor dear Tabbies and Grimalkins! Poor dear everybody except the woman who is going to risk her life to create another life! Tavy: don't you be a selfish ass. Away with you and talk to Violet; and bring her down here if she cares to come. (OCTAVIUS *rises.*) Tell her we'll stand by her.

RAMSDEN (*rising*). No, sir—

TANNER (*rising also and interrupting him*). Oh, we understand: it's against your conscience; but still you'll do it.

OCTAVIUS. I assure you all, on my word, I never meant to be selfish. It's so hard to know what to do when one wishes earnestly to do right.

TANNER. My dear Tavy, your pious English habit of regarding the world as a moral gymnasium, built expressly to strengthen your character in, occasionally leads you to think about your own confounded principles when you should be thinking about other people's necessities. The need of the present hour is a happy mother and a healthy baby. Bend your energies on that; and you will see your way clearly enough.

(OCTAVIUS, *much perplexed, goes out.*)

RAMSDEN (*facing* TANNER *impressively*). And Morality, sir? What is to become of that?

TANNER. Meaning a weeping Magdalen and an innocent child branded with her shame. Not in our circle, thank you. Morality can go to its father the devil.

RAMSDEN. I thought so, sir. Morality sent to the devil to please our libertines, male and female. That is to be the future of England, is it?

TANNER. Oh, England will survive your disapproval. Meanwhile, I understand that you agree with me as to the practical course we are to take?

RAMSDEN. Not in your spirit, sir. Not for your reasons.

TANNER. You can explain that if anybody calls you to account, here or hereafter. (*He turns away, and plants himself in front of Mr. Herbert Spencer, at whom he stares gloomily.*)

ANN (*rising and coming to* RAMSDEN). Granny: hadn't you better go up to the drawingroom and tell them what we intend to do?

RAMSDEN (*looking pointedly at* TANNER). I hardly like to leave you alone with this gentleman. Will you not come with me?

ANN. Miss Ramsden would not like to speak about it before me, Granny. I ought not to be present.

RAMSDEN. You are right: I should have thought of that. You are a good girl, Annie.

(*He pats her on the shoulder. She looks up at him with beaming eyes; and he goes out, much moved. Having disposed of him, she looks at* TANNER. *His back being turned to her, she gives a moment's attention to her personal appearance, then softly goes to him and speaks almost into his ear.*)

ANN. Jack (*he turns with a start*): are you glad that you are my guardian? You don't mind being made responsible for me, I hope.

TANNER. The latest addition to your collection of scapegoats, eh?

ANN. Oh, that stupid old joke of yours about me! Do please drop it. Why do you say things that you know must pain me? I do my best to please you, Jack: I suppose I may tell you so now that you are my guardian. You will make me so unhappy if you refuse to be friends with me.

TANNER (*studying her as gloomily as he studied the bust*). You need not go begging for my regard. How unreal our judgments are! You seem to me to have absolutely no conscience—only hypocrisy; and you can't see the difference—yet there is a sort of fascination about you. I always attend to you, somehow. I should miss you if I lost you.

ANN (*tranquilly slipping her arm into his and walking about with him*). But isn't that only natural, Jack? We have known each other since we were children. Do you remember—

TANNER (*abruptly breaking loose*). Stop! I remember everything.

ANN. Oh, I daresay we were often very silly; but—

TANNER. I won't have it, Ann. I am no more that schoolboy now than I am the dotard of ninety I shall grow into if I live long enough. It is over: let me forget it.

ANN. Wasn't it a happy time? (*She attempts to take his arm again.*)

TANNER. Sit down and behave yourself. (*He makes her sit down in the chair next to the writing table.*) No doubt it was a happy time for you. You were a good girl and never compromised yourself. And yet the wickedest child that ever was slapped could hardly have had a better time. I can understand the success with which you bullied the other girls: your virtue imposed on them. But tell me this: did you ever know a good boy?

ANN. Of course. All boys are foolish sometimes; but Tavy was always a really good boy.

TANNER (*struck by this*). Yes, you're right. For some reason you never tempted Tavy.

ANN. Tempted! Jack!

TANNER. Yes, my dear Lady Mephistopheles, tempted. You were insatiably curious as to what a boy might be capable of, and diabolically clever at getting through his guard and surprising his inmost secrets.

ANN. What nonsense! All because you used to tell me long stories of the wicked things you had done—silly boys' tricks! And you call such things inmost secrets! Boys' secrets are just like men's; and you know what they are!

TANNER (*obstinately*). No I don't. What are they, pray?

ANN. Why, the things they tell everybody, of course.

TANNER. Now I swear I told you things I told no one else. You lured me into a compact by which we were to have no secrets from one another. We were to tell one another everything. I didn't notice that you never told me anything.

ANN. You didn't want to talk about me, Jack. You wanted to talk about yourself.

TANNER. Ah, true, horribly true. But what a devil of a child you must have been to know that weakness and to play on it for the satisfaction of your own curiosity! I wanted to brag to you, to make myself interesting. And I found myself doing all sorts of mischievous things simply to have something to tell you about. I fought with boys I didn't hate; I lied about things I might just as well have told the truth about; I stole things I didn't want; I kissed little girls I didn't care for. It was all bravado: passionless and therefore unreal.

ANN. I never told of you, Jack.

TANNER. No; but if you had wanted to stop me you would have told of me. You wanted me to go on.

ANN (*flashing out*). Oh, that's not true: it's not true, Jack. I never wanted you to do those dull, disappointing, brutal, stupid, vulgar things. I always hoped that it would be something really heroic at last. (*Recovering herself.*) Excuse me, Jack; but the things you did were never a bit like the things I wanted you to do. They often gave me great uneasiness; but I could not tell of you and get you into trouble. And you were only a boy. I knew you would grow out of them. Perhaps I was wrong.

TANNER (*sardonically*). Do not give way to remorse, Ann. At least nineteen twentieths of the exploits I confessed to you were pure lies. I soon noticed that you didn't like the true stories.

ANN. Of course I knew that some of the things couldn't have happened. But—

TANNER. You are going to remind me that some of the most disgraceful ones did.

ANN (*fondly, to his great terror*). I don't want to remind you of anything. But I knew the people they happened to, and heard about them.

TANNER. Yes; but even the true stories were touched up for telling. A sensitive boy's humiliations may be very good fun for ordinary thickskinned grown-ups; but to the boy himself they are so acute, so ignominious, that he cannot confess them—cannot but deny them passionately. However, perhaps it was as well for me that I romanced a bit; for, on the one occasion when I told you the truth, you threatened to tell of me.

ANN. Oh, never. Never once.

TANNER. Yes, you did. Do you remember a dark-eyed girl named Rachel Rosetree? (ANN*'s brows contract for an instant involuntarily.*) I got up a love affair with her; and we met one night in the garden and walked about very uncomfortably with our arms round one another, and kissed at parting, and were most conscientiously romantic. If that love affair had gone on, it would have bored me to death; but it didn't go on; for the next thing that happened was that Rachel cut me because she found out that I had told you. How did she find it out? From you. You went to her and held the guilty secret over her head, leading her a life of abject terror and humiliation by threatening to tell on her.

ANN. And a very good thing for her, too. It was my duty to stop her misconduct; and she is thankful to me for it now.

TANNER. Is she?

ANN. She ought to be, at all events.

TANNER. It was not your duty to stop my misconduct, I suppose.

ANN. I did stop it by stopping her.

TANNER. Are you sure of that? You stopped my telling you about my adventures; but how do you know that you stopped the adventures?

ANN. Do you mean to say that you went on in the same way with other girls?

TANNER. No. I had enough of that sort of romantic tomfoolery with Rachel.

ANN (*unconvinced*). Then why did you break off our confidences and become quite strange to me?

TANNER (*enigmatically*). It happened just then that I got something that I wanted to keep all to myself instead of sharing it with you.

ANN. I am sure I shouldn't have asked for any of it if you had grudged it.

TANNER. It wasn't a box of sweets, Ann. It was something you'd never have let me call my own.

ANN (*incredulously*). What?

TANNER. My soul.

ANN. Oh, do be sensible, Jack. You know you're talking nonsense.

TANNER. The most solemn earnest, Ann. You didn't notice at that time that you were getting a soul too. But you were. It was not for nothing that you suddenly found you had a moral duty to chastise and reform Rachel. Up to that time you had traded pretty extensively in being a good child; but you had never set up a sense of duty to others. Well, I set one up too. Up to that time I had played the boy buccaneer with no more conscience than a fox in a poultry farm. But now I began to have scruples, to feel obligations, to find that veracity and honor were no longer goody-goody expressions in the mouths of grown up people, but compelling principles in myself.

ANN (*quietly*). Yes, I suppose you're right. You were beginning to be a man, and I to be a woman.

TANNER. Are you sure it was not that we were beginning to be something more? What does the beginning of manhood and womanhood mean in most people's mouths? You know: it means the beginning of love. But love began long before that for me. Love played its part in the earliest dreams and follies and romances I can remember—may I say the earliest follies and romances we can remember?—though we did not understand it at the time. No: the change that came to me was the birth in me of moral passion; and I declare that according to my experience moral passion is the only real passion.

ANN. All passions ought to be moral, Jack.

TANNER. Ought! Do you think that anything is strong enough to impose oughts on a passion except a stronger passion still?

ANN. Our moral sense controls passion, Jack. Don't be stupid.

TANNER. Our moral sense! And is that not a passion? Is the devil to have all the passions as well as all the good tunes? If it were not a passion—if it were not the mightiest of the passions, all the other passions would sweep it away like a leaf before a hurricane. It is the birth of that passion that turns a child into a man.

ANN. There are other passions, Jack. Very strong ones.

TANNER. All the other passions were in me before; but they were idle and aimless —mere childish greedinesses and cruelties, curiosities and fancies, habits and superstitions, grotesque and ridiculous to the mature intelligence. When they suddenly began to shine like newly lit flames it was by no light of their own, but by the radiance of the dawning moral passion. That passion dignified them, gave them conscience and meaning, found them a mob of appetites and organized them into an army of purposes and principles. My soul was born of that passion.

ANN. I noticed that you got more sense. You were a dreadfully destructive boy before that.

TANNER. Destructive! Stuff! I was only mischievous.

ANN. Oh Jack, you were very destructive. You ruined all the young fir trees by chopping off their leaders with a wooden sword. You broke all the cucumber frames with your catapult. You set fire to the common: the police arrested Tavy for it because he ran away when he couldn't stop you. You—

TANNER. Pooh! pooh! pooh! these were battles, bombardments, stratagems to save our scalps from the red Indians. You have no imagination, Ann. I am ten times more destructive now than I was then. The moral passion has taken my destructiveness in hand and directed it to moral ends. I have become a reformer, and, like all reformers, an iconoclast. I no longer break cucumber frames and burn gorse bushes: I shatter creeds and demolish idols.

ANN (*bored*). I am afraid I am too feminine to see any sense in destruction. Destruction can only destroy.

TANNER. Yes. That is why it is so useful. Construction cumbers the ground with institutions made by busybodies. Destruction clears it and gives us breathing space and liberty.

ANN. It's no use, Jack. No woman will agree with you there.

TANNER. That's because you confuse construction and destruction with creation and murder. They're quite different: I adore creation and abhor murder. Yes: I adore it in tree and flower, in bird and beast, even in you. (*A flush of interest and delight suddenly chases the growing perplexity and boredom from her face.*) It was the creative instinct that led you to attach me to you by bonds that have left their mark on me to this day. Yes, Ann: the old childish compact between us was an unconscious love compact—

ANN. Jack!

TANNER. Oh, don't be alarmed—

ANN. I am not alarmed.

TANNER (*whimsically*). Then you ought to be: where are your principles?

ANN. Jack: are you serious or are you not?

TANNER. Do you mean about the moral passion?

ANN. No, no; the other one. (*Confused.*) Oh! you are so silly: one never knows how to take you.

TANNER. You must take me quite seriously. I am your guardian; and it is my duty to improve your mind.

ANN. The love compact is over, then, is it? I suppose you grew tired of me?

TANNER. No; but the moral passion made our childish relations impossible. A jealous sense of my new individuality arose in me—

ANN. You hated to be treated as a boy any longer. Poor Jack!

TANNER. Yes, because to be treated as a boy was to be taken on the old footing. I had become a new person; and those who knew the old person laughed at me. The only man who behaved sensibly was my tailor: he took my measure anew every time he saw me, while all the rest went on with their old measurements and expected them to fit me.

ANN. You became frightfully self-conscious.

TANNER. When you go to heaven, Ann, you will be frightfully conscious of your wings for the first year or so. When you meet your relatives there, and they persist in treating you as if you were still a mortal, you will not be able to bear them. You will try to get into a circle which has never known you except as an angel.

ANN. So it was only your vanity that made you run away from us after all?

TANNER. Yes, only my vanity, as you call it.

ANN. You need not have kept away from me on that account.

TANNER. From you above all others. You fought harder than anybody against my emancipation.

ANN (*earnestly*). Oh, how wrong you are! I would have done anything for you.

TANNER. Anything except let me get loose from you. Even then you had acquired by instinct that damnable woman's trick of heaping obligations on a man, of placing yourself so entirely and helplessly at his mercy that at last he dare not take a step without running to you for leave. I know a poor wretch whose one desire in life is to run away from his wife. She prevents him by threatening to throw herself in front of the engine of the train he leaves her in. That is what all women do. If we try to go where you do not want us to go there is no law to prevent us; but when we take the first step your breasts are under our foot as it descends: your bodies are under our wheels as we start. No woman shall ever enslave me in that way.

ANN. But, Jack, you cannot get through life without considering other people a little.

TANNER. Ay; but what other people? It is this consideration of other people—or rather this cowardly fear of them which we call consideration—that makes us the sentimental slaves we are. To consider you, as you call it, is to substitute your will for my own. How if it be a baser will than mine? Are women taught better than men or worse? Are mobs of voters taught better than statesmen or worse? Worse, of course, in both cases. And then what sort of world are you going to get, with its public men considering its voting mobs, and its private men considering their wives? What does Church and State mean nowadays? The Woman and the Ratepayer.

ANN (*placidly*). I am so glad you understand politics, Jack: it will be most useful to you if you go into parliament. (*He collapses like a pricked bladder.*) But I am sorry you thought my influence a bad one.

TANNER. I don't say it was a bad one. But bad or good, I didn't choose to be cut to your measure. And I won't be cut to it.

ANN. Nobody wants you to, Jack. I assure you—really on my word—I don't mind your queer opinions one little bit. You know we have all been brought up to have advanced opinions. Why do you persist in thinking me so narrow minded?

TANNER. That's the danger of it. I know you don't mind, because you've found out that it doesn't matter. The boa constrictor doesn't mind the opinions of a stag one little bit when once she has got her coils round it.

ANN (*rising in sudden enlightenment*). O-o-o-o-oh! now I understand why you warned Tavy that I am a boa constrictor. Granny told me. (*She laughs and throws her boa round his neck.*) Doesn't it feel nice and soft, Jack?

TANNER (*in the coils*). You scandalous woman, will you throw away even your hypocrisy?

ANN. I am never hypocritical with you, Jack. Are you angry? (*She withdraws the boa and throws it on a chair.*) Perhaps I shouldn't have done that.

TANNER (*contemptuously*). Pooh, prudery! Why should you not, if it amuses you?

ANN (*shyly*). Well, because—because I suppose what you really meant by the boa constrictor was this. (*She puts her arms round his neck.*)

TANNER (*staring at her*). Magnificent audacity! (*She laughs and pats his cheeks.*) Now just to think that if I mentioned this episode not a soul would believe me except the people who would cut me for telling, while if you accused me of it nobody would believe my denial!

ANN (*taking her arms away with perfect dignity*). You are incorrigible, Jack. But you should not jest about our affection for one another. Nobody could possibly misunderstand it. You do not misunderstand it, I hope.

TANNER. My blood interprets for me, Ann. Poor Ricky Ticky Tavy!

ANN (*looking quickly at him as if this were a new light*). Surely you are not so absurd as to be jealous of Tavy.

TANNER. Jealous! Why should I be? But I don't wonder at your grip of him. I feel the coils tightening round my very self, though you are only playing with me.

ANN. Do you think I have designs on Tavy?

TANNER. I know you have.

ANN (*earnestly*). Take care, Jack. You may make Tavy very unhappy if you mislead him about me.

TANNER. Never fear: he will not escape you.

ANN. I wonder are you really a clever man!

TANNER. Why this sudden misgiving on the subject?

ANN. You seem to understand all the things I don't understand; but you are a perfect baby in the things I do understand.

TANNER. I understand how Tavy feels for you, Ann: you may depend on that, at all events.

ANN. And you think you understand how I feel for Tavy, don't you?

TANNER. I know only too well what is going to happen to poor Tavy.

ANN. I should laugh at you, Jack, if it were not for poor papa's death. Mind! Tavy will be very unhappy.

TANNER. Yes; but he won't know it, poor devil. He is a thousand times too good for you. That's why he is going to make the mistake of his life about you.

ANN. I think men make more mistakes by being too clever than by being too good. (*She sits down, with a trace of contempt for the whole male sex in the elegant carriage of her shoulders.*)

TANNER. Oh, I know you don't care very much about Tavy. But there is always one who kisses and one who only allows the kiss. Tavy will kiss; and you will only turn the cheek. And you will throw him over if anybody better turns up.

ANN (*offended*). You have no right to say such things, Jack. They are not true, and not delicate. If you and Tavy choose to be stupid about me, that is not my fault.

TANNER (*remorsefully*). Forgive my brutalities, Ann. They are leveled at this wicked world, not at you. (*She looks up at him, pleased and forgiving. He becomes cautious at once.*) All the same, I wish Ramsden would come back. I never feel safe with you: there is a devilish charm—or no: not a charm, a subtle interest (*she laughs*)—Just so: you know it; and you triumph in it. Openly and shamelessly triumph in it!

ANN. What a shocking flirt you are, Jack!

TANNER. A flirt!! I!!!

ANN. Yes, a flirt. You are always abusing and offending people; but you never really mean to let go your hold of them.

TANNER. I will ring the bell. This conversation has already gone further than I intended.

(RAMSDEN *and* OCTAVIUS *come back with* MISS RAMSDEN, *a hardheaded old maiden lady in a plain brown silk gown, with enough rings, chains and brooches to show that her plainness of dress is a matter of principle, not of poverty. She comes into the room very determinedly: the two men, perplexed and downcast, following her.* ANN *rises and goes eagerly to meet her.* TANNER *retreats to the wall between the busts and pretends to study the pictures.* RAMSDEN *goes to his table as usual; and* OCTAVIUS *clings to the neighborhood of* TANNER.)

MISS RAMSDEN (*almost pushing* ANN *aside as she comes to* MRS. WHITEFIELD'*s chair and plants herself there resolutely*). I wash my hands of the whole affair.

OCTAVIUS (*very wretched*). I know you wish me to take Violet away, Miss Ramsden. I will. (*He turns irresolutely to the door.*)

RAMSDEN. No no—

MISS RAMSDEN. What is the use of saying no, Roebuck? Octavius knows that I would not turn any truly contrite and repentant woman from your doors. But when a woman is not only wicked, but intends to go on being wicked, she and I part company.

ANN. Oh, Miss Ramsden, what do you mean? What has Violet said?

RAMSDEN. Violet is certainly very obstinate. She won't leave London. I don't understand her.

MISS RAMSDEN. I do. It's as plain as the nose on your face, Roebuck, that she won't go because she doesn't want to be separated from this man, whoever he is.

ANN. Oh, surely, surely! Octavius: did you speak to her?

OCTAVIUS. She won't tell us anything. She won't make any arrangement until she has consulted somebody. It can't be anybody else than the scoundrel who has betrayed her.

TANNER (*to* OCTAVIUS). Well, let her consult him. He will be glad enough to have her sent abroad. Where is the difficulty?

MISS RAMSDEN (*taking the answer out of* OCTAVIUS'*s mouth*). The difficulty, Mr. Jack, is that when I offered to help her I didn't offer to become her accomplice in her wickedness. She either pledges her word never to see that man again, or else she finds some new friends; and the sooner the better.

(*The* PARLORMAID *appears at the door.* ANN *hastily resumes her seat, and looks as unconcerned as possible.* OCTAVIUS *instinctively imitates her.*)

THE MAID. The cab is at the door, ma'am.

MISS RAMSDEN. What cab?

THE MAID. For Miss Robinson.

MISS RAMSDEN. Oh! (*Recovering herself.*) All right. (*The* MAID *withdraws.*) She has sent for a cab.

TANNER. I wanted to send for that cab half an hour ago.

MISS RAMSDEN. I am glad she understands the position she has placed herself in.

RAMSDEN. I don't like her going away in this fashion, Susan. We had better not do anything harsh.

OCTAVIUS. No: thank you again and again; but Miss Ramsden is quite right. Violet cannot expect to stay.

ANN. Hadn't you better go with her, Tavy?

OCTAVIUS. She won't have me.

MISS RAMSDEN. Of course she won't. She's going straight to that man.

TANNER. As a natural result of her virtuous reception here.

RAMSDEN (*much troubled*). There, Susan! You hear! and there's some truth in it. I wish you could reconcile it with your principles to be a little patient with this poor girl. She's very young; and there's a time for everything.

MISS RAMSDEN. Oh, she will get all the sympathy she wants from the men. I'm surprised at you, Roebuck.

TANNER. So am I, Ramsden, most favorably.

(VIOLET *appears at the door. She is as impenitent and self-possessed a young lady as one would desire to see among the best behaved of her sex. Her small head and tiny resolute mouth and chin; her haughty crispness of speech and trimness of carriage; the ruthless elegance of her equipment, which includes a very smart hat with a dead bird in it, mark a personality which is as formidable as it is exquisitely pretty. She is not a siren, like* ANN: *admiration comes to her without any compulsion or even interest on her part; besides, there is some fun in* ANN, *but in this woman none, perhaps no mercy either: if anything restrains her, it is intelligence and pride, not compassion. Her voice might be the voice of a schoolmistress addressing a class of girls who had disgraced themselves, as she proceeds with complete composure and some disgust to say what she has come to say.*)

VIOLET. I have only looked in to tell Miss Ramsden that she will find her birthday present to me, the filagree bracelet, in the housekeeper's room.

TANNER. Do come in, Violet, and talk to us sensibly.

VIOLET. Thank you: I have had quite enough of the family conversation this morning. So has your mother, Ann: she has gone home crying. But at all events, I have found out what some of my pretended friends are worth. Goodbye.

TANNER. No, no: one moment. I have something to say which I beg you to hear. (*She looks at him without the slightest curiosity, but waits, apparently as much to finish getting her glove on as to hear what he has to say.*) I am altogether on your side in this matter. I congratulate you, with the sincerest respect, on having the courage to do what you have done. You are entirely in the right; and the family is entirely in the wrong.

(*Sensation.* ANN *and* MISS RAMSDEN *rise and turn towards the two.* VIOLET, *more surprised than any of the others, forgets her glove, and comes forward into the middle of the room, both puzzled and displeased.* OCTAVIUS *alone does not move or raise his head: he is overwhelmed with shame.*)

ANN (*pleading to* TANNER *to be sensible*). Jack!

MISS RAMSDEN (*outraged*). Well, I must say!

VIOLET (*sharply to* TANNER). Who told you?

TANNER. Why, Ramsden and Tavy of course. Why should they not?

VIOLET. But they don't know.

TANNER. Don't know what?

VIOLET. They don't know that I am in the right, I mean.

TANNER. Oh, they know it in their hearts, though they think themselves bound to blame you by their silly superstitions about morality and propriety and so forth. But I know, and the whole world really knows, though it dare not say so, that you were right to follow your instinct; that vitality and bravery are the greatest qualities a woman can have, and motherhood her solemn initiation into womanhood; and that the fact of your not being legally married matters not one scrap either to your own worth or to our real regard for you.

VIOLET (*flushing with indignation*). Oh! You think me a wicked woman, like the rest. You think I have not only been vile, but that I share your abominable opinions. Miss Ramsden: I have borne your hard words because I knew you would be sorry for them when you found out the truth. But I won't bear such a horrible insult as to be complimented by

Jack on being one of the wretches of whom he approves. I have kept my marriage a secret for my husband's sake. But now I claim my right as a married woman not to be insulted.

OCTAVIUS (*raising his head with inexpressible relief*). You are married!

VIOLET. Yes; and I think you might have guessed it. What business had you all to take it for granted that I had no right to wear my wedding ring? Not one of you even asked me: I cannot forget that.

TANNER (*in ruins*). I am utterly crushed. I meant well. I apologize—abjectly apologize.

VIOLET. I hope you will be more careful in future about the things you say. Of course one does not take them seriously; but they are very disagreeable, and rather in bad taste, I think.

TANNER (*bowing to the storm*). I have no defense: I shall know better in future than to take any woman's part. We have all disgraced ourselves in your eyes, I am afraid, except Ann. She befriended you. For Ann's sake, forgive us.

VIOLET. Yes: Ann has been very kind; but then Ann knew.

TANNER. Oh!

MISS RAMSDEN (*stiffly*). And who, pray, is the gentleman who does not acknowledge his wife?

VIOLET (*promptly*). That is my business, Miss Ramsden, and not yours. I have my reasons for keeping my marriage a secret for the present.

RAMSDEN. All I can say is that we are extremely sorry, Violet. I am shocked to think of how we have treated you.

OCTAVIUS (*awkwardly*). I beg your pardon, Violet. I can say no more.

MISS RAMSDEN (*still loth to surrender*). Of course what you say puts a very different complexion on the matter. All the same, I owe it to myself—

VIOLET (*cutting her short*). You owe me an apology, Miss Ramsden: that's what you owe both to yourself and to me. If you were a married woman you would not like sitting in the housekeeper's room and being treated like a naughty child by young girls and old ladies without any serious duties and responsibilities.

TANNER. Don't hit us when we're down, Violet. We seem to have made fools of ourselves; but really it was you who made fools of us.

VIOLET. It was no business of yours, Jack, in any case.

TANNER. No business of mine! Why, Ramsden as good as accused me of being the unknown gentleman.

(RAMSDEN *makes a frantic demonstration; but* VIOLET*'s cool keen anger extinguishes it.*)

VIOLET. You! Oh, how infamous! how abominable! how disgracefully you have all been talking about me! If my husband knew it he would never let me speak to any of you again. (*To* RAMSDEN.) I think you might have spared me that, at least.

RAMSDEN. But I assure you I never—at least it is a monstrous perversion of something I said that—

MISS RAMSDEN. You needn't apologize, Roebuck. She brought it all on herself. It is for her to apologize for having deceived us.

VIOLET. I can make allowances for you, Miss Ramsden: you cannot understand how I feel on this subject, though I should have expected rather better taste from people of greater experience. However, I quite feel that you have all placed yourselves in a very painful position; and the most truly considerate thing for me to do is to go at once. Good morning.

(*She goes, leaving them staring.*)

MISS RAMSDEN. Well, I must say!

RAMSDEN (*plaintively*). I don't think she is quite fair to us.

TANNER. You must cower before the wedding ring like the rest of us, Ramsden. The cup of our ignominy is full.

ACT II

On the carriage drive in the park of a country house near Richmond a motor car has broken down. It stands in front of a clump of trees round which the drive sweeps to the house, which is partly visible through them: indeed TANNER, *standing in the drive with the car on his right hand, could get an unobstructed view of the west corner of the house on his left were he not far too much interested in a pair of supine legs in blue serge trousers which protrude from beneath the machine. He is watching them intently with bent back and hands supported on his knees. His leathern overcoat and peaked cap proclaim him one of the dismounted passengers.*

THE LEGS. Aha! I got him.

TANNER. All right now?

THE LEGS. Aw rawt nah.

(TANNER *stoops and takes the legs by the ankles, drawing their owner forth like a wheelbarrow, walking on his hands, with a hammer in his mouth. He is a young man in a neat suit of blue serge, clean shaven, dark eyed, square fingered, with short well brushed black hair and rather irregular skeptically turned eyebrows. When he is manipulating the car his movements are swift and sudden, yet attentive and deliberate. With* TANNER *and* TANNER'*s friends his manner is not in the least deferential, but cool and reticent, keeping them quite effectually at a distance while giving them no excuse for complaining of him. Nevertheless he has a vigilant eye on them always, and that, too, rather cynically, like a man who knows the world well from its seamy side. He speaks slowly and with a touch of sarcasm; and as he does not at all affect the gentleman in his speech, it may be inferred that his smart appearance is a mark of respect to himself and his own class, not to that which employs him.*

He now gets into the car to test his machinery and put his cap and overcoat on again. TANNER *takes off his leathern overcoat and pitches it into the car.* THE CHAUFFEUR (*or automobilist or motoreer or whatever England may presently decide to call him*) *looks round inquiringly in the act of stowing away his hammer.*)

THE CHAUFFEUR. Had enough of it, eh?

TANNER. I may as well walk to the house and stretch my legs and calm my nerves a little. (*Looking at his watch.*) I suppose you know that we have come from Hyde Park Corner to Richmond in twenty-one minutes.

THE CHAUFFEUR. I'd ha' done it under fifteen if I'd had a clear road all the way.

TANNER. Why do you do it? Is it for love of sport or for the fun of terrifying your unfortunate employer?

THE CHAUFFEUR. What are you afraid of?

TANNER. The police, and breaking my neck.

THE CHAUFFEUR. Well, if you like easy going, you can take a bus, you know. It's cheaper. You pay me to save your time and give you the value of your thousand pound car. (*He sits down calmly.*)

TANNER. I am the slave of that car and of you too. I dream of the accursed thing at night.

THE CHAUFFEUR. You'll get over that. If you're going up to the house, may I ask how long you're goin' to stay there? Because if you mean to put in the whole morning talkin' to the ladies, I'll put the car in the stables and make myself comfortable. If not, I'll keep the car on the go about here till you come.

TANNER. Better wait here. We shan't be long. There's a young American gentleman, a Mr. Malone, who is driving Mr. Robinson down in his new American steam car.

THE CHAUFFEUR (*springing up and coming hastily out of the car to* TAN-

NER). American steam car! Wot! racin' us dahn from London!

TANNER. Perhaps they're here already.

THE CHAUFFEUR. If I'd known it! (*With deep reproach.*) Why didn't you tell me. Mr. Tanner?

TANNER. Because I've been told that this car is capable of 84 miles an hour; and I already know what you are capable of when there is a rival car on the road. No, Henry: there are things it is not good for you to know; and this was one of them. However, cheer up: we are going to have a day after your own heart. The American is to take Mr. Robinson and his sister and Miss Whitefield. We are to take Miss Rhoda.

THE CHAUFFEUR (*consoled, and musing on another matter*). That's Miss Whitefield's sister, isn't it?

TANNER. Yes.

THE CHAUFFEUR. And Miss Whitefield herself is goin' in the other car? Not with you?

TANNER. Why the devil should she come with me? Mr. Robinson will be in the other car. (THE CHAUFFEUR *looks at* TANNER *with cool incredulity, and turns to the car, whistling a popular air softly to himself.* TANNER, *a little annoyed, is about to pursue the subject when he hears the footsteps of* OCTAVIUS *on the gravel.* OCTAVIUS *is coming from the house, dressed for motoring, but without his overcoat.*) We've lost the race, thank Heaven: here's Mr. Robinson. Well, Tavy, is the steam car a success?

OCTAVIUS. I think so. We came from Hyde Park Corner here in seventeen minutes. (THE CHAUFFEUR, *furious, kicks the car with a groan of vexation.*) How long were you?

TANNER. Oh, about three quarters of an hour or so.

THE CHAUFFEUR (*remonstrating*). Now, now, Mr. Tanner, come now! We could ha' done it easy under fifteen.

TANNER. By the way, let me introduce you. Mr. Octavius Robinson: Mr. Enry Straker.

STRAKER. Pleased to meet you, sir. Mr. Tanner is gittin at you with 'is Enry Straker, you know. You call it Henery. But I don't mind, bless you.

TANNER. You think it's simply bad taste in me to chaff him, Tavy. But you're wrong. This man takes more trouble to drop his aitches than ever his father did to pick them up. It's a mark of caste to him. I have never met anybody more swollen with the pride of class than Enry is.

STRAKER. Easy, easy! A little moderation, Mr. Tanner.

TANNER. A little moderation, Tavy, you observe. You would tell me to draw it mild. But this chap has been educated. What's more, he knows that we haven't. What was that Board School of yours, Straker?

STRAKER. Sherbrooke Road.

TANNER. Sherbrooke Road! Would any of us say Rugby! Harrow! Eton! in that tone of intellectual snobbery? Sherbrooke Road is a place where boys learn something: Eton is a boy farm where we are sent because we are nuisances at home, and because in after life, whenever a Duke is mentioned, we can claim him as an old school fellow.

STRAKER. You don't know nothing about it, Mr. Tanner. It's not the Board School that does it: it's the Polytechnic.

TANNER. His university, Octavius. Not Oxford, Cambridge, Durham, Dublin or Glasgow. Not even those Nonconformist holes in Wales. No, Tavy. Regent Street, Chelsea, the Borough—I don't know half their confounded names: these are his universities, not mere shops for selling class limitations like ours. You despise Oxford, Enry, don't you?

STRAKER. No, I don't. Very nice sort of place, Oxford, I should think, for people that like that sort of place. They teach you to be a gentleman there. In the

Polytechnic they teach you to be an engineer or such like. See?

TANNER. Sarcasm, Tavy, sarcasm! Oh, if you could only see into Enry's soul, the depth of his contempt for a gentleman, the arrogance of his pride in being an engineer, would appall you. He positively likes the car to break down because it brings out my gentlemanly helplessness and his workmanlike skill and resource.

STRAKER. Never you mind him, Mr. Robinson. He likes to talk. We know him, don't we?

OCTAVIUS (*earnestly*). But there's a great truth at the bottom of what he says. I believe most intensely in the dignity of labor.

STRAKER (*unimpressed*). That's because you never done any, Mr. Robinson. My business is to do away with labor. You'll get more out of me and a machine than you will out of twenty laborers, and not so much to drink either.

TANNER. For Heaven's sake, Tavy, don't start him on political economy. He knows all about it; and we don't. You're only a poetic Socialist, Tavy: he's a scientific one.

STRAKER (*unperturbed*). Yes. Well, this conversation is very improvin'; but I've got to look after the car; and you two want to talk about your ladies. *I* know. (*He retires to busy himself about the car; and presently saunters off towards the house.*)

TANNER. That's a very momentous social phenomenon.

OCTAVIUS. What is?

TANNER. Straker is. Here have we literary and cultured persons been for years setting up a cry of the New Woman whenever some unusually old fashioned female came along; and never noticing the advent of the New Man. Straker's the New Man.

OCTAVIUS. I see nothing new about him, except your way of chaffing him. But I don't want to talk about him just now. I want to speak to you about Ann.

TANNER. Straker knew even that. He learned it at the Polytechnic, probably. Well, what about Ann? Have you proposed to her?

OCTAVIUS (*self-reproachfully*). I was brute enough to do so last night.

TANNER. Brute enough! What do you mean?

OCTAVIUS (*dithyrambically*). Jack: we men are all coarse: we never understand how exquisite a woman's sensibilities are. How could I have done such a thing!

TANNER. Done what, you maudlin idiot?

OCTAVIUS. Yes, I am an idiot, Jack: if you had heard her voice! if you had seen her tears! I have lain awake all night thinking of them. If she had reproached me, I could have borne it better.

TANNER. Tears! that's dangerous. What did she say?

OCTAVIUS. She asked me how she could think of anything now but her dear father. She stifled a sob— (*He breaks down.*)

TANNER (*patting him on the back*). Bear it like a man, Tavy, even if you feel it like an ass. It's the old game: she's not tired of playing with you yet.

OCTAVIUS (*impatiently*). Oh, don't be a fool, Jack. Do you suppose this eternal shallow cynicism of yours has any real bearing on a nature like hers?

TANNER. Hm! Did she say anything else?

OCTAVIUS. Yes; and that is why I expose myself and her to your ridicule by telling you what passed.

TANNER (*remorsefully*). No, dear Tavy, not ridicule, on my honor! However, no matter. Go on.

OCTAVIUS. Her sense of duty is so devout, so perfect, so—

TANNER. Yes: I know. Go on.

OCTAVIUS. You see, under this new arrangement, you and Ramsden are her guardians; and she considers that all her duty to her father is now transferred to you. She said she thought I ought to have spoken to you both in the first instance. Of course she is right; but somehow it seems rather absurd that I am to come to you and formally ask to be received as a suitor for your ward's hand.

TANNER. I am glad that love has not totally extinguished your sense of humor, Tavy.

OCTAVIUS. That answer won't satisfy her.

TANNER. My official answer is, obviously, Bless you, my children: may you be happy!

OCTAVIUS. I wish you would stop playing the fool about this. If it is not serious to you, it is to me, and to her.

TANNER. You know very well that she is as free to choose as you are.

OCTAVIUS. She does not think so

TANNER. Oh, doesn't she! just! However, say what you want me to do.

OCTAVIUS. I want you to tell her sincerely and earnestly what you think about me. I want you to tell her that you can trust her to me—that is, if you feel you can.

TANNER. I have no doubt that I can trust her to you. What worries me is the idea of trusting you to her. Have you read Maeterlinck's book about the bee?

OCTAVIUS (*keeping his temper with difficulty*). I am not discussing literature at present.

TANNER. Be just a little patient with me. *I* am not discussing literature: the book about the bee is natural history. It's an awful lesson to mankind. You think that you are Ann's suitor; that you are the pursuer and she the pursued; that it is your part to woo, to persuade, to prevail, to overcome. Fool: it is you who are the pursued, the marked down quarry, the destined prey. You need not sit looking longingly at the bait through the wires of the trap: the door is open, and will remain so until it shuts behind you forever.

OCTAVIUS. I wish I could believe that, vilely as you put it.

TANNER. Why, man, what other work has she in life but to get a husband? It is a woman's business to get married as soon as possible, and a man's to keep unmarried as long as he can. You have your poems and your tragedies to work at: Ann has nothing.

OCTAVIUS. I cannot write without inspiration. And nobody can give me that except Ann.

TANNER. Well, hadn't you better get it from her at a safe distance? Petrarch didn't see half as much of Laura, nor Dante of Beatrice, as you see of Ann now; and yet they wrote first-rate poetry —at least so I'm told. They never exposed their idolatry to the test of domestic familiarity; and it lasted them to their graves. Marry Ann; and at the end of a week you'll find no more inspiration in her than in a plate of muffins.

OCTAVIUS. You think I shall tire of her!

TANNER. Not at all: you don't get tired of muffins. But you don't find inspiration in them; and you won't in her when she ceases to be a poet's dream and becomes a solid eleven stone wife. You'll be forced to dream about somebody else; and then there will be a row.

OCTAVIUS. This sort of talk is no use, Jack. You don't understand. You have never been in love.

TANNER. I! I have never been out of it. Why, I am in love even with Ann. But I am neither the slave of love nor its dupe. Go to the bee, thou poet: consider her ways and be wise. By Heaven, Tavy, if women could do without our work, and we ate their children's bread instead of making it, they would kill us as the spider kills her mate or as the bees kill the drone. And they would be right if we were good for nothing but love.

OCTAVIUS. Ah, if we were only good

enough for Love! There is nothing like Love: there is nothing else but Love: without it the world would be a dream of sordid horror.

TANNER. And this—this is the man who asks me to give him the hand of my ward! Tavy: I believe we were changed in our cradles, and that you are the real descendant of Don Juan.

OCTAVIUS. I beg you not to say anything like that to Ann.

TANNER. Don't be afraid. She has marked you for her own; and nothing will stop her now. You are doomed. (STRAKER *comes back with a newspaper.*) Here comes the New Man, demoralizing himself with a halfpenny paper as usual.

STRAKER. Now would you believe it, Mr. Robinson, when we're out motoring we take in two papers, the Times for him, the Leader or the Echo for me. And do you think I ever see my paper? Not much. He grabs the Leader and leaves me to stodge myself with the Times.

OCTAVIUS. Are there no winners in the Times?

TANNER. Enry don't 'old with bettin', Tavy. Motor records are his weakness. What's the latest?

STRAKER. Paris to Biskra at forty mile an hour average, not countin' the Mediterranean.

TANNER. How many killed?

STRAKER. Two silly sheep. What does it matter? Sheep don't cost such a lot: they were glad to 'ave the price without the trouble o' sellin' 'em to the butcher. All the same, d'y'see, there'll be a clamor agin it presently; and then the French Government'll stop it; an our chance'll be gone, see? That's what makes me fairly mad: Mr. Tanner won't do a good run while he can.

TANNER. Tavy: do you remember my Uncle James?

OCTAVIUS. Yes. Why?

TANNER. Uncle James had a first rate cook: he couldn't digest anything except what she cooked. Well, the poor man was shy and hated society. But his cook was proud of her skill, and wanted to serve up dinners to princes and ambassadors. To prevent her from leaving him, that poor old man had to give a big dinner twice a month, and suffer agonies of awkwardness. Now here am I; and here is this chap Enry Straker, the New Man. I loathe traveling; but I rather like Enry. He cares for nothing but tearing along in a leather coat and goggles, with two inches of dust all over him, at sixty miles an hour and the risk of his life and mine. Except, of course, when he is lying on his back in the mud under the machine trying to find out where it has given way. Well, if I don't give him a thousand mile run at least once a fortnight I shall lose him. He will give me the sack and go to some American millionaire; and I shall have to put up with a nice respectful groom-gardener-amateur, who will touch his hat and know his place. I am Enry's slave, just as Uncle James was his cook's slave.

STRAKER (*exasperated*). Garn! I wish I had a car that would go as fast as you can talk, Mr. Tanner. What I say is that you lose money by a motor car unless you keep it workin'. Might as well 'ave a pram and a nussmaid to wheel you in it as that car and me if you don't git the last inch out of us both.

TANNER (*soothingly*). All right, Henry, all right. We'll go out for half an hour presently.

STRAKER (*in disgust*). Arf an ahr! (*He returns to his machine; seats himself in it; and turns up a fresh page of his paper in search of more news.*)

OCTAVIUS. Oh that reminds me. I have a note for you from Rhoda. (*He gives* TANNER *a note.*)

TANNER (*opening it*). I rather think Rhoda is heading for a row with Ann. As a rule there is only one person an English girl hates more than she hates her mother; and that's her eldest sister. But Rhoda positively prefers her mother to Ann. She— (*Indignantly.*) Oh, I say!

OCTAVIUS. What's the matter?

TANNER. Rhoda was to have come with me for a ride in the motor car. She says Ann has forbidden her to go out with me.

(STRAKER *suddenly begins whistling his favorite air with remarkable deliberation. Surprised by this burst of larklike melody, and jarred by a sardonic note in its cheerfulness, they turn and look inquiringly at him. But he is busy with his paper; and nothing comes of their movement.*)

OCTAVIUS (*recovering himself*). Does she give any reason?

TANNER. Reason! An insult is not a reason. Ann forbids her to be alone with me on any occasion. Says I am not a fit person for a young girl to be with. What do you think of your paragon now?

OCTAVIUS. You must remember that she has a very heavy responsibility now that her father is dead. Mrs. Whitefield is too weak to control Rhoda.

TANNER (*staring at him*). In short, you agree with Ann.

OCTAVIUS. No; but I think I understand her. You must admit that your views are hardly suited for the formation of a young girl's mind and character.

TANNER. I admit nothing of the sort. I admit that the formation of a young lady's mind and character usually consists in telling her lies; but I object to the particular lie that I am in the habit of abusing the confidence of girls.

OCTAVIUS. Ann doesn't say that, Jack.

TANNER. What else does she mean?

STRAKER (*catching sight of* ANN *coming from the house*). Miss Whitefield, gentlemen. (*He dismounts and strolls away down the avenue with the air of a man who knows he is no longer wanted.*)

ANN (*coming between* OCTAVIUS *and* TANNER). Good morning, Jack. I have come to tell you that poor Rhoda has got one of her headaches and cannot go out with you today in the car. It is a cruel disappointment to her, poor child!

TANNER. What do you say now, Tavy?

OCTAVIUS. Surely you cannot misunderstand, Jack. Ann is showing you the kindest consideration, even at the cost of deceiving you.

ANN. What do you mean?

TANNER. Would you like to cure Rhoda's headache, Ann?

ANN. Of course.

TANNER. Then tell her what you said just now; and add that you arrived about two minutes after I had received her letter and read it.

ANN. Rhoda has written to you!

TANNER. With full particulars.

OCTAVIUS. Never mind him, Ann. You were right—quite right. Ann was only doing her duty, Jack; and you know it. Doing it in the kindest way, too.

ANN (*going to* OCTAVIUS). How kind you are, Tavy! How helpful! How well you understand!

(OCTAVIUS *beams.*)

TANNER. Ay: tighten the coils. You love her, Tavy, don't you?

OCTAVIUS. She knows I do.

ANN. Hush. For shame, Tavy!

TANNER. Oh, I give you leave. I am your guardian; and I commit you to Tavy's care for the next hour. I am off for a turn in the car.

ANN. No, Jack. I must speak to you about Rhoda. Ricky: will you go back to the house and entertain your American friend. He's rather on Mamma's hands so early in the morning. She wants to finish her housekeeping.

OCTAVIUS. I fly, dearest Ann. (*He kisses her hand.*)

ANN (*tenderly*). Ricky Ticky Tavy!

(*He looks at her with an eloquent blush, and runs off.*)

TANNER (*bluntly*). Now look here,

Ann. This time you've landed yourself; and if Tavy were not in love with you past all salvation he'd have found out what an incorrigible liar you are.

ANN. You misunderstand, Jack. I didn't dare tell Tavy the truth.

TANNER. No: your daring is generally in the opposite direction. What the devil do you mean by telling Rhoda that I am too vicious to associate with her? How can I ever have any human or decent relations with her again, now that you have poisoned her mind in that abominable way?

ANN. I know you are incapable of behaving badly—

TANNER. Then why did you lie to her?

ANN. I had to.

TANNER. Had to!

ANN. Mother made me.

TANNER (*his eyes flashing*). Ha! I might have known it. The mother! Always the mother!

ANN. It was that dreadful book of yours. You know how timid mother is. All timid women are conventional: we must be conventional. Even you, who are a man, cannot say what you think without being misunderstood and vilified—yes: I admit it: I have had to vilify you. Do you want to have poor Rhoda misunderstood and vilified in the same way? Would it be right for mother to let her expose herself to such treatment before she is old enough to judge for herself?

TANNER. In short, the way to avoid misunderstanding is for everybody to lie and slander and insinuate and pretend as hard as they can. That is what obeying your mother comes to.

ANN. I love my mother, Jack.

TANNER (*working himself up into a sociological rage*). Is that any reason why you are not to call your soul your own? Oh, I protest against this vile abjection of youth to age! Look at fashionable society as you know it. What does it pretend to be? An exquisite dance of nymphs. What is it? A horrible procession of wretched girls, each in the claws of a cynical, cunning, avaricious, disillusioned, ignorantly experienced, foul-minded old woman whom she calls mother, and whose duty it is to corrupt her mind and sell her to the highest bidder. Why do these unhappy slaves marry anybody, however old and vile, sooner than not marry at all? Because marriage is their only means of escape from these decrepit fiends who hide their selfish ambitions, their jealous hatreds of the young rivals who have supplanted them, under the mask of maternal duty and family affection. Such things are abominable: the voice of nature proclaims for the daughter a father's care and for the son a mother's. The law for father and son and mother and daughter is not the law of love: it is the law of revolution, of emancipation, of final supersession of the old and worn-out by the young and capable. I tell you, the first duty of manhood and womanhood is a Declaration of Independence: the man who pleads his father's authority is no man: the woman who pleads her mother's authority is unfit to bear citizens to a free people.

ANN (*watching him with quiet curiosity*). I suppose you will go in seriously for politics some day, Jack.

TANNER (*heavily let down*). Eh? What? Wh—? (*Collecting his scattered wits.*) What has that got to do with what I have been saying?

ANN. You talk so well.

TANNER. Talk! Talk! It means nothing to you but talk. Well, go back to your mother, and help her to poison Rhoda's imagination as she has poisoned yours. It is the tame elephants who enjoy capturing the wild ones.

ANN. I am getting on. Yesterday I was a boa constrictor: today I am an elephant.

TANNER. Yes. So pack your trunk and begone: I have no more to say to you.

ANN. You are so utterly unreasonable and impracticable. What can I do?

TANNER. Do! Break your chains. Go your way according to your own conscience and not according to your mother's. Get your mind clean and vigorous; and learn to enjoy a fast ride in a motor car instead of seeing nothing in it but an excuse for a detestable intrigue. Come with me to Marseilles and across to Algiers and to Biskra, at sixty miles an hour. Come right down to the Cape if you like. That will be a Declaration of Independence with a vengeance. You can write a book about it afterwards. That will finish your mother and make a woman of you.

ANN (*thoughtfully*). I don't think there would be any harm in that, Jack. You are my guardian: you stand in my father's place by his own wish. Nobody could say a word against our traveling together. It would be delightful: thank you a thousand times, Jack. I'll come.

TANNER (*aghast*). You'll come!!!

ANN. Of course.

TANNER. But— (*He stops, utterly appalled; then resumes feebly.*) No: look here, Ann: if there's no harm in it there's no point in doing it.

ANN. How absurd you are! You don't want to compromise me, do you?

TANNER. Yes: that's the whole sense of my proposal.

ANN. You are talking the greatest nonsense; and you know it. You would never do anything to hurt me.

TANNER. Well, if you don't want to be compromised, don't come.

ANN (*with simple earnestness*). Yes, I will come, Jack, since you wish it. You are my guardian; and I think we ought to see more of one another and come to know one another better. (*Gratefully.*) It's very thoughtful and very kind of you, Jack, to offer me this lovely holiday, especially after what I said about Rhoda. You really are good—much better than you think. When do we start?

TANNER. But—

(*The conversation is interrupted by the arrival of* MRS. WHITEFIELD *from the house. She is accompanied by the American gentleman, and followed by* RAMSDEN *and* OCTAVIUS.

HECTOR MALONE *is an Eastern American; but he is not at all ashamed of his nationality. This makes English people of fashion think well of him, as of a young fellow who is manly enough to confess to an obvious disadvantage without any attempt to conceal or extenuate it. They feel that he ought not to be made to suffer for what is clearly not his fault, and make a point of being specially kind to him. His chivalrous manners to women, and his elevated moral sentiments, being both gratuitous and unusual, strike them as being a little unfortunate; and though they find his vein of easy humor rather amusing when it has ceased to puzzle them (as it does at first), they have had to make him understand that he really must not tell anecdotes unless they are strictly personal and scandalous, and also that oratory is an accomplishment which belongs to a cruder stage of civilization than that in which his migration has landed him. On these points* HECTOR *is not quite convinced: he still thinks that the British are apt to make merits of their stupidities, and to represent their various incapacities as points of good breeding. English life seems to him to suffer from a lack of edifying rhetoric (which he calls moral tone); English behavior to show a want of respect for womanhood; English pronunciation to fail very vulgarly in tackling such words as world, girl, bird, etc.; English society to be plain spoken to an extent which stretches occasionally to intolerable coarseness; and English intercourse to need enlivening by games and stories and other pastimes; so he does not feel called upon to acquire these defects after taking great pains to cultivate himself in a first rate manner before venturing across the Atlantic. To this culture he finds English people either totally indifferent, as they very commonly are to all culture, or else politely evasive, the truth being that* HECTOR'*s culture is nothing but a state of saturation with our literary exports of thirty years ago, reimported by him to be unpacked at a moment's notice and hurled at the head of English literature, science and art, at every conversational opportunity. The dismay set up by these sallies encourages him in his belief that he is helping to educate England. When he finds people chattering harmlessly about Anatole France and Nietzsche, he devastates them with Matthew Arnold, the Autocrat of the Breakfast Table, and even Macauley; and as he is devoutly religious at bottom, he first leads the unwary, by humorous irreverences, to leave popular theology out of account in discussing moral questions with him, and then scatters them in confusion by demanding whether the carrying out of his ideals of conduct was not the manifest object of God Almighty in creating honest men and pure women. The engaging freshness of his personality and the dumbfoundering staleness of his culture make it extremely difficult to decide whether he is worth knowing; for while his company is undeniably pleasant and enlivening, there is intellectually nothing new to be got out of him, especially as he despises politics, and is careful not to talk commercial shop, in which department he is probably much in advance of his English capitalist friends. He gets on best with romantic Christians of the amoristic sect: hence the friendship which has sprung up between him and* OCTAVIUS.

In appearance HECTOR *is a neatly built young man of twenty-four, with a short, smartly trimmed black beard, clear, well shaped eyes, and an ingratiating vivacity of expression. He is, from the fashionable point of view, faultlessly dressed. As he comes along the drive from the house with* MRS. WHITEFIELD *he is sedulously making himself agreeable and entertaining, and thereby placing on her slender wit a burden it is unable to bear. An Englishman would let her alone, accepting boredom and indifference as their common lot; and the poor lady wants to be either let alone or let prattle about the things that interest her.*

(RAMSDEN *strolls over to inspect the motor car.* OCTAVIUS *joins* HECTOR.)

ANN (*pouncing on her mother joyously*). Oh, mamma, what do you think! Jack is going to take me to Nice in his motor car. Isn't it lovely? I am the happiest person in London.

TANNER (*desperately*). Mrs. Whitefield objects. I am sure she objects. Doesn't she, Ramsden?

RAMSDEN. I should think it very likely indeed.

ANN. You don't object, do you, mother?

MRS. WHITEFIELD. *I* object! Why should I? I think it will do you good, Ann. (*Trotting over to* TANNER.) I meant to ask you to take Rhoda out for a run occasionally: she is too much in the house; but it will do when you come back.

TANNER. Abyss beneath abyss of perfidy!

ANN (*hastily, to distract attention from this outburst*). Oh, I forgot: you have not met Mr. Malone. Mr. Tanner, my guardian: Mr. Hector Malone.

HECTOR. Pleased to meet you, Mr. Tanner. I should like to suggest an extension of the traveling party to Nice, if I may.

ANN. Oh, we're all coming. That's understood, isn't it?

HECTOR. I also am the modest possessor of a motor car. If Miss Robinson will allow me the privilege of taking her, my car is at her service.

OCTAVIUS. Violet!

(*General constraint.*)

ANN (*subduedly*). Come, mother: we must leave them to talk over the arrangements. I must see to my traveling kit.

(MRS. WHITEFIELD *looks bewildered; but* ANN *draws her discreetly away; and they disappear round the corner towards the house.*)

HECTOR. I think I may go so far as to say that I can depend on Miss Robinson's consent.

(*Continued embarrassment.*)

OCTAVIUS. I'm afraid we must leave Violet behind. There are circumstances which make it impossible for her to come on such an expedition.

HECTOR (*amused and not at all convinced*). Too American, eh? Must the young lady have a chaperone?

OCTAVIUS. It's not that, Malone—at least not altogether.

HECTOR. Indeed! May I ask what other objection applies?

TANNER (*impatiently*). Oh, tell him, tell him. We shall never be able to keep the secret unless everybody knows what it is. Mr. Malone: if you go to Nice with Violet, you go with another man's wife. She is married.

HECTOR (*thunderstruck*). You don't tell me so!

TANNER. We do. In confidence.

RAMSDEN (*with an air of importance, lest* MALONE *should suspect a misalliance*). Her marriage has not yet been made known: she desires that it shall not be mentioned for the present.

HECTOR. I shall respect the lady's wishes. Would it be indiscreet to ask who her husband is, in case I should have an opportunity of consulting him about this trip?

TANNER. We don't know who he is.

HECTOR (*retiring into his shell in a very marked manner*). In that case, I have no more to say.

(*They become more embarrassed than ever.*)

OCTAVIUS. You must think this very strange.

HECTOR. A little singular. Pardon me for saying so.

RAMSDEN (*half apologetic, half huffy*). The young lady was married secretly; and her husband has forbidden her, it seems, to declare his name. It is only right to tell you, since you are interested in Miss—er—in Violet.

OCTAVIUS (*sympathetically*). I hope this is not a disappointment to you.

HECTOR (*softened, coming out of his shell again*). Well: it is a blow. I can hardly understand how a man can leave his wife in such a position. Surely it's not customary. It's not manly. It's not considerate.

OCTAVIUS. We feel that, as you may imagine, pretty deeply.

RAMSDEN (*testily*). It is some young fool who has not enough experience to know what mystifications of this kind lead to.

HECTOR (*with strong symptoms of moral repugnance*). I hope so. A man need be very young and pretty foolish too to be excused for such conduct. You take a very lenient view, Mr. Ramsden. Too lenient to my mind. Surely marriage should ennoble a man.

TANNER (*sardonically*). Ha!

HECTOR. Am I to gather from that cachinnation that you don't agree with me, Mr. Tanner?

TANNER (*drily*). Get married and try. You may find it delightful for a while: you certainly won't find it ennobling. The greatest common measure of a man and a woman is not necessarily greater than the man's single measure.

HECTOR. Well, we think in America that a woman's moral number is higher than a man's, and that the purer nature of a woman lifts a man right out of himself, and makes him better than he was.

OCTAVIUS (*with conviction*). So it does.

TANNER. No wonder American women prefer to live in Europe! It's more comfortable than standing all their lives on an altar to be worshiped. Anyhow, Violet's husband has not been ennobled. So what's to be done?

HECTOR (*shaking his head*). I can't dismiss that man's conduct as lightly as you do, Mr. Tanner. However, I'll say no more. Whoever he is, he's Miss Robinson's husband; and I should be glad for her sake to think better of him.

OCTAVIUS (*touched; for he divines a secret sorrow*). I'm very sorry, Malone. Very sorry.

HECTOR (*gratefully*). You're a good fellow, Robinson. Thank you.

TANNER. Talk about something else. Violet's coming from the house.

HECTOR. I should esteem it a very great favor, gentlemen, if you would take the opportunity to let me have a few words with the lady alone. I shall have to cry off this trip; and it's rather a delicate—

RAMSDEN (*glad to escape*). Say no more. Come, Tanner. Come, Tavy. (*He strolls away into the park with* OCTAVIUS and TANNER, *past the motor car.*)

(*Violet comes down the avenue to Hector.*)

VIOLET. Are they looking?

HECTOR. No.

(*She kisses him.*)

VIOLET. Have you been telling lies for my sake?

HECTOR. Lying! Lying hardly describes it. I overdo it. I get carried away in an ecstasy of mendacity. Violet: I wish you'd let me own up.

VIOLET (*instantly becoming serious and resolute*). No, no, Hector: you promised me not to.

HECTOR. I'll keep my promise until you release me from it. But I feel mean, lying to those men, and denying my wife. Just dastardly.

VIOLET. I wish your father were not so unreasonable.

HECTOR. He's not unreasonable. He's right from his point of view. He has a prejudice against the English middle class.

VIOLET. It's too ridiculous. You know how I dislike saying such things to you, Hector; but if I were to—oh, well, no matter.

HECTOR. I know. If you were to marry the son of an English manufacturer of office furniture, your friends would consider it a misalliance. And here's my silly old dad, who is the biggest office furniture man in the world, would show me the door for marrying the most perfect lady in England merely because she has no handle to her name. Of course it's just absurd. But I tell you, Violet, I don't like deceiving him. I feel as if I was stealing his money. Why won't you let me own up?

VIOLET. We can't afford it. You can be as romantic as you please about love, Hector; but you mustn't be romantic about money.

HECTOR (*divided between his uxoriousness and his habitual elevation of moral sentiment*). That's very English. (*Appealing to her impulsively.*) Violet: dad's bound to find us out someday.

VIOLET. Oh yes, later on of course. But don't let's go over this every time we meet, dear. You promised—

HECTOR. All right, all right, I—

VIOLET (*not to be silenced*). It is I and not you who suffer by this concealment; and as to facing a struggle and poverty and all that sort of thing I simply will not do it. It's too silly.

HECTOR. You shall not. I'll sort of borrow the money from my dad until I get on my own feet; and then I can own up and pay up at the same time.

VIOLET (*alarmed and indignant*). Do

you mean to work? Do you want to spoil our marriage?

HECTOR. Well, I don't mean to let marriage spoil my character. Your friend Mr. Tanner has got the laugh on me a bit already about that; and—

VIOLET. The beast! I hate Jack Tanner.

HECTOR (*magnanimously*). Oh, he's all right: he only needs the love of a good woman to ennoble him. Besides, he's proposed a motoring trip to Nice; and I'm going to take you.

VIOLET. How jolly!

HECTOR. Yes; but how are we going to manage? You see, they've warned me off going with you, so to speak. They've told me in confidence that you're married. That's just the most overwhelming confidence I've ever been honored with.

(TANNER *returns with Straker, who goes to his car.*)

TANNER. Your car is a great success, Mr. Malone. Your engineer is showing it off to Mr. Ramsden.

HECTOR (*eagerly—forgetting himself*). Let's come, Vi.

VIOLET (*coldly, warning him with her eyes*). I beg your pardon, Mr. Malone, I did not quite catch

HECTOR (*recollecting himself*). I ask to be allowed the pleasure of showing you my little American steam car, Miss Robinson.

VIOLET. I shall be very pleased. (*They go off together down the avenue.*)

TANNER. About this trip, Straker.

STRAKER (*preoccupied with the car*). Yes?

TANNER. Miss Whitefield is supposed to be coming with me.

STRAKER. So I gather.

TANNER. Mr. Robinson is to be one of the party.

STRAKER. Yes.

TANNER. Well, if you can manage so as to be a good deal occupied with me, and leave Mr. Robinson a good deal occupied with Miss Whitefield, he will be deeply grateful to you.

STRAKER (*looking round at him*). Evidently.

TANNER. "Evidently"! Your grandfather would have simply winked.

STRAKER. My grandfather would have touched his 'at.

TANNER. And I should have given your good nice respectful grandfather a sovereign.

STRAKER. Five shillins, more likely. (*He leaves the car and approaches* TANNER.) What about the lady's views?

TANNER. She is just as willing to be left to Mr. Robinson as Mr. Robinson is to be left to her. (STRAKER *looks at his principal with cool skepticism; then turns to the car whistling his favorite air.*) Stop that aggravating noise. What do you mean by it? (STRAKER *calmly resumes the melody and finishes it.* TANNER *politely hears it out before he again addresses* STRAKER, *this time with elaborate seriousness.*) Enry: I have ever been a warm advocate of the spread of music among the masses; but I object to your obliging the company whenever Miss Whitefield's name is mentioned. You did it this morning, too.

STRAKER (*obstinately*). It's not a bit o' use. Mr. Robinson may as well give it up first as last.

TANNER. Why?

STRAKER. Garn! You know why. Course it's not my business; but you needn't start kiddin' me about it.

TANNER. I am not kidding. I don't know why.

STRAKER (*cheerfully sulky*). Oh, very well. All right. It ain't my business.

TANNER (*impressively*). I trust, Enry, that, as between employer and engineer, I shall always know how to keep my proper distance, and not intrude my private affairs on you. Even our business arrangements are subject to the approval of your Trade Union. But don't abuse your advantages. Let me remind you that Voltaire said that what was too silly to be said could be sung.

STRAKER. It wasn't Voltaire: it was Bow Mar Shay.

TANNER. I stand corrected: Beaumarchais of course. Now you seem to think that what is too delicate to be said can be whistled. Unfortunately your whistling, though melodious, is unintelligible. Come! there's nobody listening: neither my genteel relatives nor the secretary of your confounded Union. As man to man, Enry, why do you think that my friend has no chance with Miss Whitefield?

STRAKER. Cause she's arter summun else.

TANNER. Bosh! who else?

STRAKER. You.

TANNER. Me!!!

STRAKER. Mean to tell me you didn't know? Oh, come, Mr. Tanner!

TANNER (*in fierce earnest*). Are you playing the fool, or do you mean it?

STRAKER (*with a flash of temper*). I'm not playin' no fool. (*More coolly.*) Why, it's as plain as the nose on your face. If you ain't spotted that, you don't know much about these sort of things. (*Serene again.*) Ex-cuse me, you know, Mr. Tanner; but you asked me as man to man; and I told you as man to man.

TANNER (*wildly appealing to the heavens*). Then I—*I* am the bee, the spider, the marked down victim, the destined prey.

STRAKER. I dunno about the bee and the spider. But the marked down victim, that's what you are and no mistake; and a jolly job for you, too, I should say.

TANNER (*momentously*). Henry Straker: the golden moment of your life has arrived.

STRAKER. What d'y'mean?

TANNER. That record to Biskra.

STRAKER (*eagerly*). Yes?

TANNER. Break it.

STRAKER (*rising to the height of his destiny*). D'y'mean it?

TANNER. I do.

STRAKER. When?

TANNER. Now. Is that machine ready to start?

STRAKER (*quailing*). But you can't—

TANNER (*cutting him short by getting into the car*). Off we go. First to the bank for money; then to my rooms for my kit; then to your rooms for your kit; then break the record from London to Dover or Folkestone; then across the channel and away like mad to Marseilles, Gibraltar, Genoa, any port which we can sail to a Mahometan country where men are protected from women.

STRAKER. Garn! you're kiddin'.

TANNER (*resolutely*). Stay behind then. If you won't come I'll do it alone. (*He starts the motor.*)

STRAKER (*running after him*). Here! Mister! arf a mo! steady on! (*He scrambles in as the car plunges forward.*)

ACT III

Evening in the Sierra Nevada. Rolling slopes of brown, with olive trees instead of apple trees in the cultivated patches, and occasional prickly pears instead of gorse and bracken in the wilds. Higher up, tall stone peaks and precipices, all handsome and distinguished. No wild nature here: rather a most aristocratic mountain landscape made by a fastidious artist-creator. No vulgar profusion of vegetation: even a touch of aridity in the frequent patches of stones: Spanish magnificence and Spanish economy everywhere.

Not very far north of a spot at which the high road over one of the passes crosses a tunnel on the railway from Malaga to Granada, is one of the moun-

tain amphitheaters of the Sierra. Looking at it from the wide end of the horse-shoe, one sees, a little to the right, in the face of the cliff, a romantic cave which is really an abandoned quarry, and towards the left a little hill, commanding a view of the road, which skirts the amphitheater on the left, maintaining its higher level on embankments and an occasional stone arch. On the hill, watching the road, is a man who is either a Spaniard or a Scotchman. Probably a Spaniard, since he wears the dress of a Spanish goatherd and seems at home in the Sierra Nevada, but very like a Scotchman for all that. In the hollow, on the slope leading to the quarry-cave, are about a dozen men who, as they recline at their ease round a heap of smoldering white ashes of dead leaf as picturesque scoundrels honoring the Sierra by using it as an effective pictorial background. As a matter of artistic fact they are not picturesque; and the mountains tolerate them as lions tolerate lice. An English policeman or Poor Law Guardian would recognize them as a selected band of tramps and ablebodied paupers.

This description of them is not wholly contemptuous. Whoever has intelligently observed the tramp, or visited the ablebodied ward of a workhouse, will admit that our social failures are not all drunkards and weaklings. Some of them are men who do not fit the class they were born into. Precisely the same qualities that make the educated gentleman an artist may make an uneducated manual laborer an ablebodied pauper. There are men who fall helplessly into the workhouse because they are good for nothing; but there are also men who are there because they are strongminded enough to disregard the social convention (obviously not a disinterested one on the part of the ratepayer) which bids a man live by heavy and badly paid drudgery when he has the alternative of walking into the workhouse, announcing himself as a destitute person, and legally compelling the Guardians to feed, clothe and house him better than he could feed, clothe and house himself without great exertion. When a man who is born a poet refuses a stool in a stockbroker's office, and starves in a garret, sponging on a poor landlady or on his friends and relatives sooner than work against his grain; or when a lady, because she is a lady, will face any extremity of parasitic dependence rather than take a situation as cook or parlormaid, we make large allowances for them. To such allowances the ablebodied pauper, and his nomadic variant the tramp, are equally entitled.

Further, the imaginative man, if his life is to be tolerable to him, must have leisure to tell himself stories, and a position which lends itself to imaginative decoration. The ranks of unskilled labor offer no such positions. We misuse our laborers horribly; and when a man refuses to be misused, we have no right to say that he is refusing honest work. Let us be frank in this matter before we go on with our play; so that we may enjoy it without hypocrisy. If we are reasoning, farsighted people, four fifths of us would go straight to the Guardians for relief, and knock the whole social system to pieces with most beneficial reconstructive results. The reason we do not do this is because we work like bees or ants, by instinct or habit, not reasoning about the matter at all. Therefore when a man comes along who can and does reason, and who, applying the Kantian test to his conduct, can truly say to us, If everybody did as I do, the world would be compelled to reform itself industrially, and abolish slavery and squalor, which exist only because everybody does as you do, let us honor that man and seriously consider the advisabil-

ity of following his example. Such a man is the able-bodied, able-minded pauper. Were he a gentleman doing his best to get a pension or a sinecure instead of sweeping a crossing, nobody would blame him for deciding that so long as the alternative lies between living mainly at the expense of the community and allowing the community to live mainly at his, it would be folly to accept what is to him personally the greater of the two evils.

We may therefore contemplate the tramps of the Sierra without prejudice, admitting cheerfully that our objects—briefly, to be gentlemen of fortune—are much the same as theirs, and the difference in our position and methods merely accidental. One or two of them, perhaps, it would be wiser to kill without malice in a friendly and frank manner; for there are bipeds, just as there are quadrupeds, who are too dangerous to be left unchained and unmuzzled; and these cannot fairly expect to have other men's lives wasted in the work of watching them. But as society has not the courage to kill them, and, when it catches them, simply wreaks on them some superstitious expiatory rites of torture and degradation, and then lets them loose with heightened qualifications for mischief, it is just as well that they are at large in the Sierra, and in the hands of a chief who looks as if he might possibly, on provocation, order them to be shot.

This chief, seated in the center of the group on a squared block of stone from the quarry, is a tall strong man, with a striking cockatoo nose, glossy black hair, pointed beard, upturned moustache, and a Mephistophelean affection which is fairly imposing, perhaps because the scenery admits of a larger swagger than Piccadilly, perhaps because of a certain sentimentality in the man which gives him that touch of grace which alone can excuse deliberate picturesqueness. His eyes and mouth are by no means rascally; he has a fine voice and a ready wit; and whether he is really the strongest man in the party or not, he looks it. He is certainly the best fed, the best dressed, and the best trained. The fact that he speaks English is not unexpected, in spite of the Spanish landscape; for with the exception of one man who might be guessed as a bullfighter ruined by drink, and one unmistakable Frenchman, they are all cockney or American; therefore, in a land of cloaks and sombreros, they mostly wear seedy overcoats, woolen mufflers, hard hemispherical hats, and dirty brown gloves. Only a very few dress after their leader, whose broad sombrero with a cock's feather in the band, and voluminous cloak descending to his high boots, are as un-English as possible. None of them are armed; and the ungloved ones keep their hands in their pockets because it is their national belief that it must be dangerously cold in the open air with the night coming on. (It is as warm an evening as any reasonable man could desire.)

Except the bullfighting inebriate there is only one person in the company who looks more than, say, thirty-three. He is a small man with reddish whiskers, weak eyes, and the anxious look of a small tradesman in difficulties. He wears the only tall hat visible: it shines in the sunset with the sticky glow of some sixpenny patent hat reviver, often applied and constantly tending to produce a worse state of the original surface than the ruin it was applied to remedy. He has a collar and cuffs of celluloid; and his brown Chesterfield overcoat, with velvet collar, is still presentable. He is pre-eminently the respectable man of the party, and is certainly over forty, possibly over fifty. He is the corner man on the leader's right, opposite three men in scarlet ties on his left. One of these three is the Frenchman. Of the remaining two, who are both English, one is argumentative, solemn, and obstinate; the other rowdy and mischievous.

The chief, with a magnificent fling of the end of his cloak across his left shoulder, rises to address them. The applause which greets him shows that he is a favorite orator.

THE CHIEF. Friends and fellow brigands. I have a proposal to make to this meeting. We have now spent three evenings in discussing the question Have Anarchists or Social-Democrats the most personal courage? We have gone into the principles of Anarchism and Social-Democracy at great length. The cause of Anarchy has been ably represented by our one Anarchist, who doesn't know what Anarchism means (*laughter*)—

THE ANARCHIST (*rising*). A point of order, Mendoza—

MENDOZA (*forcibly*). No, by thunder: your last point of order took half an hour. Besides, Anarchists don't believe in order.

THE ANARCHIST (*mild, polite but persistent: he is, in fact, the respectable looking elderly man in the celluloid collar and cuffs*). That is a vulgar error. I can prove—

MENDOZA. Order, order.

THE OTHERS (*shouting*). Order, order. Sit down. Chair! Shut up.

(THE ANARCHIST *is suppressed.*)

MENDOZA. On the other hand we have three Social-Democrats among us. They are not on speaking terms; and they have put before us three distinct and incompatible views of Social-Democracy.

THE THREE MEN IN SCARLET TIES. 1. Mr. Chairman, I protest. A personal explanation. 2. It's a lie. I never said so. Be fair, Mendoza. 3. Je demande la parole. C'est absolument faux. C'est faux! faux!! faux!!! Assas-s-s-s-sin!!!!!!

MENDOZA. Order, order.

THE OTHERS. Order, order, order! Chair!

(THE SOCIAL-DEMOCRATS *are suppressed.*)

MENDOZA. Now, we tolerate all opinions here. But after all, comrades, the vast majority of us are neither Anarchists nor Socialists, but gentlemen and Christians.

THE MAJORITY (*shouting assent*). Hear, hear! So we are. Right.

THE ROWDY SOCIAL-DEMOCRAT (*smarting under suppression*). You ain't no Christian. You're a Sheeny, you are.

MENDOZA (*with crushing magnanimity*). My friend: *I* am an exception to all rules. It is true that I have the honor to be a Jew; and when the Zionists need a leader to reassemble our race on its historic soil of Palestine, Mendoza will not be the last to volunteer (*sympathetic applause—hear, hear, etc.*) But I am not a slave to any superstition. I have swallowed all the formulas, even that of Socialism; though, in a sense, once a Socialist, always a Socialist.

THE SOCIAL-DEMOCRATS. Hear, hear!

MENDOZA. But I am well aware that the ordinary man—even the ordinary brigand, who can scarcely be called an ordinary man (hear, hear!)—is not a philosopher. Common sense is good enough for him; and in our business affairs common sense is good enough for me. Well, what is our business here in the Sierra Nevada, chosen by the Moors as the fairest spot in Spain? Is it to discuss abstruse questions of political economy? No: it is to hold up motor cars and secure a more equitable distribution of wealth.

THE SULKY SOCIAL-DEMOCRAT. All made by labor, mind you.

MENDOZA (*urbanely*). Undoubtedly. All made by labor, and on its way to be squandered by wealthy vagabonds in the dens of vice that disfigure the sunny shores of the Mediterranean. We intercept that wealth. We restore it to circulation among the class that produced it and that chiefly needs it—the working class. We do this at the risk of our lives and liberties, by the exercise of the virtues of courage, endurance, foresight, and abstinence—especially abstinence. I myself have eaten nothing but prickly pears and broiled rabbit for three days.

THE SULKY SOCIAL-DEMOCRAT (*stubbornly*). No more ain't we.

MENDOZA (*indignantly*). Have I taken more than my share?

THE SULKY SOCIAL-DEMOCRAT (*unmoved*). Why should you?

THE ANARCHIST. Why should he not? To each according to his needs: from each according to his means.

THE FRENCHMAN (*shaking his fist at the Anarchist*). Fumiste!

MENDOZA (*diplomatically*). I agree with both of you.

THE GENUINELY ENGLISH BRIGANDS. Hear, hear! Bravo, Mendoza!

MENDOZA. What I say is, let us treat one another as gentlemen, and strive to excel in personal courage only when we take the field.

THE ROWDY SOCIAL-DEMOCRAT (*derisively*). Shikespear.

(*A whistle comes from the goatherd on the hill. He springs up and points excitedly forward along the road to the north.*)

THE GOATHERD. Automobile! Automobile! (*He rushes down the hill and joins the rest, who all scramble to their feet.*)

MENDOZA (*in ringing tones*). To arms! Who has the gun?

THE SULKY SOCIAL-DEMOCRAT (*handing a rifle to* MENDOZA). Here.

MENDOZA. Have the nails been strewn in the road?

THE ROWDY SOCIAL-DEMOCRAT. Two ahnces of em.

MENDOZA. Good! (*To the Frenchman.*) With me, Duval. If the nails fail, puncture their tires with a bullet. (*He gives the rifle to* DUVAL, *who follows him up the hill.* MENDOZA *produces an opera glass. The others hurry across the road and disappear to the north.*)

MENDOZA (*on the hill, using his glass*). Two only, a capitalist and his chauffeur. They look English.

DUVAL. Angliche! Aoh yess. Cochons. (*Handling the rifle.*) Faut tirer, n'est-ce-pas?

MENDOZA. No: the nails have gone home. Their tire is down: they stop.

DUVAL (*shouting to the others*). Fondez sur eux, nom de Dieu!

MENDOZA (*rebuking his excitement*). Du calme, Duval: keep your hair on. They take it quietly. Let us descend and receive them.

(MENDOZA *descends, passing behind the fire and coming forward while* TANNER *and* STRAKER, *in their motoring goggles, leather coats, and caps, are led in from the road by the brigands.*)

TANNER. Is this the gentleman you describe as your boss? Does he speak English?

THE ROWDY SOCIAL-DEMOCRAT. Course he does. Y' downt suppowz we Hinglishmen lets ahrselves be bossed by a bloomin Spenniard, do you?

MENDOZA (*with dignity*). Allow me to introduce myself: Mendoza, President of the League of the Sierra! (*Posing loftily.*) I am a brigand: I live by robbing the rich.

TANNER (*promptly*). I am a gentleman: I live by robbing the poor. Shake hands.

THE ENGLISH SOCIAL-DEMOCRATS. Hear, hear!

(*General laughter and good humor.* TANNER *and* MENDOZA *shake hands. The Brigands drop into their former places.*)

STRAKER. Ere! Where do I come in?

TANNER (*introducing*). My friend and chauffeur.

THE SULKY SOCIAL-DEMOCRAT (*suspi-*

ciously). Well, which is he? friend or show-foor? It makes all the difference, you know.

MENDOZA (*explaining*). We should expect ransom for a friend. A professional chauffeur is free of the mountains. He even takes a trifling percentage of his principal's ransom if he will honor us by accepting it.

STRAKER. I see. Just to encourage me to come this way again. Well, I'll think about it.

DUVAL (*impulsively rushing across to* STRAKER). Mon frère! (*He embraces him rapturously and kisses him on both cheeks.*)

STRAKER (*disgusted*). Ere, git out: don't be silly. Who are you, pray?

DUVAL. Duval: Social-Democrat.

STRAKER. Oh, you're a Social-Democrat are you?

THE ANARCHIST. He means he has sold out to the parliamentary humbugs and the bourgeoisie. Compromise! that is his faith.

DUVAL (*furiously*). I understand what he say. He say Bourgeois. He say Compromise. Jamais de la vie! Misérable menteur—

STRAKER. See here, Captain Mendoza, ow much o this sort o thing do you put up with here? Are we avin a pleasure trip in the mountains, or are we at a Socialist meetin?

THE MAJORITY. Hear, hear! Shut up. Chuck it. Sit down, &c &c. (THE SOCIAL-DEMOCRATS *and* THE ANARCHIST *are bustled into the background.* STRAKER, *after superintending this proceeding with satisfaction, places himself on* MENDOZA'*s left,* TANNER *being on his right.*)

MENDOZA. Can we offer you anything? Broiled rabbit and prickly pears—

TANNER. Thank you: we have dined.

MENDOZA (*to his followers*). Gentlemen: business is over for the day. Go as you please until morning.

(THE BRIGANDS *disperse into groups lazily. Some go into the cave. Others sit down or lie down to sleep in the open. A few produce a pack of cards and move off towards the road; for it is now starlight; and they know that motor cars have lamps which can be turned to account for lighting a card party.*)

STRAKER (*calling after them*). Don't none of you go fooling with that car, d'ye hear?

MENDOZA. No fear, Monsieur le Chauffeur. The first one we captured cured us of that.

STRAKER (*interested*). What did it do?

MENDOZA. It carried three brave comrades of ours, who did not know how to stop it, into Granada, and capsized them opposite the police station. Since then we never touch one without sending for the chauffeur. Shall we chat at our ease?

TANNER. By all means.

(TANNER, MENDOZA, *and* STRAKER *sit down on the turf by the fire.* MENDOZA *delicately waives his presidential dignity, of which the right to sit on the squared stone block is the appanage, by sitting on the ground like his guests, and using the stone only as a support for his back.*)

MENDOZA. It is the custom in Spain always to put off business until tomorrow. In fact, you have arrived out of office hours. However, if you would prefer to settle the question of ransom at once, I am at your service.

TANNER. Tomorrow will do for me. I am rich enough to pay anything in reason.

MENDOZA (*respectfully, much struck by this admission*). You are a remarkable man, sir. Our guests usually describe themselves as miserably poor.

TANNER. Pooh! Miserably poor people don't own motor cars.

MENDOZA. Precisely what we say to them.

TANNER. Treat us well: we shall not prove ungrateful.

STRAKER. No prickly pears and broiled

rabbits, you know. Don't tell me you can't do us a bit better than that if you like.

MENDOZA. Wine, kids, milk, cheese and bread can be procured for ready money.

STRAKER (*graciously*). Now you're talking.

TANNER. Are you all Socialists here, may I ask?

MENDOZA (*repudiating this humiliating misconception*). Oh no, no, no: nothing of the kind, I assure you. We naturally have modern views as to the justice of the existing distribution of wealth: otherwise we should lose our self-respect. But nothing that you could take exception to, except two or three faddists.

TANNER. I had no intention of suggesting anything discreditable. In fact, I am a bit of a Socialist myself.

STRAKER (*drily*). Most rich men are, I notice.

MENDOZA. Quite so. It has reached us, I admit. It is in the air of the century.

STRAKER. Socialism must be looking up a bit if your chaps are taking to it.

MENDOZA. That is true, sir. A movement which is confined to philosophers and honest men can never exercise any real political influence: there are too few of them. Until a movement shows itself capable of spreading among brigands, it can never hope for a political majority.

TANNER. But are your brigands any less honest than ordinary citizens?

MENDOZA. Sir: I will be frank with you. Brigandage is abnormal. Abnormal professions attract two classes: those who are not good enough for ordinary bourgeois life and those who are too good for it. We are dregs and scum, sir: the dregs very filthy, the scum very superior.

STRAKER. Take care; some of the dregs'll hear you.

MENDOZA. It does not matter: each brigand thinks himself scum, and likes to hear the others called dregs.

TANNER. Come! you are a wit. (MENDOZA *inclines his head, flattered.*) May one ask you a blunt question?

MENDOZA. As blunt as you please.

TANNER. How does it pay a man of your talent to shepherd such a flock as this on broiled rabbit and prickly pears? I have seen men less gifted, and I'll swear less honest, supping at the Savoy on foie gras and champagne.

MENDOZA. Pooh! They have all had their turn at the broiled rabbit, just as I shall have my turn at the Savoy. Indeed, I have had a turn there already—as waiter.

TANNER. A waiter! You astonish me!

MENDOZA (*reflectively*). Yes: I, Mendoza of the Sierra, was a waiter. Hence, perhaps, my cosmopolitanism. (*With sudden intensity.*) Shall I tell you the story of my life?

STRAKER (*apprehensively*). If it ain't too long, old chap—

TANNER (*interrupting him*). Tsh-sh: you are a Philistine, Henry: you have no romance in you. (*To* MENDOZA.) You interest me extremely, President. Never mind Henry: he can go to sleep.

MENDOZA. The woman I loved—

STRAKER. Oh, this is a love story, is it? Right you are. Go on: I was only afraid you were going to talk about yourself.

MENDOZA. Myself! I have thrown myself away for her sake: that is why I am here. No matter: I count the world well lost for her. She had, I pledge you my word, the most magnificent head of hair I ever saw. She had humor; she had intellect; she could cook to perfection; and her highly strung temperament made her uncertain, incalculable, variable, capricious, cruel, in a word, enchanting.

STRAKER. A six shillin novel sort o woman, all but the cookin. Er name was Lady Gladys Plantagenet, wasn't it?

MENDOZA. No, sir: she was not an earl's daughter. Photography, reproduced by the half-tone process, has made me familiar with the appearance of the daughters of the English peerage; and I can honestly say that I would have sold the lot, faces, dowries, clothes, titles, and all, for a smile from this woman. Yet she was a woman of the people, a worker: otherwise—let me reciprocate your bluntness—I should have scorned her.

TANNER. Very properly. And did she respond to your love?

MENDOZA. Should I be here if she did? She objected to marry a Jew.

TANNER. On religious grounds?

MENDOZA. No: she was a freethinker. She said that every Jew considers in his heart that English people are dirty in their habits.

TANNER (*surprised*). Dirty!

MENDOZA. It showed her extraordinary knowledge of the world; for it is undoubtedly true. Our elaborate sanitary code makes us unduly contemptuous of the Gentile.

TANNER. Did you ever hear that, Henry?

STRAKER. I've heard my sister say so. She was cook in a Jewish family once.

MENDOZA. I could not deny it; neither could I eradicate the impression it made on her mind. I could have got round any other objection; but no woman can stand a suspicion of indelicacy as to her person. My entreaties were in vain: she always retorted that she wasn't good enough for me, and recommended me to marry an accursed barmaid named Rebecca Lazarus, whom I loathed. I talked of suicide: she offered me a packet of beetle poison to do it with. I hinted at murder: she went into hysterics; and as I am a living man I went to America so that she might sleep without dreaming that I was stealing upstairs to cut her throat. In America I went out west and fell in with a man who was wanted by the police for holding up trains. It was he who had the idea of holding up motor cars in the South of Europe: a welcome idea to a desperate and disappointed man. He gave me some valuable introductions to capitalists of the right sort. I formed a syndicate; and the present enterprise is the result. I became leader, as the Jew always becomes leader, by his brains and imagination. But with all my pride of race I would give everything I possess to be an Englishman. I am like a boy: I cut her name on the trees and her initials on the sod. When I am alone I lie down and tear my wretched hair and cry Louisa—

STRAKER (*startled*). Louisa!

MENDOZA. It is her name—Louisa—Louisa Straker—

TANNER. Straker!

STRAKER (*scrambling up on his knees most indignantly*). Look here: Louisa Straker is my sister, see? Wot do you mean by gassin about her like this? Wot she got to do with you?

MENDOZA. A dramatic coincidence! You are Enry, her favorite brother!

STRAKER. Oo are you callin Enry? What call have you to take a liberty with my name or with hers? For two pins I'd punch your fat ed, so I would.

MENDOZA (*with grandiose calm*). If I let you do it, will you promise to brag of it afterwards to her? She will be reminded of her Mendoza: that is all I desire.

TANNER. This is genuine devotion, Henry. You should respect it.

STRAKER (*fiercely*). Funk, more likely.

MENDOZA (*springing to his feet*). Funk! Young man: I come of a famous family of fighters; and as your sister well knows, you would have as much chance against me as a perambulator against your motor car.

STRAKER (*secretly daunted, but rising*

from his knees with an air of reckless pugnacity). I ain't afraid of you. With your Louisa! Louisa! Miss Straker is good enough for you, I should think.

MENDOZA. I wish you could persuade her to think so.

STRAKER (*exasperated*). Here—

TANNER (*rising quickly and interposing*). Oh come, Henry: even if you could fight the President you can't fight the whole League of the Sierra. Sit down again and be friendly. A cat may look at a king; and even a President of brigands may look at your sister. All this family pride is really very old fashioned.

STRAKER (*subdued, but grumbling*). Let him look at her. But wot does he mean by makin out that she ever looked at im? (*Reluctantly resuming his couch on the turf.*) Ear him talk, one ud think she was keepin company with him. (*He turns his back on them and composes himself to sleep.*)

MENDOZA (*to* TANNER, *becoming more confidential as he finds himself virtually alone with a sympathetic listener in the still starlight of the mountains; for all the rest are asleep by this time*). It was just so with her, sir. Her intellect reached forward into the twentieth century: her social prejudices and family affections reached back into the dark ages. Ah, sir, how the words of Shakespear seem to fit every crisis in our emotions!

I loved Louisa: 40,000 brothers
Could not with all their quantity of love
Make up my sum.

And so on. I forget the rest. Call it madness if you will—infatuation. I am an able man, a strong man: in ten years I should have owned a first-class hotel. I met her; and—you see!—I am a brigand, an outcast. Even Shakespear cannot do justice to what I feel for Louisa. Let me read you some lines that I have written about her myself. However slight their literary merit may be, they express what I feel better than any casual words can. (*He produces a packet of hotel bills scrawled with manuscript, and kneels at the fire to decipher them, poking it with a stick to make it glow.*)

TANNER (*slapping him rudely on the shoulder*). Put them in the fire, President.

MENDOZA (*startled*). Eh?

TANNER. You are sacrificing your career to a monomania.

MENDOZA. I know it.

TANNER. No you don't. No man would commit such a crime against himself if he really knew what he was doing. How can you look round at these august hills, look up at this divine sky, taste this finely tempered air, and then talk like a literary hack on a second floor in Bloomsbury?

MENDOZA (*shaking his head*). The Sierra is no better than Bloomsbury when once the novelty has worn off. Besides, these mountains make you dream of women—of women with magnificent hair.

TANNER. Of Louisa, in short. They will not make me dream of women, my friend: I am heartwhole.

MENDOZA. Do not boast until morning, sir. This is a strange country for dreams.

TANNER. Well, we shall see. Goodnight. (*He lies down and composes himself to sleep.*)

(MENDOZA, *with a sigh, follows his example; and for a few moments there is peace in the Sierra. Then* MENDOZA *sits up suddenly and says pleading to* TANNER —)

MENDOZA. Just allow me to read a few lines before you go to sleep. I should really like your opinion of them.

TANNER (*drowsily*). Go on. I am listening.

MENDOZA. I saw thee first in Whitsun week
Louisa, Louisa—

TANNER (*rousing himself*). My dear President, Louisa is a very pretty name; but it really doesn't rhyme well to Whitsun week.

MENDOZA. Of course not. Louisa is not the rhyme, but the refrain.

TANNER (*subsiding*). Ah, the refrain. I beg your pardon. Go on.

MENDOZA. Perhaps you do not care for that one: I think you will like this better. (*He recites, in rich soft tones, and in slow time.*)

Louisa, I love thee.
I love thee, Louisa.
Louisa, Louisa, Louisa, I love thee.
One name and one phrase make my music, Louisa.
Louisa, Louisa, Louisa, I love thee.

Mendoza thy lover,
Thy lover, Mendoza,
Mendoza adoringly lives for Louisa.
There's nothing but that in the world for Mendoza.
Louisa, Louisa, Mendoza adores thee.

(*Affected.*) There is no merit in producing beautiful lines upon such a name. Louisa is an exquisite name, is it not?

TANNER (*all but asleep, responds with a faint groan*).

MENDOZA. O wert thou, Louisa
The wife of Mendoza,
Mendoza's Louisa, Louisa Mendoza,
How blest were the life of Louisa's Mendoza!
How painless his longing of love for Louisa!

That is real poetry—from the heart—from the heart of hearts. Don't you think it will move her?

(*No answer.*)

(*Resignedly.*) Asleep, as usual. Doggrel to all the world: heavenly music to me! Idiot that I am to wear my heart on my sleeve. (*He composes himself to sleep, murmuring.*) Louisa, I love thee; I love thee, Louisa; Louisa, Louisa, Louisa, I—

(STRAKER *snores; rolls over on his side; and relapses into sleep. Stillness settles on the Sierra; and the darkness deepens. The fire has again buried itself in white ash and ceased to glow. The peaks show unfathomably dark against the starry firmament; but now the stars dim and vanish; and the sky seems to steal away out of the universe. Instead of the Sierra there is nothing; omnipresent nothing. No sky, no peaks, no light, no sound, no time nor space, utter void. Then somewhere the beginning of a pallor, and with it a faint throbbing buzz as of a ghostly violoncello palpitating on the same note endlessly. A couple of ghostly violins presently takes advantage of this bass and*

therewith the pallor reveals a man in the void, an incorporeal but visible man, seated, absurdly enough, on nothing. For a moment he raises his head as the music passes him by. Then, with a heavy sigh, he droops in utter dejection; and the violins, discouraged, retrace their melody in despair and at last give it up, extinguished by wailings from uncanny wind instruments, thus:—

It is all very odd. One recognizes the Mozartian strain; and on this hint, and

by the aid of certain sparkles of violet light in the pallor, the man's costume explains itself as that of a Spanish nobleman of the XV-XVI century. DON JUAN, *of course; but where? why? how? Besides, in the brief lifting of his face, now hidden by his hat brim, there was a curious suggestion of* TANNER. *A more critical, fastidious, handsome face, paler and colder, without* TANNER'S *impetuous credulity and enthusiasm, and without a touch of his modern plutocratic vulgarity, but still a resemblance, even an identity. The name too: Don Juan Tenorio, John Tanner. Where on earth—or elsewhere—have we got to from the XX century and the Sierra?*

Another pallor in the void, this time not violet, but a disagreeable smoky yellow. With it, the whisper of a ghostly clarinet turning this tune into infinite sadness:

The yellowish pallor moves: there is an old crone wandering in the void, bent and toothless; draped, as well as one can guess, in the coarse brown frock of some religious order. She wanders and wanders in her slow hopeless way, much as a wasp flies in its rapid busy way, until she blunders against the thing she seeks: companionship. With a sob of relief the poor old creature clutches at the presence of the man and addresses him in her dry unlovely voice, which can still express pride and resolution as well as suffering.)

THE OLD WOMAN. Excuse me; but I am so lonely; and this place is so awful.

DON JUAN. A newcomer?

THE OLD WOMAN. Yes: I suppose I died this morning. I confessed; I had extreme unction; I was in bed with my family about me and my eyes fixed on the cross. Then it grew dark; and when the light came back it was this light by which I walk seeing nothing. I have wandered for hours in horrible loneliness.

DON JUAN (*sighing*). Ah! you have not yet lost the sense of time. One soon does, in eternity.

THE OLD WOMAN. Where are we?

DON JUAN. In hell.

THE OLD WOMAN (*proudly*). Hell! I in hell! How dare you?

DON JUAN (*unimpressed*). Why not, Señora?

THE OLD WOMAN. You do not know to whom you are speaking. I am a lady, and a faithful daughter of the Church.

DON JUAN. I do not doubt it.

THE OLD WOMAN. But how then can I be in hell? Purgatory, perhaps: I have not been perfect: who has? But hell! oh, you are lying.

DON JUAN. Hell, Señora, I assure you; hell at its best: that is, its most solitary—though perhaps you would prefer company.

THE OLD WOMAN. But I have sincerely repented; I have confessed—

DON JUAN. How much?

THE OLD WOMAN. More sins than I really committed. I loved confession.

DON JUAN. Ah, that is perhaps as bad as confessing too little. At all events, Señora, whether by oversight or intention, you are certainly damned, like myself; and there is nothing for it now but to make the best of it.

THE OLD WOMAN (*indignantly*). Oh! and I might have been so much wickeder! All my good deeds wasted! It is unjust.

DON JUAN. No. you were fully and clearly warned. For your bad deeds, vicarious atonement, mercy without justice. For your good deeds, justice without mercy. We have many good people here.

THE OLD WOMAN. Were you a good man?

DON JUAN. I was a murderer.

THE OLD WOMAN. A murderer! Oh, how dare they send me to herd with murderers! I was not as bad as that: I was a good woman. There is some mistake: where can I have it set right?

DON JUAN. I do not know whether mistakes can be corrected here. Probably they will not admit a mistake even if they have made one.

THE OLD WOMAN. But whom can I ask?

DON JUAN. I should ask the Devil, Señora: he understands the ways of this place, which is more than I ever could.

THE OLD WOMAN. The Devil! *I* speak to the Devil!

DON JUAN. In hell, Señora, the Devil is the leader of the best society.

THE OLD WOMAN. I tell you, wretch, I know I am not in hell.

DON JUAN. How do you know?

THE OLD WOMAN. Because I feel no pain.

DON JUAN. Oh, then there is no mistake: you are intentionally damned.

THE OLD WOMAN. Why do you say that?

DON JUAN. Because hell, Señora, is a place for the wicked The wicked are quite comfortable in it: it was made for them. You tell me you feel no pain. I conclude you are one of those for whom hell exists.

THE OLD WOMAN. Do you feel no pain?

DON JUAN. I am not one of the wicked, Señora; therefore it bores me, bores me beyond description, beyond belief.

THE OLD WOMAN. Not one of the wicked! You said you were a murderer.

DON JUAN. Only a duel. I ran my sword through an old man who was trying to run his through me.

THE OLD WOMAN. If you were a gentleman, that was not a murder.

DON JUAN. The old man called it murder, because he was, he said, defending his daughter's honor. By this he meant that because I foolishly fell in love with her and told her so, she screamed; and he tried to assassinate me after calling me insulting names.

THE OLD WOMAN. You were like all men. Libertines and murderers all, all, all!

DON JUAN. And yet we meet here, dear lady.

THE OLD WOMAN. Listen to me. My father was slain by just such a wretch as you, in just such a duel, for just such a cause. I screamed: it was my duty. My father drew on my assailant: his honor demanded it. He fell: that was the reward of honor. I am here: in hell, you tell me: that is the reward of duty. Is there justice in heaven?

DON JUAN. No; but there is justice in hell: heaven is far above such idle human personalities. You will be welcome in hell, Señora. Hell is the home of honor, duty, justice, and the rest of the seven deadly virtues. All the wickedness on earth is done in their name: where else but in hell should they have their reward? Have I not told you that the truly damned are those who are happy in hell?

THE OLD WOMAN. And are you happy here?

DON JUAN (*springing to his feet*). No; and that is the enigma on which I ponder in darkness Why am I here? I, who repudiated all duty, trampled honor underfoot, and laughed at justice!

THE OLD WOMAN. Oh, what do I care why you are here? Why am *I* here? I, who sacrificed all my inclinations to womanly virtue and propriety!

DON JUAN. Patience, lady: you will be perfectly happy and at home here. As saith the poet, "Hell is a city much like Seville."

THE OLD WOMAN. Happy! here! where I am nothing! where I am nobody!

DON JUAN. Not at all: you are a lady; and wherever ladies are is hell. Do not be surprised or terrified: you will find everything here that a lady can desire, including devils who will serve you from sheer love of servitude, and magnify your importance for the sake of dignifying their service—the best of servants.

THE OLD WOMAN. My servants will be devils!

DON JUAN. Have you ever had servants who were not devils?

THE OLD WOMAN. Never: they were devils, perfect devils, all of them. But that is only a manner of speaking. I thought you meant that my servants here would be real devils.

DON JUAN. No more real devils than you will be a real lady. Nothing is real here. That is the horror of damnation.

THE OLD WOMAN. Oh, this is all madness. This is worse than fire and the worm.

DON JUAN. For you, perhaps, there are consolations. For instance: how old were you when you changed from time to eternity?

THE OLD WOMAN. Do not ask me how old I was—as if I were a thing of the past. I am 77.

DON JUAN. A ripe age, Señora. But in hell old age is not tolerated. It is too real. Here we worship Love and Beauty. Our souls being entirely damned, we cultivate our hearts. As a lady of 77, you would not have a single acquaintance in hell.

THE OLD WOMAN. How can I help my age, man?

DON JUAN. You forget that you have left your age behind you in the realm of time. You are no more 77 than you are 7 or 17 or 27.

THE OLD WOMAN. Nonsense!

DON JUAN. Consider, Señora: was not this true even when you lived on earth? When you were 70, were you really older underneath your wrinkles and your gray hairs than when you were 30?

THE OLD WOMAN. No, younger: at 30 I was a fool. But of what use is it to feel younger and look older?

DON JUAN. You see, Señora, the look was only an illusion. Your wrinkles lied, just as the plump smooth skin of many a stupid girl of 17, with heavy spirits and decrepit ideas, lies about her age. Well, here we have no bodies: we see each other as bodies only because we learned to think about one another under that aspect when we were alive; and we still think in that way, knowing no other. But we can appear to one another at what age we choose. You have but to will any of your old looks back, and back they will come.

THE OLD WOMAN. It cannot be true.

DON JUAN. Try.

THE OLD WOMAN. Seventeen!

DON JUAN. Stop. Before you decide, I had better tell you that these things are a matter of fashion. Occasionally we have a rage for 17; but it does not last long. Just at present the fashionable age is 40—or say 37; but there are signs of a change. If you were at all good-looking at 27, I should suggest your trying that, and setting a new fashion.

THE OLD WOMAN. I do not believe a word you are saying. However, 27 be it. (*Whisk! the old woman becomes a young one, and so handsome that in the radiance into which her dull yellow halo has suddenly lightened one might almost mistake her for* ANN WHITEFIELD.)

DON JUAN. Doña Ana de Ulloa!

ANA. What? You know me!

DON JUAN. And you forget me!

ANA. I cannot see your face. (*He raises his hat.*) Don Juan Tenorio! Monster! You who slew my father! even here you pursue me.

DON JUAN. I protest I do not pursue you. Allow me to withdraw. (*Going.*)

ANA (*seizing his arm*). You shall not leave me alone in this dreadful place.

DON JUAN. Provided my staying be not interpreted as pursuit.

ANA (*releasing him*). You may well

wonder how I can endure your presence. My dear, dear father!

DON JUAN. Would you like to see him?

ANA. My father here!!!

DON JUAN. No: he is in heaven.

ANA. I knew it. My noble father! He is looking down on us now. What must he feel to see his daughter in this place, and in conversation with his murderer!

DON JUAN. By the way, if we should meet him—

ANA. How can we meet him? He is in heaven.

DON JUAN. He condescends to look in upon us here from time to time. Heaven bores him. So let me warn you that if you meet him he will be mortally offended if you speak of me as his murderer! He maintains that he was a much better swordsman than I, and that if his foot had not slipped he would have killed me. No doubt he is right: I was not a good fencer. I never dispute the point; so we are excellent friends.

ANA. It is no dishonor to a soldier to be proud of his skill in arms.

DON JUAN. You would rather not meet him, probably.

ANA. How dare you say that?

DON JUAN. Oh, that is the usual feeling here. You may remember that on earth —though of course we never confessed it—the death of anyone we knew, even those we liked best, was always mingled with a certain satisfaction at being finally done with them.

ANA. Monster! Never, never.

DON JUAN (*placidly*). I see you recognize the feeling. Yes: a funeral was always a festivity in black, especially the funeral of a relative. At all events, family ties are rarely kept up here. Your father is quite accustomed to this: he will not expect any devotion from you.

ANA. Wretch: I wore mourning for him all my life.

DON JUAN. Yes: it became you. But a life of mourning is one thing: an eternity of it quite another. Besides, here you are as dead as he. Can anything be more ridiculous than one dead person mourning for another? Do not look shocked, my dear Ana; and do not be alarmed: there is plenty of humbug in hell (indeed there is hardly anything else); but the humbug of death and age and change is dropped because here we are all dead and all eternal. You will pick up our ways soon.

ANA. And will all the men call me their dear Ana?

DON JUAN. No. That was a slip of the tongue. I beg your pardon.

ANA (*almost tenderly*). Juan: did you really love me when you behaved so disgracefully to me?

DON JUAN (*impatiently*). Oh, I beg you not to begin talking about love. Here they talk of nothing else but love—its beauty, its holiness, its spirituality, its devil knows what!—excuse me; but it does so bore me. They don't know what they're talking about. I do. They think they have achieved the perfection of love because they have no bodies. Sheer imaginative debauchery! Faugh!

ANA. Has even death failed to refine your soul, Juan? Has the terrible judgment of which my father's statue was the minister taught you no reverence?

DON JUAN. How is that very flattering statue, by the way? Does it still come to supper with naughty people and cast them into this bottomless pit?

ANA. It has been a great expense to me. The boys in the monastery school would not let it alone: the mischievous ones broke it; and the studious ones wrote their names on it. Three new noses in two years, and fingers without end. I had to leave it to its fate at last; and now I fear it is shockingly mutilated. My poor father!

DON JUAN. Hush! Listen! (*Two great chords rolling on syncopated waves of sound break forth: D minor and its dom-*

inant: a sound of dreadful joy to all musicians.) Ha! Mozart's statue music. It is your father. You had better disappear until I prepare him. (*She vanishes.*)

(*From the void comes a living statue of white marble, designed to represent a majestic old man. But he waives his majesty with infinite grace; walks with a feather-like step; and makes every wrinkle in his war worn visage brim over with holiday joyousness. To his sculptor he owes a perfectly trained figure, which he carries erect and trim; and the ends of his moustache curl up, elastic as watch-springs, giving him an air which, but for its Spanish dignity, would be called jaunty. He is on the pleasantest terms with* DON JUAN. *His voice, save for a much more distinguished intonation, is so like the voice of* ROEBUCK RAMSDEN *that it calls attention to the fact that they are not unlike one another in spite of their very different fashions of shaving.*)

DON JUAN. Ah, here you are, my friend. Why don't you learn to sing the splendid music Mozart has written for you?

THE STATUE. Unluckily he has written it for a bass voice. Mine is a counter tenor. Well: have you repented yet?

DON JUAN. I have too much consideration for you to repent, Don Gonzalo. If I did, you would have no excuse for coming from Heaven to argue with me.

THE STATUE. True. Remain obdurate, my boy. I wish I had killed you, as I should have done but for an accident. Then I should have come here; and you would have had a statue and a reputation for piety to live up to. Any news?

DON JUAN. Yes: your daughter is dead.

THE STATUE (*puzzled*). My daughter? (*Recollecting.*) Oh! the one you were taken with. Let me see: what was her name?

DON JUAN. Ana.

THE STATUE. To be sure: Ana. A good-looking girl, if I recollect aright. Have you warned Whatshisname—her husband?

DON JUAN. My friend Ottavio? No: I have not seen him since Ana arrived.

(ANA *comes indignantly to light.*)

ANA. What does this mean? Ottavio here and your friend! And you, father, have forgotten my name. You are indeed turned to stone.

THE STATUE. My dear: I am so much more admired in marble than I ever was in my own person that I have retained the shape the sculptor gave me. He was one of the first men of his day: you must acknowledge that.

ANA. Father! Vanity! personal vanity! from you!

THE STATUE. Ah, you outlived that weakness, my daughter: you must be nearly 80 by this time. I was cut off (by an accident) in my 64th year, and am considerably your junior in consequence. Besides, my child, in this place, what our libertine friend here would call the farce of parental wisdom is dropped. Regard me, I beg, as a fellow creature, not as a father.

ANA. You speak as this villain speaks.

THE STATUE. Juan is a sound thinker, Ana. A bad fencer, but a sound thinker.

ANA (*horror creeping upon her*). I begin to understand. These are devils, mocking me. I had better pray.

THE STATUE (*consoling her*). No, no, no, my child: do not pray. If you do, you will throw away the main advantage of this place. Written over the gate here are the words "Leave every hope behind, ye who enter." Only think what a relief that is! For what is hope? A form of moral responsibility. Here there is no hope, and consequently no duty, no work, nothing to be gained by praying, nothing to be lost by doing what you like. Hell, in short, is a place where you have nothing to do but amuse yourself. (DON JUAN *sighs deeply.*) You sigh, friend Juan; but if you dwelt in heaven, as I do, you would realize your advantages.

DON JUAN. You are in good spirits today, Commander. You are positively brilliant. What is the matter?

THE STATUE. I have come to a momentous decision, my boy. But first, where is our friend the Devil? I must consult him in the matter. And Ana would like to make his acquaintance, no doubt.

ANA. You are preparing some torment for me.

DON JUAN. All that is superstition, Ana. Reassure yourself. Remember: the devil is not so black as he is painted.

THE STATUE. Let us give him a call.

(*At the wave of the statue's hand the great chords roll out again; but this time Mozart's music gets grotesquely adulterated with Gounod's. A scarlet halo begins to glow; and into it* THE DEVIL *rises, very Mephistophelean, and not at all unlike* MENDOZA, *though not so interesting. He looks older; is getting prematurely bald; and, in spite of an effusion of good nature and friendliness, is peevish and sensitive when his advances are not reciprocated. He does not inspire much confidence in his powers of hard work or endurance, and is, on the whole, a disagreeably self-indulgent looking person; but he is clever and plausible, though perceptibly less well bred than the two other men, and enormously less vital than the woman.*)

THE DEVIL (*heartily*). Have I the pleasure of again receiving a visit from the illustrious Commander of Calatrava? (*Coldly.*) Don Juan, your servant. (*Politely.*) And a strange lady? My respects, Señora.

ANA. Are you—

THE DEVIL (*bowing*). Lucifer, at your service.

ANA. I shall go mad.

THE DEVIL (*gallantly*). Ah, Señora, do not be anxious. You come to us from earth, full of the prejudices and terrors of that priest-ridden place. You have heard me ill spoken of; and yet, believe me, I have hosts of friends there.

ANA. Yes: you reign in their hearts.

THE DEVIL (*shaking his head*). You flatter me, Señora; but you are mistaken. It is true that the world cannot get on without me; but it never gives me credit for that: in its heart it mistrusts and hates me. Its sympathies are all with misery, with poverty, with starvation of the body and of the heart. I call on it to sympathize with joy, with love, with happiness, with beauty—

DON JUAN (*nauseated*). Excuse me: I am going. You know I cannot stand this.

THE DEVIL (*angrily*). Yes: I know that you are no friend of mine.

THE STATUE. What harm is he doing you, Juan? It seems to me that he was talking excellent sense when you interrupted him.

THE DEVIL (*warmly shaking* THE STATUE'*s hand*). Thank you, my friend: thank you. You have always understood me: he has always disparaged and avoided me.

DON JUAN. I have treated you with perfect courtesy.

THE DEVIL. Courtesy! What is courtesy? I care nothing for mere courtesy. Give me warmth of heart, true sincerity, the bond of sympathy with love and joy—

DON JUAN. You are making me ill.

THE DEVIL. There! (*Appealing to* THE STATUE.) You hear, sir! Oh, by what irony of fate was this cold selfish egotist sent to my kingdom, and you taken to the icy mansions of the sky!

THE STATUE. I can't complain. I was a hypocrite; and it served me right to be sent to heaven.

THE DEVIL. Why, sir, do you not join us, and leave a sphere for which your temperament is too sympathetic, your heart too warm, your capacity for enjoyment too generous?

THE STATUE. I have this day resolved to do so. In future, excellent Son of the Morning, I am yours. I have left Heaven for ever.

THE DEVIL (*again grasping his hand*). Ah, what an honor for me! What a triumph for our cause! Thank you, thank you. And now, my friend—I may call you so at last—could you not persuade him to take the place you have left vacant above?

THE STATUE (*shaking his head*). I cannot conscientiously recommend anybody with whom I am on friendly terms to deliberately make himself dull and uncomfortable.

THE DEVIL. Of course not; but are you sure he would be uncomfortable? Of course you know best: you brought him here originally; and we had the greatest hopes of him. His sentiments were in the best taste of our best people. You remember how he sang? (*He begins to sing in a nasal operatic baritone, tremulous from an eternity of misuse in the French manner.*)

Vivan le femmine!
Viva il buon vino!

THE STATUE (*taking up the tune an octave higher in his counter tenor*).

Sostegno e gloria
D'umanità.

THE DEVIL. Precisely. Well, he never sings for us now.

DON JUAN. Do you complain of that? Hell is full of musical amateurs: music is the brandy of the damned. May not one lost soul be permitted to abstain?

THE DEVIL. You dare blaspheme against the sublimest of the arts!

DON JUAN (*with cold disgust*). You talk like a hysterical woman fawning on a fiddler.

THE DEVIL. I am not angry. I merely pity you. You have no soul; and you are unconscious of all that you lose. Now you, Señor Commander, are a born musician. How well you sing! Mozart would be delighted if he were still here; but he moped and went to heaven. Curious how these clever men, whom you would have supposed born to be popular here, have turned out social failures, like Don Juan!

DON JUAN. I am really very sorry to be a social failure.

THE DEVIL. Not that we don't admire your intellect, you know. We do. But I look at the matter from your own point of view. You don't get on with us. The place doesn't suit you. The truth is, you have—I won't say no heart; for we know that beneath all your affected cynicism you have a warm one—

DON JUAN (*shrinking*). Don't, please don't.

THE DEVIL (*nettled*). Well, you've no capacity for enjoyment. Will that satisfy you?

DON JUAN. It is a somewhat less insufferable form of cant than the other. But if you'll allow me, I'll take refuge, as usual, in solitude.

THE DEVIL. Why not take refuge in Heaven? That's the proper place for you. (*To* ANA.) Come, Señora! could you not persuade him for his own good to try change of air?

ANA. But can he go to Heaven if he wants to?

THE DEVIL. What's to prevent him?

ANA. Can anybody—can *I* go to Heaven if I want to?

THE DEVIL (*rather contemptuously*). Certainly, if your taste lies that way.

ANA. But why doesn't everybody go to Heaven, then?

THE STATUE (*chuckling*). *I* can tell you that, my dear. It's because heaven is the most angelically dull place in all creation: that's why.

THE DEVIL. His excellency the Commander puts it with military bluntness; but the strain of living in Heaven is intolerable. There is a notion that I was turned out of it; but as a matter of fact nothing could have induced me to stay there. I simply left it and organized this place.

THE STATUE. I don't wonder at it. Nobody could stand an eternity of heaven.

THE DEVIL. Oh, it suits some people. Let us be just, Commander: it is a question of temperament. I don't admire the heavenly temperament: I don't understand it: I don't know that I particularly want to understand it; but it takes all sorts to make a universe. There is no accounting for tastes: there are people who like it. I think Don Juan would like it.

DON JUAN. But—pardon my frankness—could you really go back there if you desired to; or are the grapes sour?

THE DEVIL. Back there! I often go back there. Have you never read the book of Job? Have you any canonical authority for assuming that there is any barrier between our circle and the other one?

ANA. But surely there is a great gulf fixed.

THE DEVIL. Dear lady: a parable must not be taken literally. The gulf is the difference between the angelic and the diabolic temperament. What more impassable gulf could you have? Think of what you have seen on earth. There is no physical gulf between the philosopher's class room and the bull ring; but the bull fighters do not come to the class room for all that. Have you ever been in the country where I have the largest following—England? There they have great racecourses, and also concert rooms where they play the classical compositions of his Excellency's friend Mozart. Those who go to the racecourses can stay away from them and go to the classical concerts instead if they like: there is no law against it; for Englishmen never will be slaves: they are free to do whatever the Government and public opinion allow them to do. And the classical concert is admitted to be a higher, more cultivated, poetic, intellectual, ennobling place than the racecourse. But do the lovers of racing desert their sport and flock to the concert room? Not they. They would suffer there all the weariness the Commander has suffered in heaven. There is the great gulf of the parable between the two places. A mere physical gulf they could bridge; or at least I could bridge it for them (the earth is full of Devil's Bridges); but the gulf of dislike is impassable and eternal. And that is the only gulf that separates my friends here from those who are invidiously called the blest.

ANA. I shall go to heaven at once.

THE STATUE. My child: one word of warning first. Let me complete my friend Lucifer's similitude of the classical concert. At every one of those concerts in England you will find rows of weary people who are there, not because they really like classical music, but because they think they ought to like it. Well, there is the same thing in heaven. A number of people sit there in glory, not because they are happy, but because they think they owe it to their position to be in heaven. They are almost all English.

THE DEVIL. Yes: the Southerners give it up and join me just as you have done. But the English really do not seem to know when they are thoroughly miserable. An Englishman thinks he is moral when he is only uncomfortable.

THE STATUE. In short, my daughter, if you go to Heaven without being naturally qualified for it, you will not enjoy yourself there.

ANA. And who dares say that I am not

naturally qualified for it? The most distinguished princes of the Church have never questioned it. I owe it to myself to leave this place at once.

THE DEVIL (*offended*). As you please, Señora, I should have expected better taste from you.

ANA. Father: I shall expect you to come with me. You cannot stay here. What will people say?

THE STATUE. People! Why, the best people are here—princes of the church and all. So few go to Heaven, and so many come here, that the blest, once called a heavenly host, are a continually dwindling minority. The saints, the fathers, the elect of long ago are the cranks, the faddists, the outsiders of today.

THE DEVIL. It is true. From the beginning of my career I knew that I should win in the long run by sheer weight of public opinion, in spite of the long campaign of misrepresentation and calumny against me. At bottom the universe is a constitutional one; and with such a majority as mine I cannot be kept permanently out of office.

DON JUAN. I think, Ana, you had better stay here.

ANA (*jealously*). You do not want me to go with you.

DON JUAN. Surely you do not want to enter Heaven in the company of a reprobate like me.

ANA. All souls are equally precious. You repent, do you not?

DON JUAN. My dear Ana, you are silly. Do you suppose heaven is like earth, where people persuade themselves that what is done can be undone by repentance; that what is spoken can be unspoken by withdrawing it; that what is true can be annihilated by a general agreement to give it the lie? No: heaven is the home of the masters of reality: that is why I am going thither.

ANA. Thank you: I am going to heaven for happiness. I have had quite enough of reality on earth.

DON JUAN. Then you must stay here; for hell is the home of the unreal and of the seekers for happiness. It is the only refuge from heaven, which is, as I tell you, the home of the masters of reality, and from earth, which is the home of the slaves of reality. The earth is a nursery in which men and women play at being heroes and heroines, saints and sinners; but they are dragged down from their fool's paradise by their bodies: hunger and cold and thirst, age and decay and disease, death above all, make them slaves of reality: thrice a day meals must be eaten and digested: thrice a century a new generation must be engendered: ages of faith, of romance, and of science are all driven at last to have but one prayer "Make me a healthy animal." But here you escape this tyranny of the flesh; for here you are not an animal at all: you are a ghost, an appearance, an illusion, a convention, deathless, ageless: in a word, bodiless. There are no social questions here, no political questions, no religious questions, best of all, perhaps, no sanitary questions. Here you call your appearance beauty, your emotions love, your sentiments heroism, your aspirations virtue, just as you did on earth; but here there are no hard facts to contradict you, no ironic contrast of your needs with your pretensions, no human comedy, nothing but a perpetual romance, a universal melodrama. As our German friend put it in his poem, "the poetically nonsensical here is good sense; and the Eternal Feminine draws us ever upward and on"—without getting us a step farther. And yet you want to leave this paradise!

ANA. But if Hell be so beautiful as this, how glorious must heaven be!

(THE DEVIL, THE STATUE, *and* DON JUAN *all begin to speak at once in violent protest; then stop, abashed.*)

DON JUAN. I beg your pardon.

THE DEVIL. Not at all. I interrupted you.

THE STATUE. You were going to say something.

DON JUAN. After you, gentlemen.

THE DEVIL (*to* DON JUAN). You are been so eloquent on the advantages of my dominions that I leave you to do equal justice to the drawbacks of the alternative establishment.

DON JUAN. In Heaven, as I picture it, dear lady, you live and work instead of playing and pretending. You face things as they are; you escape nothing but glamour; and your steadfastness and your peril are your glory. If the play still goes on here and on earth, and all the world is a stage, Heaven is at least behind the scenes. But Heaven cannot be described by metaphor. Thither I shall go presently, because there I hope to escape at last from lies and from the tedious, vulgar pursuit of happiness, to spend my eons in contemplation—

THE STATUE. Ugh!

DON JUAN. Señor Commander: I do not blame your disgust: a picture gallery is a dull place for a blind man. But even as you enjoy the contemplation of such romantic mirages as beauty and pleasure; so would I enjoy the contemplation of that which interests me above all things: namely, Life: the force that ever strives to attain greater power of contemplating itself. What made this brain of mine, do you think? Not the need to move my limbs; for a rat with half my brains moves as well as I. Not merely the need to do, but the need to know what I do, lest in my blind efforts to live I should be slaying myself.

THE STATUE. You would have slain yourself in your blind efforts to fence but for my foot slipping, my friend.

DON JUAN. Audacious ribald: your laughter will finish in hideous boredom before morning.

THE STATUE. Ha ha! Do you remember how I frightened you when I said something like that to you from my pedestal in Seville? It sounds rather flat without my trombones.

DON JUAN. They tell me it generally sounds flat with them, Commander.

ANA. Oh, do not interrupt with these frivolities, father. Is there nothing in Heaven but contemplation, Juan?

DON JUAN. In the Heaven I seek, no other joy. But there is the work of helping Life in its struggle upward. Think of how it wastes and scatters itself, how it raises up obstacles to itself and destroys itself in its ignorance and blindness. It needs a brain, this irresistible force, lest in its ignorance it should resist itself. What a piece of work is man! says the poet. Yes: but what a blunderer! Here is the highest miracle of organization yet attained by life, the most intensely alive thing that exists, the most conscious of all the organisms, and yet, how wretched are his brains! Stupidity made sordid and cruel by the realities learned from toil and poverty: Imagination resolved to starve sooner than face these realities, piling up illusions to hide them, and calling itself cleverness, genius! And each accusing the other of its own defect: Stupidity accusing Imagination of folly, and Imagination accusing Stupidity of ignorance: whereas, alas! Stupidity has all the knowledge, and Imagination all the intelligence.

THE DEVIL. And a pretty kettle of fish they make of it between them. Did I not say, when I was arranging that affair of Faust's, that all Man's reason has done for him is to make him beastlier than any beast. One splendid body is worth the brains of a hundred dyspeptic, flatulent philosophers.

DON JUAN. You forget that brainless magnificence of body has been tried. Things immeasurably greater than man in every respect but brain have existed and perished. The megatherium, the icthyosaurus have paced the earth with seven-league steps and hidden the day with cloud vast wings. Where are they now? Fossils in museums, and so few and imperfect at that, that a knuckle bone or a tooth of one of them is prized beyond the lives of a thousand soldiers. These things lived and wanted to live; but for lack of brains they did not know how to carry out their purpose, and so destroyed themselves.

THE DEVIL. And is Man any the less destroying himself for all this boasted brain of his? Have you walked up and down upon the earth lately? I have; and I have examined Man's wonderful inventions. And I tell you that in the arts of life man invents nothing; but in the arts of death he outdoes Nature herself, and produces by chemistry and machinery all the slaughter of plague, pestilence and famine. The peasant I tempt today eats and drinks what was eaten and drunk by the peasants of ten thousand years ago; and the house he lives in has not altered as much in a thousand centuries as the fashion of a lady's bonnet in a score of weeks. But when he goes out to slay, he carries a marvel of mechanism that lets loose at the touch of his finger all the hidden molecular energies, and leaves the javelin, the arrow, the blowpipe of his fathers far behind. In the arts of peace Man is a bungler. I have seen his cotton factories and the like, with machinery that a greedy dog could have invented if it had wanted money instead of food. I know his clumsy typewriters and bungling locomotives and tedious bicycles: they are toys compared to the Maxim gun, the submarine torpedo boat. There is nothing in Man's industrial machinery but his greed and sloth: his heart is in his weapons. This marvelous force of Life of which you boast is a force of Death: Man measures his strength by his destructiveness. What is his religion? An excuse for hating me. What is his law? An excuse for hanging you. What is his morality? Gentility! an excuse for consuming without producing. What is his art? An excuse for gloating over pictures of slaughter. What are his politics? Either the worship of a despot because a despot can kill, or parliamentary cockfighting. I spent an evening lately in a certain celebrated legislature, and heard the pot lecturing the kettle for its blackness, and ministers answering questions. When I left I chalked up on the door the old nursery saying "Ask no questions and you will be told no lies." I bought a sixpenny family magazine, and found it full of pictures of young men shooting and stabbing one another. I saw a man die: he was a London bricklayer's laborer with seven children. He left seventeen pounds club money; and his wife spent it all on his funeral and went into the workhouse with the children next day. She would not have spent sevenpence on her children's schooling: the law had to force her to let them be taught gratuitously; but on death she spent all she had. Their imagination glows, their energies rise up at the idea of death, these people: they love it; and the more horrible it is the more they enjoy it. Hell is a place far above their comprehension: they derive their notion of it from two of the greatest fools that ever lived, an Italian and an Englishman. The Italian described it as a place of mud, frost, filth, fire, and venomous serpents: all torture. This ass, when he was not lying about me, was maundering about some woman whom he saw once in the street. The Englishman described me as being expelled from Heaven by cannons and gunpowder; and to this day every Briton believes that the whole of his silly story is in the Bible. What else he says I do not know; for it is all in a long poem which neither I nor anyone else ever succeeded in wading through. It is the same in everything. The highest form of literature is the tragedy, a play in which everybody is murdered at the end. In the old chronicles you read of earthquakes and pestilences, and are told that these showed the power and majesty of God and the littleness of Man. Nowadays the chronicles describe battles. In a battle two bodies of men shoot at one another with bullets and explosive shells until one body runs away, when the others chase the fugitives on horseback and cut them to pieces as they fly. And this, the chronicle concludes, shows the greatness and majesty of empires, and the littleness of the vanquished. Over such battles the people run about the streets yelling with delight, and egg their Governments on to spend hundreds of millions of money in the slaughter, while the strongest Ministers dare not spend an extra penny in the pound against the poverty and pestilence through which they themselves daily walk. I could give you a thousand instances; but they all come to the same thing: the power that governs the earth is not the power of Life but of Death; and the inner need that has nerved Life to the effort of organizing itself into the human being is not the need for higher life but for a more efficient engine of destruction. The plague, the famine, the earthquake, the tempest were too spasmodic in their action; the tiger and crocodile were too easily satiated and not cruel enough: something more constantly, more ruthlessly, more ingeniously destructive was needed; and that something was Man, the inventor of the rack, the stake, the gallows, and the electrocutor; of the sword and gun; above all, of justice, duty, patriotism and all the other isms by which even those who are clever enough to be humanely disposed are persuaded to become the most destructive of all the destroyers.

DON JUAN. Pshaw! all this is old. Your weak side, my diabolic friend, is that you have always been a gull: you take Man at his own valuation. Nothing would flatter him more than your opinion of him. He loves to think of himself as bold and bad. He is neither one nor the other: he is only a coward. Call him tyrant, murderer, pirate, bully; and he will adore you, and swagger about with the consciousness of having the blood of the old sea kings in his veins. Call him liar and thief; and he will only take an action against you for libel. But call him coward; and he will go mad with rage: he will face death to outface that stinging truth. Man gives every reason for his conduct save one, every excuse for his crimes save one, every plea for his safety save one; and that one is his cowardice. Yet all his civilization is founded on his cowardice, on his abject tameness, which he calls his respectability. There are limits to what a mule or an ass will stand, but Man will suffer himself to be degraded until his vileness becomes so loathsome to his oppressors that they themselves are forced to reform it.

THE DEVIL. Precisely. And these are the creatures in whom you discover what you call a Life Force!

DON JUAN. Yes; for now comes the most surprising part of the whole business.

THE STATUE. What's that?

DON JUAN. Why, that you can make any of these cowards brave by simply putting an idea into his head.

THE STATUE. Stuff! As an old soldier I admit the cowardice: it's as universal as sea sickness, and matters just as little. But that about putting an idea into a man's head is stuff and nonsense. In a battle all you need to make you fight is a little hot blood and the knowledge that it's more dangerous to lose than to win.

DON JUAN. That is perhaps why battles are so useless. But men never really overcome fear until they imagine they are fighting to further a universal purpose—fighting for an idea, as they call it. Why was the Crusader braver than the pirate? Because he fought, not for himself, but for the Cross. What force was it that met him with a valor as reckless as his own? The force of men who fought, not for themselves, but for Islam. They took Spain from us, though we were fighting for our very hearths and homes; but when we, too, fought for that mighty idea, a Catholic Church, we swept them back to Africa.

THE DEVIL (*ironically*). What! You a Catholic, Señor Don Juan. A devotee! My congratulations.

THE STATUE (*seriously*). Come, come! as a soldier, I can listen to nothing against the Church.

DON JUAN. Have no fear, Commander: this idea of a Catholic Church will survive Islam, will survive the Cross, will survive even that vulgar pageant of incompetent school-boyish gladiators that you call the Army.

THE STATUE. Juan: you will force me to call you to account for this.

DON JUAN. Useless: I cannot fence. Every idea for which Man will die will be a Catholic idea. When the Spaniard learns at last that he is no better than the Saracen, and his prophet no better than Mahomet, he will arise, more Catholic than ever, and die on a barricade across the filthy slum be starves in, for universal liberty and equality.

THE STATUE. Bosh!

DON JUAN. What you can bosh is the only thing men dare die for. Later on, Liberty will not be Catholic enough: men will die for human perfection, to which they will sacrifice all their liberty gladly.

THE DEVIL. Ay: they will never be at a loss for an excuse for killing one another.

DON JUAN. What of that? It is not death that matters, but the fear of death. It is not killing and dying that degrades us, but base living, and accepting the wages and profits of degradation. Better ten dead men than one live slave or his master. Men shall yet rise up, father against son and brother against brother, and kill one another for the great Catholic idea of abolishing slavery.

THE DEVIL. Yes, when the Liberty and Equality of which you prate shall have made free white Christians cheaper in the labor market than black heathen slaves sold by auction at the block.

DON JUAN. Never fear! the white laborer shall have his turn too. But I am not now defending the illusory forms the great ideas take. I am giving you examples of the fact that this creature Man, who in his own selfish affairs is a coward to the backbone, will fight for an idea like a hero. He may be abject as a citizen; but he is dangerous as a fanatic. He can only be enslaved while he is spiritually weak enough to listen to reason. I tell you, gentlemen, if you can show a man a piece of what he now calls God's work to do, and what he will later on call by many new names, you can make him entirely reckless of the consequences to himself personally.

ANA. Yes: he shirks all his responsibilities, and leaves his wife to grapple with them.

THE STATUE. Well said, daughter. Do not let him talk you out of your common sense.

THE DEVIL. Alas! Señor Commander, now that we have got on to the subject of Woman, he will talk more than ever. However, I confess it is for me the one supremely interesting subject.

DON JUAN. To a woman, Señora, man's duties and responsibilities begin and end with the task of getting bread for her children. To her, Man is only a means to the end of getting children and rearing them.

ANA. Is that your idea of a woman's mind? I call it cynical and disgusting materialism.

DON JUAN. Pardon me, Ana: I said nothing about a woman's whole mind. I

spoke of her view of Man as a separate sex. It is no more cynical than her view of herself as above all things a Mother. Sexually, Woman is Nature's contrivance for perpetuating its highest achievement. Sexually, Man is Woman's contrivance for fulfilling Nature's behest in the most economical way. She knows by instinct that far back in the evolutional process she invented him, differentiated him, created him in order to produce something better than the single-sexed process can produce. While he fulfills the purpose for which she made him, he is welcome to his dreams, his follies, his ideals, his heroisms, provided that the keystone of them all is the worship of woman, of motherhood, of the family, of the hearth. But how rash and dangerous it was to invent a separate creature whose sole function was her own impregnation! For mark what has happened. First, Man has multiplied on her hands until there are as many men as women; so that she has been unable to employ for her purposes more than a fraction of the immense energy she has left at his disposal by saving him the exhausting labor of gestation. This superfluous energy has gone to his brain and to his muscle. He has become too strong to be controlled by her bodily, and too imaginative and mentally vigorous to be content with mere self-reproduction. He has created civilization without consulting her, taking her domestic labor for granted as the foundation of it.

ANA. That is true, at all events.

THE DEVIL. Yes; and this civilization! what is it, after all?

DON JUAN. After all, an excellent peg to hang your cynical commonplaces on; but before all, it is an attempt on Man's part to make himself something more than the mere instrument of Woman's purpose. So far, the result of Life's continual effort not only to maintain itself, but to achieve higher and higher organization and completer self-consciousness, is only, at best, a doubtful campaign between its forces and those of Death and Degeneration. The battles in this campaign are mere blunders, mostly won, like actual military battles, in spite of the commanders.

THE STATUE. That is a dig at me. No matter: go on, go on.

DON JUAN. It is a dig at a much higher power than you, Commander. Still, you must have noticed in your profession that even a stupid general can win battles when the enemy's general is a little stupider.

THE STATUE (*very seriously*). Most true, Juan, most true. Some donkeys have amazing luck.

DON JUAN. Well, the Life Force is stupid; but it is not so stupid as the forces of Death and Degeneration. Besides, these are in its pay all the time. And so Life wins, after a fashion. What mere copiousness of fecundity can supply and mere greed preserve, we possess. The survival of whatever form of civilization can produce the best rifle and the best fed riflemen is assured.

THE DEVIL. Exactly! the survival, not of the most effective means of Life but of the most effective means of Death. You always come back to my point, in spite of your wrigglings and evasions and sophistries, not to mention the intolerable length of your speeches.

DON JUAN. Oh come! who began making long speeches? However, if I overtax your intellect, you can leave us and seek the society of love and beauty and the rest of your favorite boredoms.

THE DEVIL (*much offended*). This is not fair, Don Juan, and not civil. I am also on the intellectual plane. Nobody can appreciate it more than I do. I am arguing fairly with you, and, I think, utterly refuting you. Let us go on for another hour if you like.

DON JUAN. Good: let us.

THE STATUE. Not that I see any prospect of your coming to any point in particular, Juan. Still, since in this place, instead of merely killing time we have to kill eternity, go ahead by all means.

DON JUAN (*somewhat impatiently*). My point, you marbleheaded old masterpiece, is only a step ahead of you. Are we agreed that Life is a force which has made innumerable experiments in organizing itself; that the mammoth and the man, the mouse and the megatherium, the flies and the fleas and the Fathers of the Church, are all more or less successful attempts to build up that raw force into higher and higher individuals, the ideal individual being omnipotent, omniscient, infallible, and withal completely, unilludedly self-conscious: in short, a god?

THE DEVIL. I agree, for the sake of argument.

THE STATUE. I agree, for the sake of avoiding argument.

ANA. I most emphatically disagree as regards the Fathers of the Church; and I must beg you not to drag them into the argument.

DON JUAN. I did so purely for the sake of alliteration, Ana; and I shall make no further allusion to them. And now, since we are, with that exception, agreed so far, will you not agree with me further that Life has not measured the success of its attempts at godhead by the beauty or bodily perfection of the result, since in both these respects the birds, as our friend Aristophanes long ago pointed out, are so extraordinarily superior, with their power of flight and their lovely plumage, and, may I add, the touching poetry of their loves and nestings, that it is inconceivable that Life, having once produced them, should, if love and beauty were her object, start off on another line and labor at the clumsy elephant and the hideous ape, whose grandchildren we are?

ANA. Aristophanes was a heathen; and you, Juan, I am afraid, are very little better.

THE DEVIL. You conclude, then, that Life was driving at clumsiness and ugliness?

DON JUAN. No, perverse devil that you are, a thousand times no. Life was driving at brains—at its darling object: an organ by which it can attain not only self-consciousness but self-understanding.

THE STATUE. This is metaphysics, Juan. Why the devil should— (*To* THE DEVIL.) I beg your pardon.

THE DEVIL. Pray don't mention it. I have always regarded the use of my name to secure additional emphasis as a high compliment to me. It is quite at your service, Commander.

THE STATUE. Thank you: that's very good of you. Even in heaven, I never quite got out of my old military habits of speech. What I was going to ask Juan was why Life should bother itself about getting a brain. Why should it want to understand itself? Why not be content to enjoy itself?

DON JUAN. Without a brain, Commander, you would enjoy yourself without knowing it, and so lose all the fun.

THE STATUE. True, most true. But I am quite content with brain enough to know that I'm enjoying myself. I don't want to understand why. In fact, I'd rather not. My experience is that one's pleasures don't bear thinking about.

DON JUAN. That is why intellect is so unpopular. But to Life, the force behind the Man, intellect is a necessity, because without it he blunders into death. Just as Life, after ages of struggle, evolved that wonderful bodily organ the eye, so that the living organism could see where it was going and what was coming to help or threaten it, and thus avoid a thousand dangers that formerly slew it, so it is evolving today a mind's eye that shall see, not the physical world, but the purpose of Life, and thereby enable the individual to work for that purpose instead of thwarting and baffling it by setting up shortsighted personal aims as at present. Even as it is, only one sort of man has ever been happy, has ever been universally respected among all the conflicts of interests and illusions.

THE STATUE. You mean the military man.

DON JUAN. Commander: I do not mean the military man. When the military man approaches, the world locks up its spoons and packs off its womankind. No: I sing, not arms and the hero, but the philosophic man: he who seeks in contemplation to discover the inner will of the world, in invention to discover the means of fulfilling that will, and in action to do that will by the so-discovered means. Of all other sorts of men I declare myself tired. They are tedious failures. When I was on earth, professors of all sorts prowled round me feeling for an unhealthy spot in me on which they could fasten. The doctors of medicine bade me consider what I must do to save my body, and offered me quack cures for imaginary diseases. I replied that I was not a hypochondriac; so they called me Ignoramus and went their way. The doctors of divinity bade me consider what I must do to save my soul; but I was not a spiritual hypochondriac any more than a bodily one, and would not trouble myself about that either; so they called me Atheist and went their way. After them came the politician, who said there was only one purpose in Nature, and that was to get him into parliament. I told him I did not care whether he got into parliament or not; so he called me Mugwump and went his way. Then came the romantic man, the Artist, with his love songs and his paintings and his poems; and with him I had great delight for many years, and some profit; for I cultivated my senses for his sake; and his songs taught me to hear better, his paintings to see better, and his poems to feel more deeply. But he led me at last into the worship of Woman.

ANA. Juan!

DON JUAN. Yes: I came to believe that in her voice was all the music of the song, in her face all the beauty of the painting, and in her soul all the emotion of the poem.

ANA. And you were disappointed, I suppose. Well, was it her fault that you attributed all these perfections to her?

DON JUAN. Yes, partly. For with a wonderful instinctive cunning, she kept silent and allowed me to glorify her; to mistake my own visions, thoughts, and feelings for hers. Now my friend the romantic man was often too poor or too timid to approach those women who were beautiful or refined enough to seem to realize his ideal; and so he went to his grave believing in his dream. But I was more favored by nature and circumstance. I was of noble birth and rich; and when my person did not please, my conversation flattered, though I generally found myself fortunate in both.

THE STATUE. Coxcomb!

DON JUAN. Yes; but even my coxcombry pleased. Well, I found that when I had touched a woman's imagination, she would allow me to persuade myself that she loved me; but when my suit was granted she never said "I am happy: my love is satisfied": she always said, first, "At last, the barriers are down," and second, "When will you come again?"

ANA. That is exactly what men say.

DON JUAN. I protest I never said it. But all women say it. Well, these two speeches always alarmed me; for the first meant that the lady's impulse had been solely to throw down my fortifications and gain my citadel; and the second openly announced that henceforth she regarded me as her property, and counted my time as already wholly at her disposal.

THE DEVIL. That is where your want of heart came in.

THE STATUE (*shaking his head*). You shouldn't repeat what a woman says, Juan.

ANA (*severely*). It should be sacred to you.

THE STATUE. Still, they certainly do always say it. I never minded the barriers; but there was always a slight shock about the other, unless one was very hard hit indeed.

DON JUAN. Then the lady, who had been happy and idle enough before, became anxious, preoccupied with me, always intriguing, conspiring, pursuing, watching, waiting, bent wholly on making sure of her prey—I being the prey, you understand. Now this was not what I had bargained for. It may have been very proper and very natural; but it was not music, painting, poetry and joy incarnated in a beautiful woman. I ran away from it. I ran away from it very often: in fact I became famous for running away from it.

ANA. Infamous, you mean.

DON JUAN. I did not run away from you. Do you blame me for running away from the others?

ANA. Nonsense, man. You are talking to a woman of 77 now. If you had had the chance, you would have run away from me too—if I had let you. You would not have found it so easy with me as with some of the others. If men will not be faithful to their home and their duties, they must be made to be. I daresay you all want to marry lovely incarnations of music and painting and poetry. Well, you can't have them, because they don't exist. If flesh and blood is not good enough for you you must go without: that's all. Women have to put up with flesh-and-blood husbands—and little enough of that too, sometimes; and you will have to put up with flesh-and-blood wives. (THE DEVIL *looks dubious.* THE STATUE *makes a wry face.*) I see you don't like that, any of you; but it's true, for all that; so if you don't like it you can lump it.

DON JUAN. My dear lady, you have put my whole case against romance into a few sentences. That is just why I turned my back on the romantic man with the artist nature, as he called his infatuation. I thanked him for teaching me to use my eyes and ears; but I told him that his beauty worshiping and happiness hunting and woman idealizing was not worth a dump as a philosophy of life; so he called me Philistine and went his way.

ANA. It seems that Woman taught you something, too, with all her defects.

DON JUAN. She did more: she interpreted all the other teaching for me. Ah, my friends, when the barriers were down for the first time, what an astounding illumination! I had been prepared for infatuation, for intoxication, for all the illusions of love's young dream; and lo! never was my perception clearer, nor my criticism more ruthless. The most jealous rival of my mistress never saw every blemish in her more keenly than I. I was not duped: I took her without chloroform.

ANA. But you did take her.

DON JUAN. That was the revelation. Up to that moment I had never lost the sense of being my own master; never consciously taken a single step until my reason had examined and approved it. I had come to believe that I was a purely rational creature: a thinker! I said, with the foolish philosopher, "I think; therefore I am." It was Woman who taught me to say "I am; therefore I think." And also "I would think more; therefore I must be more."

THE STATUE. This is extremely abstract and metaphysical, Juan. If you would stick to the concrete, and put your discoveries in the form of entertaining anecdotes about your adventures with women, your conversation would be easier to follow.

DON JUAN. Bah! what need I add? Do you not understand that when I stood face to face with Woman, every fiber in my clear critical brain warned me to spare her and save myself. My morals said No. My conscience said No. My chivalry and pity for her said No. My prudent regard for myself said No. My ear, practiced on a thousand songs and symphonies; my eye, exercised on a thousand paintings; tore her voice, her features, her color to shreds. I caught all those tell-tale resemblances to her father and mother by which I knew what she would be like in thirty years time. I noted the gleam of gold from a dead tooth in the laughing mouth: I made curious observations of the strange odors of the chemistry of the nerves. The visions of my romantic reveries, in which I had trod the plains of heaven with a deathless, ageless creature of coral and ivory, deserted me in that supreme hour. I remembered them and desperately strove to recover their illusions; but they now seemed the emptiest of inventions: my judgment was not to be corrupted: my brain still said No on every issue. And while I was in the act of framing my excuse to the lady, Life seized me and threw me into her arms as a sailor throws a scrap of fish into the mouth of a seabird.

THE STATUE. You might as well have gone without thinking such a lot about it, Juan. You are like all the clever men: you have more brains than is good for you.

THE DEVIL. And were you not the happier for the experience, Señor Don Juan?

DON JUAN. The happier, no: the wiser, yes. That moment introduced me for the first time to myself, and, through myself, to the world. I saw then how useless it is to attempt to impose conditions on the irresistible force of Life; to preach prudence, careful selection, virtue, honor, chastity—

ANA. Don Juan: a word against chastity is an insult to me.

DON JUAN. I say nothing against your chastity, Señora, since it took the form of a husband and twelve children. What more could you have done had you been the most abandoned of women?

ANA. I could have had twelve husbands and no children: that's what I could have done, Juan. And let me tell you that that would have made all the difference to the earth which I replenished.

THE STATUE. Bravo Ana! Juan: you are floored, quelled, annihilated.

DON JUAN. No; for though that difference is the true essential difference—Doña Ana has, I admit, gone straight to the real point—yet it is not a difference of love or chastity, or even constancy; for twelve children by twelve different husbands would have replenished the earth perhaps more effectively. Suppose my friend Ottavio had died when you were thirty, you would never have remained a widow; you were too beautiful. Suppose the successor of Ottavio had died when you were forty, you would still have been irresistible; and a woman who marries twice marries three times if she becomes free to do so. Twelve lawful children borne by one highly respectable lady to three different fathers is not impossible nor condemned by public opinion. That such a lady may be more law abiding than the poor girl whom we used to spurn into the gutter for bearing one unlawful infant is no doubt true; but dare you say she is less self-indulgent?

ANA. She is less virtuous: that is enough for me.

DON JUAN. In that case, what is virtue but the Trade Unionism of the married?

Let us face the facts, dear Ana. The Life Force respects marriage only because marriage is a contrivance of its own to secure the greatest number of children and the closest care of them. For honor, chastity and all the rest of your moral figments it cares not a rap. Marriage is the most licentious of human institutions—

ANA. Juan!

THE STATUE (*protesting*). Really!—

DON JUAN (*determinedly*). I say the most licentious of human institutions: that is the secret of its popularity. And a woman seeking a husband is the most unscrupulous of all the beasts of prey. The confusion of marriage with morality has done more to destroy the conscience of the human race than any other single error. Come, Ana! do not look shocked: you know better than any of us that marriage is a mantrap baited with simulated accomplishments and delusive idealizations. When your sainted mother, by dint of scoldings and punishments, forced you to learn how to play half a dozen pieces on the spinet—which she hated as much as you did—had she any other purpose than to delude your suitors into the belief that your husband would have in his home an angel who would fill it with melody, or at least play him to sleep after dinner? You married my friend Ottavio: well, did you ever open the spinet from the hour when the Church united him to you?

ANA. You are a fool, Juan. A young married woman has something else to do than sit at the spinet without any support for her back; so she gets out of the habit of playing.

DON JUAN. Not if she loves music. No: believe me, she only throws away the bait when the bird is in the net.

ANA (*bitterly*). And men, I suppose, never throw off the mask when their bird is in the net. The husband never becomes negligent, selfish, brutal—oh never!

DON JUAN. What do these recriminations prove, Ana? Only that the hero is as gross an imposture as the heroine.

ANA. It is all nonsense: most marriages are perfectly comfortable.

DON JUAN. "Perfectly" is a strong expression, Ana. What you mean is that sensible people make the best of one another. Send me to the galleys and chain me to the felon whose number happens to be next before mine; and I must accept the inevitable and make the best of the companionship. Many such companionships, they tell me, are touchingly affectionate; and most are at least tolerably friendly. But that does not make a chain a desirable ornament nor the galleys an abode of bliss. Those who talk most about the blessings of marriage and the constancy of its vows are the very people who declare that if the chain were broken and the prisoners left free to choose, the whole social fabric would fly asunder. You cannot have the argument both ways. If the prisoner is happy, why lock him in? If he is not, why pretend that he is?

ANA. At all events, let me take an old woman's privilege again, and tell you flatly that marriage peoples the world and debauchery does not.

DON JUAN. How if a time come when this shall cease to be true? Do you not know that where there is a will there is a way—that whatever Man really wishes to do he will finally discover a means of doing? Well, you have done your best, you virtuous ladies, and others of your way of thinking, to bend Man's mind wholly towards honorable love as the highest good, and to understand by honorable love romance and beauty and happiness in the possession of beautiful, refined, delicate, affectionate women. You have taught women to value their own youth, health, shapeliness, and refinement above all things. Well, what place have squalling babies and household cares in this exquisite paradise of the senses and emotions? Is it not the inevitable end of it all that the human will shall say to the human brain: Invent me a means by which I can have love, beauty, romance, emotion, passion without their wretched penalties, their expenses, their worries, their trials, their illnesses and agonies and risks of death, their retinue of servants and nurses and doctors and schoolmasters.

THE DEVIL. All this, Señor Don Juan, is realized here in my realm.

DON JUAN. Yes, at the cost of death. Man will not take it at that price: he demands the romantic delights of your hell while he is still on earth. Well, the means will be found: the brain will not fail when the will is in earnest. The day is coming when great nations will find their numbers dwindling from census to census; when the six roomed villa will rise in price above the family mansion: when the viciously reckless poor and the stupidly pious rich will delay the extinction of the race only by degrading it; while the boldly prudent, the thriftily selfish and ambitious, the imaginative and poetic, the lovers of money and solid comfort, the worshipers of success, of art, and of love, will all oppose to the Force of Life the device of sterility.

THE STATUE. That is all very eloquent, my young friend; but if you had lived to Ana's age, or even to mine, you would have learned that the people who get rid of the fear of poverty and children and all the other family troubles, and devote themselves to having a good time of it, only leave their minds free for the fear of old age and ugliness and impotence and death. The childless laborer is more tormented by his wife's idleness and her constant demands for amusement and distraction than he could be by twenty children; and his wife is more wretched than he. I have had my share of vanity; for as a young man I was admired by women; and as a statue I am praised by art critics. But I confess that had I found nothing to do in the world but wallow in these delights I should have cut my throat. When I married Ana's mother—or perhaps, to be strictly correct, I should rather say when I at last gave in and allowed Ana's mother to marry me—I knew that I was planting thorns in my pillow, and that marriage for me, a swaggering young officer thitherto unvanquished, meant defeat and capture.

ANA (*scandalized*). Father!

THE STATUE. I am sorry to shock you, my love; but since Juan has stripped every rag of decency from the discussion I may as well tell the frozen truth.

ANA. Hmf! I suppose I was one of the thorns.

THE STATUE. By no means: you were often a rose. You see, your mother had most of the trouble you gave.

DON JUAN. Then may I ask, Commander, why you have left Heaven to come here and wallow, as you express it, in sentimental beatitudes which you confess would once have driven you to cut your throat?

THE STATUE (*struck by this*). Egad, that's true.

THE DEVIL (*alarmed*). What! You are going back from your word! (*To* DON JUAN.) And all your philosophizing has been nothing but a mask for proselytizing! (*To* THE STATUE.) Have you forgotten already the hideous dullness from which I am offering you a refuge here? (*To* DON JUAN.) And does your demonstration of the approaching sterilization and extinction of mankind lead to anything better than making the most of those pleasures of art and love which you yourself admit refined you, elevated you, developed you?

DON JUAN. I never demonstrated the extinction of mankind. Life cannot will its own extinction either in its blind amorphous state or in any of the forms into which it has organized itself. I had not finished when His Excellency interrupted me.

THE STATUE. I begin to doubt whether you ever will finish, my friend. You are extremely fond of hearing yourself talk.

DON JUAN. True; but since you have endured so much, you may as well endure to the end. Long before this sterilization which I described becomes more than a clearly foreseen possibility, the reaction will begin. The great central purpose of breeding the race, ay, breeding it to heights now deemed superhuman: that purpose which is now hidden in a mephitic cloud of love and romance and prudery and fastidiousness, will break through into clear sunlight as a purpose no longer to be confused with the gratification of personal fancies, the impossible realization of boys' and girls' dreams of bliss, or the need of older people for companionship or money. The plain-spoken marriage services of the vernacular Churches will no longer be abbreviated and half suppressed as indelicate. The sober decency, earnestness and authority of their declaration of the real purpose of marriage will be honored and accepted, while their romantic vowings and pledgings and until-death-do-us-partings and the like will be expunged as unbearable frivolities. Do my sex the justice to admit, Señora, that we have always recognized that the sex relation is not a personal or friendly relation at all.

ANA. Not a personal or friendly relation! What relation is more personal? more sacred? more holy?

DON JUAN. Sacred and holy, if you like, Ana, but not personally friendly. Your relation to God is sacred and holy: dare you call it personally friendly? In the sex relation the universal creative energy, of which the parties are both the helpless agents, over-rides and sweeps away all personal considerations and dispenses with all personal relations. The pair may be utter strangers to one another, speaking different languages, differing in race and color, in age and disposition, with no bond between them but a possibility of that fecundity for the sake of which the Life Force throws them into one another's arms at the exchange of a glance. Do we not recognize this by allowing marriages to be made by parents without consulting the woman? Have you not often expressed your disgust at the immorality of the English nation, in which women and men of noble birth become acquainted and court each other like peasants? And how much does even the peasant know of his bride or she of him before he engages himself? Why, you would not make a man your lawyer or your family doctor on so slight an acquaintance as you would fall in love with and marry him!

ANA. Yes, Juan: we know the libertine's philosophy. Always ignore the consequences to the woman.

DON JUAN. The consequences, yes: they justify her fierce grip of the man. But surely you do not call that attachment a sentimental one. As well call the policeman's attachment to his prisoner a love relation.

ANA. You see you have to confess that marriage is necessary, though, according to you, love is the slightest of all the relations.

DON JUAN. How do you know that it is not the greatest of all the relations? far too great to be a personal matter. Could your father have served his country if he had refused to kill any enemy of Spain unless he personally hated him? Can a woman serve her country if she refuses to marry any man she does not personally love? You know it is not so: the woman of noble birth marries as the man of noble birth fights, on political and family grounds, not on personal ones.

THE STATUE (*impressed*). A very clever point that, Juan: I must think it over. You are really full of ideas. How did you come to think of this one?

DON JUAN. I learned it by experience. When I was on earth, and made those proposals to ladies which, though universally condemned, have made me so interesting a hero of legend, I was not infrequently met in some such way as this. The lady would say that she would countenance my advances, provided they were honorable. On inquiring what that proviso meant, I found that it meant that I proposed to get possession of her property if she had any, or to undertake her support for life if she had not; that I desired her continual companionship, counsel and conversation to the end of my days, and would bind myself under penalties to be always enraptured by them; and, above all, that I would turn my back on all other women forever for her sake. I did not object to these conditions because they were exorbitant and inhuman: it was their extraordinary irrelevance that prostrated me. I invariably replied with perfect frankness that I had never dreamed of any of these things; that unless the lady's character and intellect were equal or superior to my own, her conversation must degrade and her counsel mislead me; that her constant companionship might, for all I knew, become intolerably tedious to me; that I could not answer for my feelings for a week in advance, much less to the end of my life; that to cut me off from all natural and unconstrained relations with the rest of my fellow creatures would narrow and warp me if I submitted to it, and, if not, would bring me under the curse of clandestinity; that, finally, my proposals to her were wholly unconnected with any of these matters, and were the outcome of a perfectly simple impulse of my manhood towards her womanhood.

ANA. You mean that it was an immoral impulse.

DON JUAN. Nature, my dear lady, is what you call immoral. I blush for it; but I cannot help it. Nature is a pander, Time a wrecker, and Death a murderer. I have always preferred to stand up to those facts and build institutions on their recognition. You prefer to propitiate the three devils by proclaiming their chastity, their thrift, and their loving kindness; and to base your institutions on these flatteries. Is it any wonder that the institutions do not work smoothly?

THE STATUE. What used the ladies to say, Juan?

DON JUAN. Oh come! Confidence for confidence. First tell me what you used to say to the ladies.

THE STATUE. I! Oh, I swore that I would be faithful to the death; that I should die if they refused me; that no woman could ever be to me what she was—

ANA. She! Who?

THE STATUE. Whoever it happened to be at the time, my dear. I had certain things I always said. One of them was that even when I was eighty, one white hair of the woman I loved would make me tremble more than the thickest gold tress from the most beautiful young head. Another was that I could not bear the thought of anyone else being the mother of my children.

DON JUAN (*revolted*). You old rascal!

THE STATUE (*stoutly*). Not a bit; for I really believed it with all my soul at the moment. I had a heart: not like you. And it was this sincerity that made me successful.

DON JUAN. Sincerity! To be fool enough to believe a ramping, stamping, thumping lie: that is what you call sincerity! To be so greedy for a woman that you deceive yourself in your eagerness to deceive her: sincerity, you call it!

THE STATUE. Oh, damn your sophistries! I was a man in love, not a lawyer. And the women loved me for it, bless them!

DON JUAN. They made you think so. What will you say when I tell you that though I played the lawyer so callously, they made me think so too? I also had my moments of infatuation in which I gushed nonsense and believed it. Sometimes the desire to give pleasure by saying beautiful things so rose in me on the flood of emotion that I said them recklessly. At other times I argued against myself with a devilish coldness that drew tears. But I found it just as hard to escape in the one case as in the others. When the lady's instinct was set on me, there was nothing for it but lifelong servitude or flight.

ANA. You dare boast, before me and my father, that every woman found you irresistible.

DON JUAN. Am I boasting? It seems to me that I cut the most pitiable of figures. Besides, I said "when the lady's instinct was set on me." It was not always so; and then, heavens! what transports of virtuous indignation! what overwhelming defiance to the dastardly seducer! what scenes of Imogen and Iachimo!

ANA. I made no scenes. I simply called my father.

DON JUAN. And he came, sword in hand, to vindicate outraged honor and morality by murdering me.

THE STATUE. Murdering! What do you mean? Did I kill you or did you kill me?

DON JUAN. Which of us was the better fencer?

THE STATUE. I was.

DON JUAN. Of course you were. And yet you, the hero of those scandalous adventures you have just been relating to us, you had the effrontery to pose as the avenger of outraged morality and condemn me to death! You would have slain me but for an accident.

THE STATUE. I was expected to, Juan. That is how things were arranged on earth. I was not a social reformer; and I always did what it was customary for a gentleman to do.

DON JUAN. That may account for your attacking me, but not for the revolting hypocrisy of your subsequent proceedings as a statue.

THE STATUE. That all came of my going to Heaven.

THE DEVIL. I still fail to see, Señor Don Juan, that these episodes in your earthly career and in that of the Señor Commander in any way discredit my view of life. Here, I repeat, you have all that you sought without anything that you shrank from.

DON JUAN. On the contrary, here I have everything that disappointed me without anything that I have not already tried and found wanting. I tell you that as long as I can conceive something better than myself I cannot be easy unless I am striving to bring it into existence or clearing the way for it. That is the law of my life. That is the working within me of Life's incessant aspiration to higher organization, wider, deeper, intenser self-consciousness, and clearer self-understanding. It was the supremacy of this purpose that reduced love for me to the mere pleasure of a moment, art for me to the mere schooling of my faculties, religion for me to a mere excuse for laziness, since it had set up a God who looked at the world and saw that it was good, against the instinct in me that looked through my eyes at the world and saw that it could be improved. I tell you that in the pursuit of my own pleasure, my own health, my own fortune, I have never known happiness. It was not love for Woman that delivered me into her hands: it was fatigue, exhaustion. When I was a child, and bruised my head against a stone, I ran to the nearest woman and cried away my pain against her apron. When I grew up, and bruised my soul against the brutalities and stupidities with which I had to strive, I did again just what I had done as a child. I have enjoyed, too, my rests, my recuperations, my breathing times, my very prostrations after strife; but rather would I be dragged through all the circles of the foolish Italian's Inferno than through the pleasures of Europe. That is what has made this place of eternal pleasures so deadly to me. It is the absence of this instinct in you that makes you that strange monster called a Devil. It is the success with which you have diverted the attention of men from their real purpose, which in one degree or another is the same as mine, to yours, that has earned you the name of The Tempter. It is the fact that they are doing your will, or rather drifting with your want of will, instead of doing their own, that makes them the uncomfortable, false, restless, artificial, petulant, wretched creatures they are.

THE DEVIL (*mortified*). Señor Don Juan: you are uncivil to my friends.

DON JUAN. Pooh! why should I be civil to them or to you? In this Palace of Lies a truth or two will not hurt you. Your friends are all the dullest dogs I know. They are not beautiful: they are only decorated. They are not clean: they are only shaved and starched. They are not dignified: they are only fashionably dressed. They are not educated: they are only college passmen. They are not religious: they are only pewrenters. They are not moral: they are only conventional. They are not virtuous: they are only cowardly. They are not even vicious: they are only "frail." They are not artistic: they are only lascivious. They are not prosperous: they are only rich. They are not loyal, they are only servile; not dutiful, only sheepish; not public spirited, only patriotic; not courageous, only quarrelsome; not determined, only obstinate; not masterful, only domineering; not self-controlled, only obtuse; not self-respecting, only vain; not kind, only sentimental; not social, only gregarious; not considerate, only polite; not intelligent, only opinionated; not progressive, only factious; not imaginative, only superstitious; not just, only vindictive; not generous, only propitiatory; not disciplined, only cowed; and not truthful at all—liars every one of them, to the very backbone of their souls.

THE STATUE. Your flow of words is simply amazing, Juan. How I wish I could have talked like that to my soldiers.

THE DEVIL. It is mere talk, though. It has all been said before; but what change has it ever made? What notice has the world ever taken of it?

DON JUAN. Yes, it is mere talk. But why is it mere talk? Because, my friend, beauty, purity, respectability, religion, morality, art, patriotism, bravery and the rest are nothing but words which I or anyone else can turn inside out like a glove. Were they realities, you would have to plead guilty to my indictment; but fortunately for your self-respect, my diabolical friend, they are not realities. As you say, they are mere words, useful for duping barbarians into adopting civilization, or the civilized poor into submitting to be robbed and enslaved. That is the family secret of the governing caste; and if we who are of that caste aimed at more Life for the world instead of at more power and luxury for our miserable selves, that secret would make us great. Now, since I, being a nobleman, am in the secret too, think how tedious to me must be your unending cant about all these moralistic figments, and how squalidly disastrous your sacrifice of your lives to them! If you even believed in your moral game enough to play it fairly, it would be interesting to watch; but you don't: you cheat at every trick; and if your opponent outcheats you, you upset the table and try to murder him.

THE DEVIL. On earth there may be some truth in this, because the people are uneducated and cannot appreciate my religion of love and beauty; but here—

DON JUAN. Oh yes: I know. Here there is nothing but love and beauty. Ugh! it is like sitting for all eternity at the first act of a fashionable play, before the complications begin. Never in my worst moments of superstitious terror on earth did I dream that Hell was so horrible. I live, like a hairdresser, in the continental contemplation of beauty, toying with silken tresses. I breathe an atmosphere of sweetness, like a confectioner's shopboy. Commander: are there any beautiful women in Heaven?

THE STATUE. None. Absolutely none. All dowdies. Not two pennorth of jewelry among a dozen of them. They might be men of fifty.

DON JUAN. I am impatient to get there. Is the word beauty ever mentioned; and are there any artistic people?

THE STATUE. I give you my word they won't admire a fine statue even when it walks past them.

DON JUAN. I go.

THE DEVIL. Don Juan: shall I be frank with you?

DON JUAN. Were you not so before?

THE DEVIL. As far as I went, yes. But I will now go further, and confess to you that men get tired of everything, of heaven no less than of hell; and that all history is nothing but a record of the oscillations of the world between these two extremes. An epoch is but a swing of the pendulum; and each generation thinks the world is progressing because it is always moving. But when you are as old as I am; when you have a thousand times wearied of heaven, like myself and the Commander, and a thousand times wearied of hell, as you are wearied now, you will no longer imagine that every swing from heaven to hell is an emancipation, every swing from hell to heaven an evolution. Where you now see reform, progress, fulfillment of upward tendency, continual ascent by Man on the stepping stones of his dead selves to higher things, you will see nothing but an infinite comedy of illusion. You will discover the profound truth of the saying of my friend Koheleth, that there is nothing new under the sun. Vanitas vanitatum—

DON JUAN (*out of all patience*). By Heaven, this is worse than your cant about love and beauty. Clever dolt that you are, is a man no better than a worm, or a dog than a wolf, because he gets tired of everything? Shall he give up eating because he destroys his appetite in the act of gratifying it? Is a field idle when it is fallow? Can the Commander expend his hellish energy here without accumulating heavenly energy for his next term of blessedness? Granted that the great Life Force has hit on the device of the clockmaker's pendulum, and uses the earth for its bob; that the history of each oscillation, which seems so novel to us the actors, is but the history of the last oscillation repeated; nay more, that in the unthinkable infinitude of time the sun throws off the earth and catches it again a thousand times as a circus rider throws up a ball, and that the total of all our epochs is but the moment between the toss and the catch, has the colossal mechanism no purpose?

THE DEVIL. None, my friend. You think, because you have a purpose, Nature must have one. You might as well expect it to have fingers and toes because you have them.

DON JUAN. But I should not have them if they served no purpose. And I, my friend, am as much a part of Nature as my own finger is a part of me. If my finger is the organ by which I grasp the sword and the mandoline, my brain is the organ by which Nature strives to understand itself. My dog's brain serves only my dog's purposes; but my brain labors at a knowledge which does nothing for me personally but make my body bitter to me and my decay and death a calamity. Were I not possessed with a purpose beyond my own I had better be a ploughman than a philosopher; for the ploughman lives as long as the philosopher, eats more, sleeps better, and rejoices in the wife of his bosom with less misgiving. This is because the philosopher is in the grip of the Life Force. This Life Force says to him "I have done a thousand wonderful things unconsciously by merely willing to live and following the line of least resistance: now I want to know myself and my destination, and choose my path; so I have made a special brain—a philosopher's brain—to grasp this knowledge for me as the husbandman's hand grasps the plough for me. And this" says the Life Force to the philosopher "must thou strive to do for me until thou diest, when I will make another brain and another philosopher to carry on the work."

THE DEVIL. What is the use of knowing?

DON JUAN. Why, to be able to choose the line of greatest advantage instead of yielding in the direction of the least resistance. Does a ship sail to its destination no better than a log drifts nowhither? The philosopher is Nature's pilot. And there you have our difference: to be in hell is to drift: to be in heaven is to steer.

THE DEVIL. On the rocks, most likely.

DON JUAN. Pooh! which ship goes oftenest on the rocks or to the bottom—the drifting ship or the ship with a pilot on board?

THE DEVIL. Well, well, go your way, Señor Don Juan. I prefer to be my own master and not the tool of any blundering universal force. I know that beauty is good to look at; that music is good to hear; that love is good to feel; and that they are all good to think about and talk about. I know that to be well exercised in these sensations, emotions, and studies is to be a refined and cultivated being. Whatever they may say of me in churches on earth, I know that it is universally admitted in good society that the Prince of Darkness is a gentleman; and that is enough for me. As to your Life Force, which you think irresistible, it is the most resisting thing in the world for a person of any character. But if you are naturally vulgar and credulous, as all reformers are, it will thrust you first into religion, where you will sprinkle water on babies to save their souls from me; then it will drive you from religion into science, where you will snatch the babies from the water sprinkling and inoculate them with disease to save them from catching it accidentally; then you will take to politics, where you will become the cat's-paw of corrupt functionaries and the henchman of ambitious humbugs; and the end will be despair and decrepitude, broken nerves and shattered hopes, vain regrets for that worst and silliest of wastes and sacrifices, the waste and sacrifice of the power of enjoyment: in a word, the punishment of the fool who pursues the better before he has secured the good.

DON JUAN. But at least I shall not be bored. The service of the Life Force has that advantage, at all events. So fare you well, Señor Satan.

THE DEVIL (*amiably*). Fare you well, Don Juan. I shall often think of our interesting chats about things in general. I wish you every happiness: Heaven, as I said before, suits some people. But if you should change your mind, do not forget that the gates are always open here to the repentant prodigal. If you feel at any time that warmth of heart, sincere unforced affection, innocent enjoyment, and warm, breathing, palpitating reality—

DON JUAN. Why not say flesh and blood at once, though we have left those two greasy commonplaces behind us?

THE DEVIL (*angrily*). You throw my friendly farewell back in my teeth, then, Don Juan?

DON JUAN. By no means. But though there is much to be learned from a cynical devil, I really cannot stand a sentimental one. Señor Commander: you know the way to the frontier of hell and heaven. Be good enough to direct me.

THE STATUE. Oh, the frontier is only the difference between two ways of looking at things. Any road will take you across it if you really want to get there.

DON JUAN. Good. (*Saluting* DOÑA ANA.) Señora: your servant.

ANA. But I am going with you.

DON JUAN. I can find my own way to heaven, Ana; but I cannot find yours. (*He vanishes.*)

ANA. How annoying!

THE STATUE (*calling after him*). Bon voyage, Juan! (*He wafts a final blast of his great rolling chords after him as a parting salute. A faint echo of the first ghostly melody comes back in acknowledgment.*) Ah; there he goes. (*Puffing a long breath out through his lips.*) Whew! How he does talk! They'll never stand it in heaven.

THE DEVIL (*gloomily*). His going is a political defeat. I cannot keep these Life Worshipers: they all go. This is the greatest loss I have had since that Dutch painter went—a fellow who would paint a hag of 70 with as much enjoyment as a Venus of 20.

THE STATUE. I remember: he came to heaven. Rembrandt.

THE DEVIL. Ay, Rembrandt. There is something unnatural about these fellows. Do not listen to their gospel, Señor Commander: it is dangerous. Beware of the pursuit of the Superhuman: it leads to an indiscriminate contempt for the Human. To a man, horses and dogs and cats are mere species, outside the moral world. Well, to the Superman, men and women are a mere species too, also outside the moral world. This Don Juan was kind to women and courteous to men as your daughter here was kind to her pet cats and dogs; but such kindness is a denial of the exclusively human character of the soul.

THE STATUE. And who the deuce is the Superman?

THE DEVIL. Oh, the latest fashion among the Life Force fanatics. Did you not meet in Heaven, among the new arrivals, that German Polish madman—what was his name? Nietzsche?

THE STATUE. Never heard of him.

THE DEVIL. Well, he came here first, before he recovered his wits. I had some hopes of him; but he was a confirmed Life Force worshiper. It was he who raked up the Superman, who is as old as Prometheus; and the 20th century will run after this newest of the old crazes when it gets tired of the world, the flesh, and your humble servant.

THE STATUE. Superman is a good cry; and a good cry is half the battle. I should like to see this Nietzsche.

THE DEVIL. Unfortunately he met Wagner here, and had a quarrel with him.

THE STATUE. Quite right, too. Mozart for me!

THE DEVIL. Oh, it was not about music. Wagner once drifted into Life Force worship, and invented a Superman called Siegfried. But he came to his senses afterwards. So when they met here, Nietzsche denounced him as a renegade; and Wagner wrote a pamphlet to prove that Nietzsche was a Jew; and it ended in Nietzsche's going to heaven in a huff. And a good riddance too. And now, my friend, let us hasten to my palace and celebrate your arrival with a grand musical service.

THE STATUE. With pleasure: you're most kind.

THE DEVIL. This way, Commander. We go down the old trap (*he places himself on the grave trap*).

THE STATUE. Good. (*Reflectively.*) All the same, the Superman is a fine conception. There is something statuesque about it. (*He places himself on the grave trap beside* THE DEVIL. *It begins to descend slowly. Red glow from the abyss.*) Ah, this reminds me of old times.

THE DEVIL. And me also.

ANA. Stop! (*The trap stops.*)

THE DEVIL. You, Señora, cannot come this way. You will have an apotheosis. But you will be at the palace before us.

ANA. That is not what I stopped you for. Tell me: where can I find the Superman?

THE DEVIL. He is not yet created, Señora.

THE STATUE. And never will be, probably. Let us proceed: the red fire will make me sneeze. (*They descend.*)

ANA. Not yet created! Then my work is not yet done. (*Crossing herself devoutly.*) I believe in the Life to Come. (*Crying to the universe.*) A father—a father for the Superman!

(*She vanishes into the void; and again there is nothing: all existence seems suspended infinitely. Then, vaguely, there is a live human voice crying somewhere. One sees, with a shock, a mountain peak showing faintly against a lighter background. The sky has returned from afar; and we suddenly remember where we were. The cry becomes distinct and urgent: it says* Automobile, Automobile. *The complete reality comes back with a rush: in a moment it is full morning in the Sierra; and the brigands are scrambling to their feet and making for the road as the goatherd runs down from the hill, warning them of the approach of another motor.* TANNER *and* MENDOZA *rise amazedly and stare at one another with scattered wits.* STRAKER *sits up to yawn for a moment before he gets on his feet, making it a point of honor not to show any undue interest in the excitement of the bandits.* MENDOZA *gives a quick look to see that his followers are attending to the alarm; then exchanges a private word with* TANNER.)

MENDOZA. Did you dream?

TANNER. Damnably. Did you?

MENDOZA. Yes. I forget what. You were in it.

TANNER. So were you. Amazing!

MENDOZA. I warned you. (*A shot is heard from the road.*) Dolts! they will play with that gun. (*The brigands come running back scared.*) Who fired that shot? (*to* DUVAL) was it you?

DUVAL (*breathless*). I have not shoot. Dey shoot first.

ANARCHIST. I told you to begin by abolishing the State. Now we are all lost.

THE ROWDY SOCIAL-DEMOCRAT (*stampeding across the amphitheater*). Run, everybody.

MENDOZA (*collaring him; throwing him on his back; and drawing a knife*). I stab the man who stirs. (*He blocks the way. The stampede is checked.*) What has happened?

THE SULKY SOCIAL-DEMOCRAT. A motor—

THE ANARCHIST. Three men—

DUVAL. Deux femmes—

MENDOZA. Three men and two women! Why have you not brought them here? Are you afraid of them?

THE ROWDY ONE (*getting up*). Thy've a hescort. Ow, de-ooh lut's ook it, Mendowza.

THE SULKY ONE. Two armored cars full o' soldiers at the 'ed o' the valley.

ANARCHIST. The shot was fired in the air. It was a signal.

(STRAKER *whistles his favorite air, which falls on the ears of the brigands like a funeral march.*)

TANNER. It is not an escort, but an expedition to capture you. We were advised to wait for it; but I was in a hurry.

THE ROWDY ONE (*in an agony of apprehension*). And Ow my good Lord, 'ere we are, wytin' for 'em! Lut's tike to the mahntns.

MENDOZA. Idiot, what do you know about the mountains? Are you a Spaniard? You would be given up by the first shepherd you met. Besides, we are already within range of their rifles.

THE ROWDY ONE. Bat—

MENDOZA. Silence. Leave this to me. (*To* TANNER.) Comrade: you will not betray us.

STRAKER. Oo are you callin' comrade?

MENDOZA. Last night the advantage was with me. The robber of the poor was at the mercy of the robber of the rich. You offered your hand: I took it.

TANNER. I bring no charge against you, comrade. We have spent a pleasant evening with you: that is all.

STRAKER. I gev my 'and to nobody, see?

MENDOZA (*turning on him impressively*). Young man, if I am tried, I shall plead guilty, and explain what drove me from England, home and duty. Do you wish to have the respectable name of Straker dragged through the mud of a Spanish criminal court? The police will search me. They will find Louisa's portrait. It will be published in the illustrated papers. You blench. It will be your doing, remember.

STRAKER (*with baffled rage*). I don't care about the court. It's 'avin' our name mixed up with yours that I object to, you blackmailin' swine, you.

MENDOZA. Language unworthy of Louisa's brother! But no matter: you are muzzled: that is enough for us. (*He turns to face his own men, who back uneasily across the amphitheater towards the cave to take refuge behind him, as a fresh party, muffled for motoring, comes from the road in riotous spirits.* ANN, *who makes straight for* TANNER, *comes first; then* VIOLET, *helped over the rough ground by* HECTOR *holding her right hand and* RAMSDEN *her left.* MENDOZA *goes to his presidential block and seats himself calmly with his rank and file grouped behind him, and his Staff, consisting of* DUVAL *and the* ANARCHIST *on his right and the two* SOCIAL-DEMOCRATS *on his left, supporting him in flank.*)

ANN. It's Jack!

TANNER. Caught!

HECTOR. Why, certainly it is. I said it was you Tanner. We've just been stopped by a puncture: the road is full of nails.

VIOLET. What are you doing here with all these men?

ANN. Why did you leave us without a word of warning?

HECTOR. I want that bunch of roses, Miss Whitefield. (*To* TANNER.) When we found you were gone, Miss Whitefield bet me a bunch of roses my car would not overtake yours before you reached Monte Carlo.

TANNER. But this is not the road to Monte Carlo.

HECTOR. No matter. Miss Whitefield tracked you at every stopping place: she is a regular Sherlock Holmes.

TANNER. The Life Force! I am lost.

OCTAVIUS (*bounding gaily down from the road into the amphitheater, and coming between* TANNER *and* STRAKER). I am so glad you are safe, old chap. We were afraid you had been captured by brigands.

RAMSDEN (*who has been staring at* MENDOZA). I seem to remember the face of your friend here. (MENDOZA *rises politely and advances with a smile between* ANN *and* RAMSDEN.)

HECTOR. Why, so do I.

OCTAVIUS. I know you perfectly well, sir; but I can't think where I have met you.

MENDOZA (*to* VIOLET). Do you remember me, madam?

VIOLET. Oh, quite well; but I am so stupid about names.

MENDOZA. It was at the Savoy Hotel. (*To* HECTOR.) You, sir, used to come with this lady (VIOLET) to lunch. (*To* OCTAVIUS.) You, sir, often brought this lady (ANN) and her mother to dinner on your way to the Lyceum Theater. (*To* RAMSDEN.) You, sir, used to come to supper, with (*dropping his voice to a confidential but perfectly audible whisper*) several different ladies.

RAMSDEN (*angrily*). Well, what is that to you, pray?

OCTAVIUS. Why, Violet, I thought you hardly knew one another before this trip, you and Malone!

VIOLET (*vexed*). I suppose this person was the manager.

MENDOZA. The waiter, madam. I have a grateful recollection of you all. I gathered from the bountiful way in which you treated me that you all enjoyed your visits very much.

VIOLET. What impertinence! (*She turns her back on him, and goes up the hill with* HECTOR.)

RAMSDEN. That will do, my friend. You do not expect these ladies to treat you as an acquaintance, I suppose, because you have waited on them at table.

MENDOZA. Pardon me: it was you who claimed my acquaintance. The ladies followed your example. However, this display of the unfortunate manners of your class closes the incident. For the future, you will please address me with the respect due to a stranger and fellow traveler. (*He turns haughtily away and resumes his presidential seat.*)

TANNER. There! I have found one man on my journey capable of reasonable conversation; and you all instinctively insult him. Even the New Man is as bad as any of you. Enry: you have behaved just like a miserable gentleman.

STRAKER. Gentleman! Not me.

RAMSDEN. Really, Tanner, this tone—

ANN. Don't mind him, Granny: you ought to know him by this time. (*She takes his arms and coaxes him away to the hill to join* VIOLET *and* HECTOR. OCTAVIUS *follows her, doglike.*)

VIOLET (*calling from the hill*). Here are the soldiers. They are getting out of their motors.

DUVAL (*panic-stricken*). Oh, nom de Dieu!

THE ANARCHIST. Fools: the State is about to crush you because you spread it at the prompting of the political hangers-on of the bourgeoisie.

THE SULKY SOCIAL-DEMOCRAT (*argumentative to the last*). On the contrary, only by capturing the State machine—

THE ANARCHIST. It is going to capture you.

THE ROWDY SOCIAL-DEMOCRAT (*his anguish culminating*). Ow, chack it. Wot are we 'ere for? Wot are we wytin' for?

MENDOZA (*between his teeth*). Go on. Talk politics, you idiots: nothing sounds more respectable. Keep it up, I tell you.

(*The soldiers line the road, commanding the amphitheater with their rifles. The brigands, struggling with an overwhelming impulse to hide behind one another, look as unconcerned as they can.* MENDOZA *rises superbly, with undaunted front.* THE OFFICER *in command steps down from the road into the amphitheater; looks hard at the brigands; and then inquiringly at* TANNER.)

THE OFFICER. Who are these men, Señor Ingles?

TANNER. My escort.

(MENDOZA, *with a Mephistophelean smile, bows profoundly. An irrepressible grin runs from face to face among the brigands. They touch their hats, except* THE ANARCHIST, *who defies the State with folded arms.)*

ACT IV

The garden of a villa in Granada. Whoever wishes to know what it is like must go to Granada and see. One may prosaically specify a group of hills dotted with villas, the Alhambra on the top of one of the hills, and a considerable town in the valley, approached by dusty white roads in which the children, no matter what they are doing or thinking about, automatically whine for halfpence and reach out little clutching brown palms for them; but there is nothing in this description except the Alhambra, the begging, and the color of the roads, that does not fit Surrey as well as Spain. The difference is that the Surrey hills are comparatively small and ugly, and should properly be called the Surrey Protuberances; but these Spanish hills are of mountain stock: the amenity which conceals their size does not compromise their dignity.

This particular garden is on a hill opposite the Alhambra; and the villa is as expensive and pretentious as a villa must be if it is to be let furnished by the week to opulent American and English visitors. If we stand on the lawn at the foot of the garden and look uphill, our horizon is the stone balustrade of a flagged platform on the edge of infinite space at the top of the hill. Between us and this platform is a flower garden with a circular basin and fountain in the center, surrounded by geometrical flower beds, gravel paths, and clipped yew trees in the genteelest order. The garden is higher than our lawn; so we reach it by a few steps in the middle of its embankment. The platform is higher again than the garden, from which we mount a couple more steps to look over the balustrade at a fine view of the town up the valley and of the hills that stretch away beyond it to where, in the remotest distance, they become mountains. On our left is the villa, accessible by steps from the left hand corner of the garden. Returning from the platform through the garden and down again to the lawn (a movement which leaves the villa behind us on our right) we find evidence of literary interests on the part of the tenants in the fact that there is no tennis net nor set of croquet hoops, but, on our left, a little iron garden table with books on it, mostly yellow-backed, and a chair beside it. A chair on the right has also a couple of open books upon it. There are no newspapers, a circumstance which, with the absence of games, might lead an intelligent spectator to the most far reaching conclusions as to the sort of people who live in the villa. Such speculations are checked, however, on this delightfully fine afternoon, by the appearance at a little gate in a paling on our left, of HENRY STRAKER *in his professional costume. He opens the gate for an elderly gentleman, and follows him on to the lawn.*

This elderly gentleman defies the Spanish sun in a black frock coat, tall silk hat, trousers in which narrow stripes of dark gray and lilac blend into a highly respectable color, and a black necktie tied into a bow over spotless linen. Probably therefore a man whose social position needs constant and scrupulous affirmation without regard to climate: one who would dress thus for the middle of the Sahara or the top of Mont Blanc. And since he has not the stamp of the class which accepts as its life-mission the advertising and maintenance of first rate tailoring and millinery, he looks vulgar in his finery, though in a working dress of any kind he would look dignified enough. He is a bullet cheeked man with a red complexion, stubbly hair, smallish eyes, a hard mouth that folds down at the corners, and a dogged chin. The looseness of skin that comes with age has attacked his throat and the laps of his cheeks; but he is still hard as an apple above the mouth; so that the upper half of his face looks younger than the lower. He has the self-confidence of one who has made money, and something of the truculence of one who has made it in a brutalizing struggle, his civility having under it a perceptible menace that he has other methods in reserve if necessary. Withal, a man to be rather pitied when he is not to be feared; for there is something pathetic about him at times, as if the huge commercial machine which has worked him into his frock coat had allowed him very little of his own way and left his affections hungry and baffled. At the first word that falls from him it is clear that he is an Irishman whose native intonation has clung to him through many changes of place and rank. One can only guess that the original material of his speech was perhaps the surly Kerry brogue; but the degradation of speech that occurs in London, Glasgow, Dublin and big cities generally has been at work on it so long that nobody but an arrant cockney would dream of calling it a brogue now; for its music is almost gone, though its surliness is still perceptible. STRAKER, *as a very obvious cockney, inspires him with implacable contempt, as a stupid Englishman who cannot even speak his own language properly.* STRAKER, *on the other hand, regards the old gentleman's accent as a joke thoughtfully provided by Providence expressly for the amusement of the British race, and treats him normally with the indulgence due to an inferior and unlucky species, but occasionally with indignant alarm when the old gentleman shows signs of intending his Irish nonsense to be taken seriously.*

STRAKER. I'll go tell the young lady. She said you'd prefer to stay here. (*He turns to go up through the garden to the villa.*)

MALONE (*who has been looking round him with lively curiosity*). The young lady? That's Miss Violet, eh?

STRAKER (*stopping on the steps with sudden suspicion*). Well, you know, don't you?

MALONE. Do I?

STRAKER (*his temper rising*). Well, do you or don't you?

MALONE. What business is that of yours?

(STRAKER, *now highly indignant, comes back from the steps and confronts the visitor.*)

STRAKER. I'll tell you what business it is of mine. Miss Robinson—

MALONE (*interrupting*). Oh, her name is Robinson, is it? Thank you.

STRAKER. Why, you don't know even her name?

MALONE. Yes I do, now that you've told me.

STRAKER (*after a moment of stupefaction at the old man's readiness in repartee*). Look here: what do you mean by gittin' into my car and lettin' me bring you here if you're not the person I took that note to?

MALONE. Who else did you take it to, pray?

STRAKER. I took it to Mr. Ector Malone, at Miss Robinson's request, see? Miss Robinson is not my principal: I took it to oblige her. I know Mr. Malone; and he ain't you, not by a long chalk. At the hotel they told me that your name is Ector Malone—

MALONE. *H*ector Malone.

STRAKER (*with calm superiority*). Hector in your own country: that's what comes o' livin' in provincial places like Ireland and America. Over here you're Ector: if you 'avn't noticed it before you soon will.

(*The growing strain of the conversation is here relieved by* VIOLET, *who has sallied from the villa and through the garden to the steps, which she now descends, coming very opportunely between* MALONE *and* STRAKER.)

VIOLET (*to* STRAKER). Did you take my message?

STRAKER. Yes, miss. I took it to the hotel and sent it up, expecting to see young Mr. Malone. Then out walks this gent, and says it's all right and he'll come with me. So as the hotel people said he was Mr. Ector Malone, I fetched him. And now he goes back on what he said. But if he isn't the gentleman you meant, say the word: it's easy enough to fetch him back again.

MALONE. I should esteem it a great favor if I might have a short conversation with you, madam. I am Hector's father, as this bright Britisher would have guessed in the course of another hour or so.

STRAKER (*coolly defiant*). No, not in another year or so. When we've 'ad you as long to polish up as we've 'ad 'im, perhaps you'll begin to look a little bit up to 'is mark. At present you fall a long way short. You've got too many aitches, for one thing. (*To* VIOLET, *amiably.*) All right, Miss: you want to talk to him: I shan't intrude. (*He nods affably to* MALONE *and goes out through the little gate in the paling.*)

VIOLET (*very civilly*). I am so sorry, Mr. Malone, if that man has been rude to you. But what can we do? He is our chauffeur.

MALONE. You what?

VIOLET. The driver of our automobile. He can drive a motor car at seventy miles an hour, and mend it when it breaks down. We are dependent on our motor cars; and our motor cars are dependent on him; so of course we are dependent on him.

MALONE. I've noticed, madam, that every thousand dollars an Englishman gets seems to add one to the number of people he's dependent on. However, you needn't apologize for your man: I made him talk on purpose. By doing so I learned that you're staying here in Grannida with a party of English, including my son Hector.

VIOLET (*conversationally*). Yes. We intended to go to Nice; but we had to follow a rather eccentric member of our party who started first and came here. Won't you sit down? (*She clears the nearest chair of the two books on it.*)

MALONE (*impressed by this attention*). Thank you. (*He sits down, examining her curiously as she goes to the iron table to put down the books. When she turns to him again, he says.*) Miss Robinson, I believe?

VIOLET (*sitting down*). Yes.

MALONE (*taking a letter from his pocket*). Your note to Hector runs as follows (VIOLET *is unable to repress a start. He pauses quietly to take out and put on his spectacles, which have gold rims*): "Dearest: they have all gone to the Alhambra for the afternoon. I have shammed headache and have the garden all to myself. Jump into Jack's motor: Straker will rattle you here in a jiffy. Quick, quick, quick. Your loving Violet." (*He looks at her; but by this time she has recovered herself, and meets his spectacles with perfect composure. He continues slowly.*) Now I don't know on what terms young people associate in English society; but in America that note would be considered to imply a very considerable degree of affectionate intimacy between the parties.

VIOLET. Yes: I know your son very well, Mr. Malone. Have you any objection?

MALONE (*somewhat taken aback*). No, no objection exactly. Provided it is understood that my son is altogether dependent on me, and that I have to be consulted in any important step he may propose to take.

VIOLET. I am sure you would not be unreasonable with him, Mr. Malone.

MALONE. I hope not, Miss Robinson; but at your age you might think many things unreasonable that don't seem so to me.

VIOLET (*with a little shrug*). Oh well, I suppose there's no use our playing at cross purposes, Mr. Malone. Hector wants to marry me.

MALONE. I inferred from your note that he might. Well, Miss Robinson, he is his own master; but if he marries you he shall not have a rap from me. (*He takes off his spectacles and pockets them with the note.*)

VIOLET (*with some severity*). That is not very complimentary to me, Mr. Malone.

MALONE. I say nothing against you, Miss Robinson: I daresay you are an amiable and excellent young lady. But I have other views for Hector.

VIOLET. Hector may not have other views for himself, Mr. Malone.

MALONE. Possibly not. Then he does without me: that's all. I daresay you are prepared for that. When a young lady writes to a young man to come to her quick, quick, quick, money seems nothing and love seems everything.

VIOLET (*sharply*). I beg your pardon, Mr. Malone: I do not think anything so foolish. Hector must have money.

MALONE (*staggered*). Oh, very well, very well. No doubt he can work for it.

VIOLET. What is the use of having money if you have to work for it? (*She rises impatiently.*) It's all nonsense, Mr. Malone: you must enable your son to keep up his position. It is his right.

MALONE (*grimly*). I should not advise you to marry him on the strength of that right, Miss Robinson.

(VIOLET, *who has almost lost her temper, controls herself with an effort; unclenches her fingers; and resumes her seat with studied tranquillity and reasonableness.*)

VIOLET. What objection have you to me, pray? My social position is as good as Hector's, to say the least. He admits it.

MALONE (*shrewdly*). You tell him so from time to time, eh? Hector's social position in England, Miss Robinson, is just what I choose to buy for him. I have made him a fair offer. Let him pick out the most historic house, castle or abbey that England contains. The day that he tells me he wants it for a wife worthy of its traditions, I buy it for him, and give him the means of keeping it up.

VIOLET. What do you mean by a wife worthy of its traditions? Cannot any well bred woman keep such a house for him?

MALONE. No: she must be born to it.

VIOLET. Hector was not born to it, was he?

MALONE. His grandmother was a barefooted Irish girl that nursed me by a turf fire. Let him marry another such, and I will not stint her marriage portion. Let him raise himself socially with my money or raise somebody else; so long as there is a social profit somewhere, I'll regard my expenditure as justified. But there must be a profit for someone. A marriage with you would leave things just where they are.

VIOLET. Many of my relations would object very much to my marrying the grandson of a common woman, Mr. Malone. That may be prejudice; but so is your desire to have him marry a title prejudice.

MALONE (*rising, and approaching her with a scrutiny in which there is a good deal of reluctant respect*). You seem a pretty straightforward downright sort of a young woman.

VIOLET. I do not see why I should be made miserably poor because I cannot make profits for you. Why do you want to make Hector unhappy?

MALONE. He will get over it all right enough. Men thrive better on disappointments in love than on disappointments in money. I daresay you think that sordid; but I know what I'm talking about. My father died of starvation in Ireland in the black '47. Maybe you've heard of it.

VIOLET. The Famine?

MALONE (*with smoldering passion*). No, the starvation. When a country is full of food, and exporting it, there can be no famine. My father was starved dead; and I was starved out to America in my mother's arms. English rule drove me and mine out of Ireland. Well, you can keep Ireland. I and my like are coming back to buy England; and we'll buy the best of it. I want no middle-class properties and no middle-class women for Hector. That's straightforward, isn't it, like yourself?

VIOLET (*icily pitying his sentimentality*). Really, Mr. Malone, I am astonished to hear a man of your age and good sense talking in that romantic way. Do you suppose English noblemen will sell their places to you for the asking?

MALONE. I have the refusal of two of the oldest family mansions in England. One historic owner can't afford to keep all the rooms dusted: the other can't afford the death duties. What do you say now?

VIOLET. Of course it is very scandalous; but surely you know that the Government will sooner or later put a stop to all these Socialistic attacks on property.

MALONE (*grinning*). D'y' think they'll be able to get that done before I buy the house—or rather the abbey? They're both abbeys.

VIOLET (*putting that aside rather impatiently*). Oh, well, let us talk sense, Mr. Malone. You must feel that we haven't been talking sense so far.

MALONE. I can't say I do. I mean all I say.

VIOLET. Then you don't know Hector as I do. He is romantic and faddy—he gets it from you, I fancy—and he wants a certain sort of wife to take care of him. Not a faddy sort of person, you know.

MALONE. Somebody like you, perhaps?

VIOLET (*quietly*). Well, yes. But you cannot very well ask me to undertake this with absolutely no means of keeping up his position.

MALONE (*alarmed*). Stop a bit, stop a bit. Where are we getting to? I'm not aware that I'm asking you to undertake anything.

VIOLET. Of course, Mr. Malone, you can make it very difficult for me to speak to you if you choose to misunderstand me.

MALONE (*half bewildered*). I don't wish to take any unfair advantage; but we seem to have got off the straight track somehow.

(STRAKER, *with the air of a man who has been making haste, opens the little gate, and admits* HECTOR, *who, snorting with indignation, comes upon the lawn, and is making for his father when* VIOLET, *greatly dismayed, springs up and intercepts him.* STRAKER *does not wait; at least he does not remain visibly within earshot.*)

VIOLET. Oh, how unlucky! Now please, Hector, say nothing. Go away until I have finished speaking to your father.

HECTOR (*inexorably*). No, Violet: I mean to have this thing out, right away. (*He puts her aside; passes her by; and faces his father, whose cheeks darken as his Irish blood begins to simmer.*) Dad: you've not played this hand straight.

MALONE. Hwat d'y' mean?

HECTOR. You've opened a letter addressed to me. You've impersonated me and stolen a march on this lady. That's dishonorable.

MALONE (*threateningly*). Now you take care what you're saying, Hector. Take care, I tell you.

HECTOR. I have taken care. I am taking care. I'm taking care of my honor and my position in English society.

MALONE (*hotly*). Your position has been got by my money: do you know that?

HECTOR. Well, you've just spoiled it all by opening that letter. A letter from an English lady, not addressed to you—a confidential letter! a delicate letter! a private letter! opened by my father! That's a sort of thing a man can't struggle against in England. The sooner we go back together the better. (*He appeals mutely to the heavens to witness the shame and anguish of two outcasts.*)

VIOLET (*snubbing him with an instinctive dislike for scene making*). Don't be unreasonable, Hector. It was quite natural of Mr. Malone to open my letter: his name was on the envelope.

MALONE. There! You've no common sense, Hector. I thank you, Miss Robinson.

HECTOR. I thank you, too. It's very kind of you. My father knows no better

MALONE (*furiously clenching his fists*). Hector—

HECTOR (*with undaunted moral force*). Oh, it's no use hectoring me. A private letter's a private letter, dad: you can't get over that.

MALONE (*raising his voice*). I won't be talked back to by you, d'y' hear?

VIOLET. Ssh! please, please. Here they all come.

(*Father and son, checked, glare mutely at one another as* TANNER *comes in through the little gate with* RAMSDEN, *followed by* OCTAVIUS *and* ANN.)

VIOLET. Back already!

TANNER. The Alhambra is not open this afternoon.

VIOLET. What a sell!

(TANNER *passes on, and presently finds himself between* HECTOR *and a strange elder, both apparently on the verge of personal combat. He looks from one to the other for an explanation. They sulkily avoid his eye, and nurse their wrath in silence.*)

RAMSDEN. Is it wise for you to be out in the sunshine with such a headache, Violet?

TANNER. Have you recovered too, Malone?

VIOLET. Oh, I forgot. We have not all met before. Mr. Malone: won't you introduce your father?

HECTOR (*with Roman firmness*). No I will not. He is no father of mine.

MALONE (*very angry*). You disown your dad before your English friends, do you?

VIOLET. Oh please don't make a scene.

(ANN *and* OCTAVIUS, *lingering near the gate, exchange an astonished glance, and discreetly withdraw up the steps to the garden, where they can enjoy the disturbance without intruding. On their way to the steps* ANN *sends a little grimace of mute sympathy to* VIOLET, *who is standing with her back to the little table, looking on in helpless annoyance as her husband soars to higher and higher moral eminences without the least regard to the old man's millions.*)

HECTOR. I'm very sorry, Miss Robinson; but I'm contending for a principle. I am a son, and, I hope, a dutiful one; but before everything I'm a Man!!! And when dad treats my private letters as his own, and takes it on himself to say that I shan't marry you if I am happy and fortunate enough to gain your consent, then I just snap my fingers and go my own way.

TANNER. Marry Violet!

RAMSDEN. Are you in your senses?

TANNER. Do you forget what we told you?

HECTOR (*recklessly*). I don't care what you told me.

RAMSDEN (*scandalized*). Tut tut, sir! Monstrous! (*He flings away towards the gate, his elbows quivering with indignation.*)

TANNER. Another madman! These men in love should be locked up. (*He gives* HECTOR *up as hopeless, and turns away towards the garden; but* MALONE, *taking offense in a new direction, follows him and compels him, by the aggressiveness of his tone, to stop.*)

MALONE. I don't understand this. Is Hector not good enough for this lady, pray?

TANNER. My dear sir, the lady is married already. Hector knows it; and yet he persists in his infatuation. Take him home and lock him up.

MALONE (*bitterly*). So this is the highborn social tone I've spoiled be me ignorant, uncultivated behavior! Makin love to a married woman! (*He comes angrily between* HECTOR *and* VIOLET, *and almost bawls into* HECTOR'*s left ear.*) You've picked up that habit of the British aristocracy, have you?

HECTOR. That's all right. Don't you trouble yourself about that. I'll answer for the morality of what I'm doing.

TANNER (*coming forward to* HECTOR'*s right hand with flashing eyes*). Well said, Malone! You also see that mere marriage laws are not morality! I agree with you; but unfortunately Violet does not.

MALONE. I take leave to doubt that, sir. (*Turning on* VIOLET.) Let me tell you, Mrs. Robinson, or whatever your right name is, you had no right to send that letter to my son when you were the wife of another man.

HECTOR (*outraged*). This is the last straw. Dad: you have insulted my wife.

MALONE. Your wife!

TANNER. You the missing husband! Another moral impostor! (*He smites his brow, and collapses into* MALONE'*s chair.*)

MALONE. You've married without my consent!

RAMSDEN. You have deliberately humbugged us, sir!

HECTOR. Here: I have had just about enough of being badgered. Violet and I are married: that's the long and the short of it. Now what have you got to say—any of you?

MALONE. I know what I've got to say. She's married a beggar.

HECTOR. No; she's married a Worker. (*His American pronunciation imparts an overwhelming intensity to this simple and unpopular word.*) I start to earn my own living this very afternoon.

MALONE (*sneering angrily*). Yes: you're very plucky now, because you got your remittance from me yesterday or this morning, I reckon. Wait till it's spent. You won't be so full of cheek then.

HECTOR (*producing a letter from his pocketbook*). Here it is (*thrusting it on his father*). Now you just take your remittance and yourself out of my life. I'm done with remittances; and I'm done with you. I don't sell the privilege of insulting my wife for a thousand dollars.

MALONE (*deeply wounded and full of concern*). Hector: you don't know what poverty is.

HECTOR (*fervidly*). Well, I want to know what it is. I want to be a Man. Violet: you come along with me, to your own home: I'll see you through.

OCTAVIUS (*jumping down from the garden to the lawn and running to* HECTOR'*s left hand*). I hope you'll shake hands with me before you go, Hector. I admire and respect you more than I can say. (*He is affected almost to tears as they shake hands.*)

VIOLET (*also almost in tears, but of vexation*). Oh don't be an idiot, Tavy.

Hector's about as fit to become a workman as you are.

TANNER (*rising from his chair on the other side of* HECTOR). Never fear: there's no question of his becoming a navvy, Mrs. Malone. (*To* HECTOR.) There's really no difficulty about capital to start with. Treat me as a friend: draw on me.

OCTAVIUS (*impulsively*). Or on me.

MALONE (*with fierce jealousy*). Who wants your durty money? Who should he draw on but his own father? (TANNER *and* OCTAVIUS *recoil,* OCTAVIUS *rather hurt,* TANNER *consoled by the solution of the money difficulty.* VIOLET *looks up hopefully.*) Hector: don't be rash, my boy. I'm sorry for what I said: I never meant to insult Violet: I take it all back. She's just the wife you want: there!

HECTOR (*patting him on the shoulder*). Well, that's all right, dad. Say no more: we're friends again. Only, I take no money from anybody.

MALONE (*pleading abjectly*). Don't be hard on me, Hector. I'd rather you quarreled and took the money than made friends and starved. You don't know what the world is: I do.

HECTOR. No, no, NO. That's fixed: that's not going to change. (*He passes his father inexorably by, and goes to* VIOLET.) Come, Mrs. Malone: you've got to move to the hotel with me, and take your proper place before the world.

VIOLET. But I must go in, dear, and tell Davis to pack. Won't you go on and make them give you a room overlooking the garden for me? I'll join you in half an hour.

HECTOR. Very well. You'll dine with us, Dad, won't you?

MALONE (*eager to conciliate him*). Yes, yes.

HECTOR. See you all later. (*He waves his hand to* ANN, *who has now been joined by* TANNER, OCTAVIUS, *and* RAMSDEN *in the garden, and goes out through the little gate, leaving his father and* VIOLET *together on the lawn.*)

MALONE. You'll try to bring him to his senses, Violet: I know you will.

VIOLET. I had no idea he could be so headstrong. If he goes on like that, what can I do?

MALONE. Don't be discurridged: domestic pressure may be slow; but it's sure. You'll wear him down. Promise me you will.

VIOLET. I will do my best. Of course I think it's the greatest nonsense deliberately making us poor like that.

MALONE. Of course it is.

VIOLET (*after a moment's reflection*). You had better give me the remittance. He will want it for his hotel bill. I'll see whether I can induce him to accept it. Not now, of course, but presently.

MALONE (*eagerly*). Yes, yes, yes: that's just the thing. (*He hands her the thousand dollar bill, and adds cunningly.*) Y'understand that this is only a bachelor allowance.

VIOLET (*coolly*). Oh, quite. (*She takes it.*) Thank you. By the way, Mr. Malone, those two houses you mentioned—the abbeys.

MALONE. Yes?

VIOLET. Don't take one of them until I've seen it. One never knows what may be wrong with these places.

MALONE. I won't. I'll do nothing without consulting you, never fear.

VIOLET (*politely, but without a ray of gratitude*). Thanks: that will be much the best way. (*She goes calmly back to the villa, escorted obsequiously by* MALONE *to the upper end of the garden.*)

TANNER (*drawing* RAMSDEN'*s attention to* MALONE'*s cringing attitude as he takes leave of* VIOLET). And that poor devil is a billionaire! one of the master spirits of the age! Led in a string like a pug dog by the first girl who takes the trouble to despise him. I wonder will it ever come to that with me. (*He comes down to the lawn.*)

RAMSDEN (*following him*). The sooner the better for you.

MALONE (*slapping his hands as he returns through the garden*). That'll be a grand woman for Hector. I wouldn't exchange her for ten duchesses. (*He descends to the lawn and comes between* TANNER *and* RAMSDEN.)

RAMSDEN (*very civil to the billionaire*). It's an unexpected pleasure to find you in this corner of the world, Mr. Malone. Have you come to buy up the Alhambra?

MALONE. Well, I don't say I mightn't. I think I could do better with it than the Spanish government. But that's not what I came about. To tell you the truth, about a month ago I overheard a deal between two men over a bundle of shares. They differed about the price: they were young and greedy, and didn't know that if the shares were worth what was bid for them they must be worth what was asked, the margin being too small to be of any account, you see. To amuse meself, I cut in and bought the shares. Well, to this day I haven't found out what the business is. The office is in this town; and the name is Mendoza, Limited. Now whether Mendoza's a mine, or a steamboat line, or a bank, or a patent article—

TANNER. He's a man. I know him: his principles are thoroughly commercial. Let us take you round the town in our motor, Mr. Malone, and call on him on the way.

MALONE. If you'll be so kind, yes. And may I ask who—

TANNER. Mr. Roebuck Ramsden, a very old friend of your daughter-in-law.

MALONE. Happy to meet you, Mr. Ramsden.

RAMSDEN. Thank you. Mr. Tanner is also one of our circle.

MALONE. Glad to know you also, Mr. Tanner.

TANNER. Thanks. (MALONE *and* RAMSDEN *go out very amicably through the little gate.* TANNER *calls to* OCTAVIUS, *who is wandering in the garden with* ANN.) *Tavy!* (TAVY *comes to the steps,* TANNER *whispers loudly to him.*) Violet has married a financier of brigands. (TANNER *hurries away to overtake* MALONE *and* RAMSDEN. ANN *strolls to the steps with an idle impulse to torment* OCTAVIUS.)

ANN. Won't you go with them, Tavy?

OCTAVIUS (*tears suddenly flushing his eyes*). You cut me to the heart, Ann, by wanting me to go. (*He comes down on the lawn to hide his face from her. She follows him caressingly.*)

ANN. Poor Ricky Ticky Tavy! Poor heart!

OCTAVIUS. It belongs to you, Ann. Forgive me: I must speak of it. I love you. You know I love you.

ANN. What's the good, Tavy? You know that my mother is determined that I shall marry Jack.

OCTAVIUS (*amazed*). Jack!

ANN. It seems absurd, doesn't it?

OCTAVIUS (*with growing resentment*). Do you mean to say that Jack has been playing with me all this time? That he has been urging me not to marry you because he intends to marry you himself?

ANN (*alarmed*). No no; you mustn't lead him to believe that I said that: I don't for a moment think that Jack knows his own mind. But it's clear from my father's will that he wished me to marry Jack. And my mother is set on it.

OCTAVIUS. But you are not bound to sacrifice yourself always to the wishes of your parents.

ANN. My father loved me. My mother loves me. Surely their wishes are a better guide than my own selfishness.

OCTAVIUS. Oh, I know how unselfish

you are, Ann. But believe me—though I know I am speaking in my own interest—there is another side to this question. Is it fair to Jack to marry him if you do not love him? Is it fair to destroy my happiness as well as your own if you can bring yourself to love me?

ANN (*looking at him with a faint impulse of pity*). Tavy, my dear, you are a nice creature—a good boy.

OCTAVIUS (*humiliated*). Is that all?

ANN (*mischievously in spite of her pity*). That's a great deal, I assure you. You would always worship the ground I trod on, wouldn't you?

OCTAVIUS. I do. It sounds ridiculous; but it's no exaggeration. I do; and I always shall.

ANN. Always is a long word, Tavy. You see, I shall have to live up always to your idea of my divinity; and I don't think I could do that if we were married. But if I marry Jack, you'll never be disillusioned—at least not until I grow too old.

OCTAVIUS. I too shall grow old, Ann. And when I am eighty, one white hair of the woman I love will make me tremble more than the thickest gold tress from the most beautiful young head.

ANN (*quite touched*). Oh, that's poetry, Tavy, real poetry. It gives me that strange sudden sense of an echo from a former existence which always seems to me such a striking proof that we have immortal souls.

OCTAVIUS. Do you believe that it is true?

ANN. Tavy: if it is to come true, you must lose me as well as love me.

OCTAVIUS. Oh! (*He hastily sits down at the little table and covers his face with his hands.*)

ANN (*with conviction*). Tavy: I wouldn't for worlds destroy your illusions. I can neither take you nor let you go. I can see exactly what will suit you. You must be a sentimental old bachelor for my sake.

OCTAVIUS (*desperately*). Ann: I'll kill myself.

ANN. Oh no you won't: that wouldn't be kind. You won't have a bad time. You will be very nice to women; and you will go a good deal to the opera. A broken heart is a very pleasant complaint for a man in London if he has a comfortable income.

OCTAVIUS (*considerably cooled, but believing that he is only recovering his self-control*). I know you mean to be kind, Ann. Jack has persuaded you that cynicism is a good tonic for me. (*He rises with quiet dignity.*)

ANN (*studying him slyly*). You see, I'm disillusionizing you already. That's what I dread.

OCTAVIUS. You do not dread disillusionizing Jack.

ANN (*her face lighting up with mischievous ecstasy—whispering*). I can't: he has no illusions about me. I shall surprise Jack the other way. Getting over an unfavorable impression is ever so much easier than living up to an ideal. Oh, I shall enrapture Jack sometimes!

OCTAVIUS (*resuming the calm phase of despair, and beginning to enjoy his broken heart and delicate attitude without knowing it*). I don't doubt that. You will enrapture him always. And he—the fool!—thinks you would make him wretched.

ANN. Yes: that's the difficulty, so far.

OCTAVIUS (*heroically*). Shall *I* tell him that you love him?

ANN (*quickly*). Oh no: he'd run away again.

OCTAVIUS (*shocked*). Ann: would you marry an unwilling man?

ANN. What a queer creature you are, Tavy! There's no such thing as a willing man when you really go for him. (*She laughs naughtily.*) I'm shocking you, I suppose. But you know you are really getting a sort of satisfaction already in being out of danger yourself.

OCTAVIUS (*startled*). Satisfaction! (*Reproachfully.*) You say that to me!

ANN. Well, if it were really agony, would you ask for more of it?

OCTAVIUS. Have I asked for more of it?

ANN. You have offered to tell Jack that I love him. That's self-sacrifice, I suppose; but there must be some satisfaction in it. Perhaps it's because you're a poet. You are like the bird that presses its breast against the sharp thorn to make itself sing.

OCTAVIUS. It's quite simple. I love you; and I want you to be happy. You don't love me; so I can't make you happy myself; but I can help another man to do it.

ANN. Yes: it seems quite simple. But I doubt if we ever know why we do things. The only really simple thing is to go straight for what you want and grab it. I suppose I don't love you, Tavy; but sometimes I feel as if I should like to make a man of you somehow. You are very foolish about women.

OCTAVIUS (*almost coldly*). I am content to be what I am in that respect.

ANN. Then you must keep away from them, and only dream about them. I wouldn't marry you for worlds, Tavy.

OCTAVIUS. I have no hope, Ann: I accept my ill luck. But I don't think you quite know how much it hurts.

ANN. You are so softhearted! It's queer that you should be so different from Violet. Violet's as hard as nails.

OCTAVIUS. Oh no. I am sure Violet is thoroughly womanly at heart.

ANN (*with some impatience*). Why do you say that? Is it unwomanly to be thoughtful and businesslike and sensible? Do you want Violet to be an idiot—or something worse, like me?

OCTAVIUS. Something worse—like you! What do you mean, Ann?

ANN. Oh well, I don't mean that, of course. But I have a great respect for Violet. She gets her own way always.

OCTAVIUS (*sighing*). So do you.

ANN. Yes; but somehow she gets it without coaxing—without having to make people sentimental about her.

OCTAVIUS (*with brotherly callousness*). Nobody could get very sentimental about Violet, I think, pretty as she is.

ANN. Oh yes they could, if she made them.

OCTAVIUS. But surely no really nice woman would deliberately practice on men's instincts in that way.

ANN (*throwing up her hands*). Oh Tavy, Tavy, Ricky Ticky Tavy, heaven help the woman who marries you!

OCTAVIUS (*his passion reviving at the name*). Oh why, why, why do you say that? Don't torment me. I don't understand.

ANN. Suppose she were to tell fibs, and lay snares for men?

OCTAVIUS. Do you think *I* could marry such a woman—I, who have known and loved you?

ANN. Hm! Well, at all events, she wouldn't let you if she were wise. So that's settled. And now I can't talk any more. Say you forgive me, and that the subject is closed.

OCTAVIUS. I have nothing to forgive; and the subject is closed. And if the wound is open, at least you shall never see it bleed.

ANN. Poetic to the last, Tavy. Goodbye, dear. (*She pats his cheek; has an impulse to kiss him and then another impulse of distaste which prevents her; finally runs away through the garden and into the villa.*)

(OCTAVIUS *again takes refuge at the table, bowing his head on his arms and sobbing softly.* MRS. WHITEFIELD, *who has been pottering round the Granada shops, and has a net full of little parcels in her hand, comes in through the gate and sees him.*)

MRS. WHITEFIELD (*running to him and lifting his head*). What's the matter, Tavy? Are you ill?

OCTAVIUS. No, nothing, nothing.

MRS. WHITEFIELD (*still holding his head, anxiously*). But you're crying. Is it about Violet's marriage?

OCTAVIUS. No, no. Who told you about Violet?

MRS. WHITEFIELD (*restoring the head to its owner*). I met Roebuck and that awful old Irishman. Are you sure you're not ill? What's the matter?

OCTAVIUS (*affectionately*). It's nothing—only a man's broken heart. Doesn't that sound ridiculous?

MRS. WHITEFIELD. But what is it all about? Has Ann been doing anything to you?

OCTAVIUS. It's not Ann's fault. And don't think for a moment that I blame you.

MRS. WHITEFIELD (*startled*). For what?

OCTAVIUS (*pressing her hand consolingly*). For nothing. I said I didn't blame you.

MRS. WHITEFIELD. But I haven't done anything. What's the matter?

OCTAVIUS (*smiling sadly*). Can't you guess? I daresay you are right to prefer Jack to me as a husband for Ann; but I love Ann; and it hurts rather. (*He rises and moves away from her towards the middle of the lawn.*)

MRS. WHITEFIELD (*following him hastily*). Does Ann say that I want her to marry Jack?

OCTAVIUS. Yes: she has told me.

MRS. WHITEFIELD (*thoughtfully*). Then I'm very sorry for you, Tavy. It's only her way of saying she wants to marry Jack. Little she cares what *I* say or what *I* want!

OCTAVIUS. But she would not say it unless she believed it. Surely you don't suspect Ann of—of deceit!!

MRS. WHITEFIELD. Well, never mind, Tavy. I don't know which is best for a young man: to know too little, like you, or too much, like Jack.

(TANNER *returns.*)

TANNER. Well, I've disposed of old Malone. I've introduced him to Mendoza, Limited; and left the two brigands together to talk it out. Hullo, Tavy! anything wrong?

OCTAVIUS. I must go wash my face, I see. (*To* MRS. WHITEFIELD.) Tell him what you wish. (*To* TANNER.) You may take it from me, Jack, that Ann approves of it.

TANNER (*puzzled by his manner*). Approves of what?

OCTAVIUS. Of what Mrs. Whitefield wishes. (*He goes his way with sad dignity to the villa.*)

TANNER (*to* MRS. WHITEFIELD). This is very mysterious. What is it you wish? It shall be done, whatever it is.

MRS. WHITEFIELD (*with sniveling gratitude*). Thank you, Jack. (*She sits down.* TANNER *brings the other chair from the table and sits close to her with his elbows on his knees, giving her his whole attention.*) I don't know why it is that other people's children are so nice to me, and that my own have so little consideration for me. It's no wonder I don't seem able to care for Ann and Rhoda as I do for you and Tavy and Violet. It's a very queer world. It used to be so straightforward and simple; and now nobody seems to think and feel as they ought. Nothing has been right since that speech that Professor Tyndall made at Belfast.

TANNER. Yes: life is more complicated than we used to think. But what am I to do for you?

MRS. WHITEFIELD. That's just what I

want to tell you. Of course you'll marry Ann whether I like it or not—

TANNER (*starting*). It seems to me that I shall presently be married to Ann whether I like it myself or not.

MRS. WHITEFIELD (*peacefully*). Oh, very likely you will: you know what she is when she has set her mind on anything. But don't put it on me: that's all I ask. Tavy has just let out that she's been saying that I am making her marry you; and the poor boy is breaking his heart about it; for he is in love with her himself, though what he sees in her so wonderful, goodness knows: *I* don't. It's no use telling Tavy that Ann puts things into people's heads by telling them that I want them when the thought of them never crossed my mind. It only sets Tavy against me. But you know better than that. So if you marry her, don't put the blame on me.

TANNER (*emphatically*). I haven't the slightest intention of marrying her.

MRS. WHITEFIELD (*slyly*). She'd suit you better than Tavy. She'd meet her match in you, Jack. I'd like to see her meet her match.

TANNER. No man is a match for a woman, except with a poker and a pair of hobnailed boots. Not always even then. Anyhow, *I* can't take the poker to her. I should be a mere slave.

MRS. WHITEFIELD. No: she's afraid of you. At all events, you would tell her the truth about herself. She wouldn't be able to slip out of it as she does with me.

TANNER. Everybody would call me a brute if I told Ann the truth about herself in terms of her own moral code. To begin with, Ann says things that are not strictly true.

MRS. WHITEFIELD. I'm glad somebody sees she is not an angel.

TANNER. In short—to put it as a husband would put it when exasperated to the point of speaking out—she is a liar. And since she has plunged Tavy head over ears in love with her without any intention of marrying him, she is a coquette, according to the standard definition of a coquette as a woman who rouses passions she has no intention of gratifying. And as she has now reduced you to the point of being willing to sacrifice me at the altar for the mere satisfaction of getting me to call her a liar to her face, I may conclude that she is a bully as well. She can't bully men as she bullies women; so she habitually and unscrupulously uses her personal fascination to make men give her whatever she wants. That makes her almost something for which I know no polite name.

MRS. WHITEFIELD (*in mild expostulation*). Well, you can't expect perfection, Jack.

TANNER. I don't. But what annoys me is that Ann does. I know perfectly well that all this about her being a liar and a bully and a coquette and so forth is a trumped-up moral indictment which might be brought against anybody. We all lie; we all bully as much as we dare; we all bid for admiration without the least intention of earning it; we all get as much rent as we can out of our powers of fascination. If Ann would admit this I shouldn't quarrel with her. But she won't. If she has children she'll take advantage of their telling lies to amuse herself by whacking them. If another woman makes eyes at me, she'll refuse to know a coquette. She will do just what she likes herself while insisting on everybody else doing what the conventional code prescribes. In short, I can stand everything except her confounded hypocrisy. That's what beats me.

MRS. WHITEFIELD (*carried away by the relief of hearing her own opinion so eloquently expressed*). Oh, she is a hypocrite. She is: she is. Isn't she?

TANNER. Then why do you want to marry me to her?

MRS. WHITEFIELD (*querulously*). There

now! put it on me, of course. I never thought of it until Tavy told me she said I did. But, you know, I'm very fond of Tavy: he's a sort of son to me; and I don't want him to be trampled on and made wretched.

TANNER. Whereas I don't matter, I suppose.

MRS. WHITEFIELD. Oh, you are different, somehow: you are able to take care of yourself. You'd serve her out. And anyhow, she must marry somebody.

TANNER. Aha! there speaks the life instinct. You detest her; but you feel that you must get her married.

MRS. WHITEFIELD (*rising, shocked*). Do you mean that I detest my own daughter! Surely you don't believe me to be so wicked and unnatural as that, merely because I see her faults.

TANNER (*cynically*). You love her, then?

MRS. WHITEFIELD. Why, of course I do. What queer things you say, Jack! We can't help loving our own blood relations.

TANNER. Well, perhaps it saves unpleasantness to say so. But for my part, I suspect that the tables of consanguinity have a natural basis in a natural repugnance. (*He rises.*)

MRS. WHITEFIELD. You shouldn't say things like that, Jack. I hope you won't tell Ann that I have been speaking to you. I only wanted to set myself right with you and Tavy. I couldn't sit mumchance and have everything put on me.

TANNER (*politely*). Quite so.

MRS. WHITEFIELD (*dissatisfied*). And now I've only made matters worse. Tavy's angry with me because I don't worship Ann. And when it's been put into my head that Ann ought to marry you, what can I say except that it would serve her right?

TANNER. Thank you.

MRS. WHITEFIELD. Now don't be silly and twist what I say into something I don't mean. I ought to have fair play—

(ANN *comes from the villa, followed presently by* VIOLET, *who is dressed for driving.*)

ANN (*coming to her mother's right hand with threatening suavity*). Well, mamma darling, you seem to be having a delightful chat with Jack. We can hear you all over the place.

MRS. WHITEFIELD (*appalled*). Have you overheard—

TANNER. Never fear: Ann is only—well, we were discussing that habit of hers just now. She hasn't heard a word.

MRS. WHITEFIELD (*stoutly*). I don't care whether she has or not: I have a right to say what I please.

VIOLET (*arriving on the lawn and coming between* MRS. WHITEFIELD *and* TANNER). I've come to say goodbye. I'm off for my honeymoon.

MRS. WHITEFIELD (*crying*). Oh don't say that, Violet. And no wedding, no breakfast, no clothes, nor anything.

VIOLET (*petting her*). It won't be for long.

MRS. WHITEFIELD. Don't let him take you to America. Promise me that you won't.

VIOLET (*very decidedly*). I should think not, indeed. Don't cry, dear: I'm only going to the hotel.

MRS. WHITEFIELD. But going in that dress, with your luggage, makes one realize— (*She chokes, and then breaks out again.*) How I wish you were my daughter, Violet!

VIOLET (*soothing her*). There, there: so I am. Ann will be jealous.

MRS. WHITEFIELD. Ann doesn't care a bit for me.

ANN. Fie, mother! Come, now: you mustn't cry any more: you know Violet doesn't like it (MRS. WHITEFIELD *dries her eyes, and subsides*).

VIOLET. Goodbye, Jack.

TANNER. Goodbye, Violet.

VIOLET. The sooner you get married too, the better. You will be much less misunderstood.

TANNER (*restively*). I quite expect to get married in the course of the afternoon. You all seem to have set your minds on it.

VIOLET. You might do worse. (*To* MRS. WHITEFIELD: *putting her arm round her.*) Let me take you to the hotel with me: the drive will do you good. Come in and get a wrap. (*She takes her towards the villa.*)

MRS. WHITEFIELD (*as they go up through the garden*). I don't know what I shall do when you are gone, with no one but Ann in the house; and she always occupied with the men! It's not to be expected that your husband will care to be bothered with an old woman like me. Oh, you needn't tell me: politeness is all very well; but I know what people think— (*She talks herself and* VIOLET *out of sight and hearing.*)

(ANN, *musing on* VIOLET*'s opportune advice, approaches* TANNER; *examines him humorously for a moment from toe to top; and finally delivers her opinion.*)

ANN. Violet is quite right. You ought to get married.

TANNER (*explosively*). Ann: I will not marry you. Do you hear? I won't, won't, won't, won't, WON'T marry you.

ANN (*placidly*). Well, nobody axd you, sir she said, sir she said, sir she said. So that's settled.

TANNER. Yes, nobody has asked me; but everybody treats the thing as settled. It's in the air. When we meet, the others go away on absurd pretexts to leave us alone together. Ramsden no longer scowls at me: his eye beams, as if he were already giving you away to me in church. Tavy refers me to your mother and gives me his blessing. Straker openly treats you as his future employer: it was he who first told me of it.

ANN. Was that why you ran away?

TANNER. Yes, only to be stopped by a lovesick brigand and run down like a truant schoolboy.

ANN. Well, if you don't want to be married, you needn't be. (*She turns away from him and sits down, much at her ease.*)

TANNER (*following her*). Does any man want to be hanged? Yet men let themselves be hanged without a struggle for life, though they could at least give the chaplain a black eye. We do the world's will, not our own. I have a frightful feeling that I shall let myself be married because it is the world's will that you should have a husband.

ANN. I daresay I shall, someday.

TANNER. But why me—me of all men? Marriage is to me apostasy, profanation of the sanctuary of my soul, violation of my manhood, sale of my birthright, shameful surrender, ignominious capitulation, acceptance of defeat. I shall decay like a thing that has served its purpose and is done with; I shall change from a man with a future to a man with a past; I shall see in the greasy eyes of all the other husbands their relief at the arrival of a new prisoner to share their ignominy. The young men will scorn me as one who has sold out: to the young women I, who have always been an enigma and a possibility, shall be merely somebody else's property—and damaged goods at that: a secondhand man at best.

ANN. Well, your wife can put on a cap and make herself ugly to keep you in countenance, like my grandmother.

TANNER. So that she may make her triumph more insolent by publicly throwing away the bait the moment the trap snaps on the victim!

ANN. After all, though, what difference would it make? Beauty is all very well at first sight; but who ever looks at it when it has been in the house three days? I thought our pictures very lovely when papa bought them; but I haven't looked at them for years. You never bother about my looks: you are too well used to me. I might be the umbrella stand.

TANNER. You lie, you vampire: you lie.

ANN. Flatterer. Why are you trying to fascinate me, Jack, if you don't want to marry me?

TANNER. The Life Force. I am in the grip of the Life Force.

ANN. I don't understand in the least: it sounds like the Life Guards.

TANNER. Why don't you marry Tavy? He is willing. Can you not be satisfied unless your prey struggles?

ANN (*turning to him as if to let him into a secret*). Tavy will never marry. Haven't you noticed that that sort of man never marries?

TANNER. What! a man who idolizes women! who sees nothing in nature but romantic scenery for love duets! Tavy, the chivalrous, the faithful, the tender-hearted and true! Tavy never marry! Why, he was born to be swept up by the first pair of blue eyes he meets in the street.

ANN. Yes, I know. All the same, Jack, men like that always live in comfortable bachelor lodgings with broken hearts, and are adored by their landladies, and never get married. Men like you always get married.

TANNER (*smiting his brow*). How frightfully, horribly true! It has been staring me in the face all my life; and I never saw it before.

ANN. Oh, it's the same with women. The poetic temperament's a very nice temperament, very amiable, very harmless and poetic, I daresay; but it's an old maid's temperament.

TANNER. Barren. The Life Force passes it by.

ANN. If that's what you mean by the Life Force, yes.

TANNER. You don't care for Tavy?

ANN (*looking round carefully to make sure that* TAVY *is not within earshot*). No.

TANNER. And you do care for me?

ANN (*rising quietly and shaking her finger at him*). Now, Jack! Behave yourself.

TANNER. Infamous, abandoned woman! Devil!

ANN. Boa-constrictor! Elephant!

TANNER. Hypocrite!

ANN (*softly*). I must be, for my future husband's sake.

TANNER. For mine! (*Correcting himself savagely.*) I mean for his.

ANN (*ignoring the correction*). Yes, for yours. You had better marry what you call a hypocrite, Jack. Women who are not hypocrites go about in rational dress and are insulted and get into all sorts of hot water. And then their husbands get dragged in too, and live in continual dread of fresh complications. Wouldn't you prefer a wife you could depend on?

TANNER. No, a thousand times no: hot water is the revolutionist's element. You clean men as you clean milkpails, by scalding them.

ANN. Cold water has its uses too. It's healthy.

TANNER (*despairingly*). Oh, you are witty: at the supreme moment the Life Force endows you with every quality. Well, I too can be a hypocrite. Your father's will appointed me your guardian, not your suitor. I shall be faithful to my trust.

ANN (*in low siren tones*). He asked me who would I have as my guardian before he made that will. I chose you!

TANNER. The will is yours then! The trap was laid from the beginning.

ANN (*concentrating all her magic*). From the beginning—from our childhood—for both of us—by the Life Force.

TANNER. I will not marry you. I will not marry you.

ANN. Oh, you will, you will.

TANNER. I tell you, no, no, no.

ANN. I tell you, yes, yes, yes.

TANNER. No.

ANN (*coaxing—imploring—almost exhausted*). Yes. Before it is too late for repentance. Yes.

TANNER (*struck by the echo from the past*). When did all this happen to me before? Are we two dreaming?

ANN (*suddenly losing her courage, with an anguish that she does not conceal*). No. We are awake; and you have said no: that is all.

TANNER (*brutally*). Well?

ANN. Well, I made a mistake: you do not love me.

TANNER (*seizing her in his arms*). It is false: I love you. The Life Force enchants me: I have the whole world in my arms when I clasp you. But I am fighting for my freedom, for my honor, for my self, one and indivisible.

ANN. Your happiness will be worth them all.

TANNER. You would sell freedom and honor and self for happiness?

ANN. It will not be all happiness for me. Perhaps death.

TANNER (*groaning*). Oh, that clutch holds and hurts. What have you grasped in me? Is there a father's heart as well as a mother's?

ANN. Take care, Jack: if anyone comes while we are like this, you will have to marry me.

TANNER. If we two stood now on the edge of a precipice, I would hold you tight and jump.

ANN (*panting, failing more and more under the strain*). Jack: let me go. I have dared so frightfully—it is lasting longer than I thought. Let me go: I can't bear it.

TANNER. Nor I. Let it kill us.

ANN. Yes: I don't care. I am at the end of my forces. I don't care. I think I am going to faint.

(*At this moment* VIOLET *and* OCTAVIUS *come from the villa with* MRS. WHITEFIELD, *who is wrapped up for driving. Simultaneously* MALONE *and* RAMSDEN, *followed by* MENDOZA *and* STRAKER, *come in through the little gate in the paling.* TANNER *shamefacedly releases* ANN, *who raises her hand giddily to her forehead.*)

MALONE. Take care. Something's the matter with the lady.

RAMSDEN. What does this mean?

VIOLET (*running between* ANN *and* TANNER). Are you ill?

ANN (*reeling, with a supreme effort*). I have promised to marry Jack. (*She swoons.* VIOLET *kneels by her and chafes her hand.* TANNER *runs round to her other hand, and tries to lift her head.* OCTAVIUS *goes to* VIOLET*'s assistance, but does not know what to do.* MRS. WHITEFIELD *hurries back into the villa.* OCTAVIUS, MALONE *and* RAMSDEN *run to* ANN *and crowd round her, stooping to assist.* STRAKER *coolly comes to* ANN*'s feet, and* MENDOZA *to her head, both upright and self-possessed.*)

STRAKER. Now then, ladies and gentlemen: she don't want a crowd round her: she wants air—all the air she can git. If you please, gents— (MALONE *and* RAMSDEN *allow him to drive them gently past* ANN *and up the lawn towards the garden, where* OCTAVIUS, *who has already become conscious of his uselessness, joins them.* STRAKER, *following them up, pauses for a moment to instruct* TANNER.) Don't lift er ed, Mr. Tanner: let it go flat so's the blood can run back into it.

MENDOZA. He is right, Mr. Tanner. Trust to the air of the Sierra. (*He withdraws delicately to the garden steps.*)

TANNER (*rising*). I yield to your su-

perior knowledge of physiology, Henry. (*He withdraws to the corner of the lawn; and* OCTAVIUS *immediately hurries down to him.*)

TAVY (*aside to* TANNER, *grasping his hand*). Jack: be very happy.

TANNER (*aside to* TAVY). I never asked her. It is a trap for me. (*He goes up the lawn towards the garden.* OCTAVIUS *remains petrified.*)

MENDOZA (*intercepting* MRS. WHITEFIELD, *who comes from the villa with a glass of brandy*). What is this, madam? (*He takes it from her.*)

MRS. WHITEFIELD. A little brandy.

MENDOZA. The worst thing you could give her. Allow me. (*He swallows it.*) Trust to the air of the Sierra, madam.

(*For a moment the men all forget* ANN *and stare at* MENDOZA.)

ANN (*in* VIOLET'*s ear, clutching her round the neck*). Violet: did Jack say anything when I fainted?

VIOLET. No.

ANN. Ah! (*With a sigh of intense relief she relapses.*)

MRS. WHITEFIELD. Oh, she's fainted again.

(*They are about to rush back to her; but* MENDOZA *stops them with a warning gesture.*)

ANN (*supine*). No I haven't. I'm quite happy.

TANNER (*suddenly walking determinedly to her, and snatching her hand from* VIOLET *to feel her pulse*). Why, her pulse is positively bounding. Come, get up. What nonsense! Up with you. (*He gets her up summarily.*)

ANN. Yes: I feel strong enough now. But you very nearly killed me, Jack, for all that.

MALONE. A rough wooer, eh? They're the best sort, Miss Whitefield. I congratulate Mr. Tanner; and I hope to meet you and him as frequent guests at the Abbey.

ANN. Thank you. (*She gets past* MALONE *to* OCTAVIUS.) Ricky Ticky Tavy: congratulate me. (*Aside to him.*) I want to make you cry for the last time.

TAVY (*steadfastly*). No more tears. I am happy in your happiness. And I believe in you in spite of everything.

RAMSDEN (*coming between* MALONE *and* TANNER). You are a happy man, Jack Tanner. I envy you.

MENDOZA (*advancing between* VIOLET *and* TANNER). Sir: there are two tragedies in life. One is not to get your heart's desire. The other is to get it. Mine and yours, sir.

TANNER. Mr. Mendoza: I have no heart's desires. Ramsden: it is very easy for you to call me a happy man: you are only a spectator. I am one of the principals; and I know better. Ann: stop tempting Tavy, and come back to me.

ANN (*complying*). You are absurd, Jack. (*She takes his proffered arm.*)

TANNER (*continuing*). I solemnly say that I am not a happy man. Ann looks happy; but she is only triumphant, successful, victorious. That is not happiness, but the price for which the strong sell their happiness. What we have both done this afternoon is to renounce happiness, renounce freedom, renounce tranquillity, above all, renounce the romantic possibilities of an unknown future, for the cares of a household and a family. I beg that no man may seize the occasion to get half drunk and utter imbecile speeches and coarse pleasantries at my expense. We propose to furnish our own house according to our own taste; and I hereby give notice that the seven or eight traveling clocks, the four or five dressing cases, the salad bowls, the carvers and fish slices, the copy of Tennyson in extra morocco, and all the other articles you are preparing to heap upon us, will be instantly sold, and the proceeds devoted to circulating free copies of the Revolutionist's Handbook. The wedding will take place three days after our return to England, by special license, at the office of the district superintendent registrar, in the presence of my solicitor and his clerk, who, like his clients, will be in ordinary walking dress—

VIOLET (*with intense conviction*). You are a brute, Jack.

ANN (*looking at him with fond pride and caressing his arm*). Never mind her, dear. Go on talking.

TANNER. Talking!

(*Universal laughter.*)

CURTAIN

THE REVOLUTIONIST'S HANDBOOK

PREFACE

"No one can contemplate the present condition of the masses of the people without desiring something like a revolution for the better." *Sir Robert Giffen.* Essays in Finance, vol. ii. p. 393.

FOREWORD

A revolutionist is one who desires to discard the existing social order and try another.

The constitution of England is revolutionary. To a Russian or Anglo-Indian bureaucrat, a general election is as much a revolution as a referendum or plebiscite in which the people fight instead of voting. The French Revolution overthrew one set of rulers and substituted another with different interests and different views. That is what a general election enables the people to do in England every seven years if they choose. Revolution is therefore a national institution in England; and its advocacy by an Englishman needs no apology.

Every man is a revolutionist concerning the thing he understands. For example, every person who has mastered a profession is a skeptic concerning it, and consequently a revolutionist.

Every genuinely religious person is a heretic and therefore a revolutionist.

All who achieve real distinction in life begin as revolutionists. The most distinguished persons become more revolutionary as they grow older, though they are commonly supposed to become more conservative owing to their loss of faith in conventional methods of reform.

Any person under the age of thirty, who, having any knowledge of the existing social order, is not a revolutionist, is an inferior

AND YET

Revolutions have never lightened the burden of tyranny: they have only shifted it to another shoulder.

JOHN TANNER

I
On Good Breeding

If there were no God, said the eighteenth-century Deist, it would be necessary to invent Him. Now this XVIII-century god was *deus ex machina,* the god who helped those who could not help themselves, the god of the lazy and incapable. The nineteenth century decided that there is indeed no such god; and now Man must take in hand all the work that he used to shirk with an idle prayer. He must, in effect, change himself into the political Providence which he formerly conceived as god; and such change is not only possible, but the only sort of change that is real. The mere transfigurations of institutions, as from military and priestly dominance to commercial and scientific dominance, from commercial dominance to proletarian democracy, from slavery to serfdom, from serfdom to capitalism, from monarchy to republicanism, from polytheism to monotheism, from monotheism to atheism, from atheism to pantheistic humanitarianism, from general illiteracy to general literacy, from romance to realism, from realism to mysticism, from metaphysics to physics, are all but changes from Tweedledum to Tweedledee: *"plus ça change, plus c'est la même chose."* But the changes from the crab apple to the pippin, from the wolf and fox to the house dog, from the charger of Henry V to the brewer's draft horse and the race-horse, are real; for here Man has played the god, subduing Nature to his intention, and ennobling or debasing Life for a set purpose. And what can be done with a wolf can be done with a man. If such monsters as the tramp and the gentleman can appear as mere by-products of Man's individual greed and folly, what might we not hope for as a main product of his universal aspiration?

This is no new conclusion. The despair of institutions, and the inexorable "ye must be born again," with Mrs. Poyser's stipulation, "and born different," recurs in every generation. The cry for the Superman did not begin with Nietzsche, nor will it end with his vogue. But it has always been silenced by the same question: what kind of person is this Superman to be? You do not ask for a superapple, but for an eatable apple; nor for a superhorse, but for a horse of greater draft or velocity. Neither is it of any use to ask for a Superman: you must furnish a specification of the sort of man you want. Unfortunately you do not know what sort of man you want. Some sort of goodlooking philosopher-athlete, with a handsome healthy woman for his mate, perhaps.

Vague as this is, it is a great advance on the popular demand for a perfect gentleman and a perfect lady. And, after all, no market demand in the world takes the form of exact technical specification of the article required. Excellent poultry and potatoes are produced to satisfy the demand of housewives who do not know the technical differences between a tuber and a chicken. They will tell you that the proof of the pudding is in the eating; and they are right. The proof of the Superman will be in the living; and we shall find out how to produce him by the old method of trial and error, and not by waiting for a completely convincing prescription of his ingredients.

Certain common and obvious mistakes may be ruled out from the beginning.

For example, we agree that we want superior mind; but we need not fall into the football club folly of counting on this as a product of superior body. Yet if we recoil so far as to conclude that superior mind consists in being the dupe of our ethical classifications of virtues and vices, in short, of conventional morality, we shall fall out of the fryingpan of the football club into the fire of the Sunday School. If we must choose between a race of athletes and a race of "good" men, let us have the athletes: better Samson and Milo than Calvin and Robespierre. But neither alternative is worth changing for: Samson is no more a Superman than Calvin. What then are we to do?

II

Property and Marriage

Let us hurry over the obstacles set up by property and marriage. Revolutionists make too much of them. No doubt it is easy to demonstrate that property will destroy society unless society destroys it. No doubt, also, property has hitherto held its own and destroyed all the empires. But that was because the superficial objection to it (that it distributes social wealth and the social labor burden in a grotesquely inequitable manner) did not threaten the existence of the race, but only the individual happiness of its units, and finally the maintenance of some irrelevant political form or other, such as a nation, an empire, or the like. Now as happiness never matters to Nature, as she neither recognizes flags and frontiers nor cares a straw whether the economic system adopted by a society is feudal, capitalistic or collectivist, provided it keeps the race afoot (the hive and the anthill being as acceptable to her as Utopia), the demonstrations of Socialists, though irrefutable, will never make any serious impression on property. The knell of that overrated institution will not sound until it is felt to conflict with some more vital matter than mere personal inequities in industrial economy. No such conflict was perceived while society had not yet grown beyond national communities too small and simple to disastrously overtax Man's limited political capacity. But we have now reached the stage of international organization. Man's political capacity and magnanimity are clearly beaten by the vastness and complexity of the problems forced on him. And it is at this anxious moment that he finds, when he looks upward for a mightier mind to help him, that the heavens are empty. He will presently see that his discarded formula that Man is the Temple of the Holy Ghost happens to be precisely true, and that it is only through his own brain and hand that this Holy Ghost, formerly the most nebulous person in the Trinity, and now become its sole survivor as it has always been its real Unity, can help him in any way. And so, if the Superman is to come, he must be born of Woman by Man's intentional and well-considered contrivance. Conviction of this will smash everything that opposes it. Even Property and Marriage, which laugh at the laborer's petty complaint that he is defrauded of "surplus value," and at the domestic miseries of the slaves of the wedding ring, will themselves be laughed aside as the lightest of trifles if they cross this conception when it becomes a fully realized vital purpose of the race.

That they must cross it becomes obvious the moment we acknowledge the futility of breeding men for special qualities as we breed cocks for game, grayhounds for speed, or sheep for mutton. What is really important in Man is the part of him that we do not yet understand. Of much of it we are not even conscious, just as we are not normally conscious of keeping up our circulation by our heart-pump, though if we neglect it we die. We are therefore driven to the conclusion that when we have carried selection as far as we can by rejecting from the list of eligible parents all persons who are uninteresting, unpromising, or blemished without any set-off, we shall still have to trust to the guidance of fancy (*alias* Voice of Nature), both in the breeders and the parents, for that superiority in the unconscious self which will be the true characteristic of the Superman.

At this point we perceive the importance of giving fancy the widest possible field. To cut humanity up into small cliques, and effectively limit the selection of the individual to his own clique, is to postpone the Superman for eons, if not forever. Not only should every person be nourished and trained as a possible parent, but there also should be no possibility of such an obstacle to natural selection as the objection of a countess to a navvy or of a duke to a charwoman. Equality is essential to good breeding; and equality, as all economists know, is incompatible with property.

Besides, equality is an essential condition of bad breeding also; and bad breeding is indispensable to the weeding out of the human race. When the conception of heredity took hold of the scientific imagination in the middle of last century, its devotees announced that it was a crime to marry the lunatic to the lunatic or the consumptive to the consumptive. But pray are we to try to correct our diseased stocks by infecting our healthy stocks with them? Clearly the attraction which disease has for diseased people is beneficial to the race. If two really unhealthy people get married, they will, as likely as not, have a great number of children who will all die before they reach maturity. This is a far more satisfactory arrangement than the tragedy of a union between a healthy and an unhealthy person. Though more costly than sterilization of the unhealthy, it has the enormous advantage that in the event of our notions of health and unhealth being erroneous (which to some extent they most certainly are), the error will be corrected by experience instead of confirmed by evasion.

One fact must be faced resolutely, in spite of the shrieks of the romantic. There is no evidence that the best citizens are the offspring of congenial marriages, or that a conflict of temperament is not a highly important part of what breeders call crossing. On the contrary, it is quite sufficiently probable that good results may be obtained from parents who would be extremely unsuitable companions and partners, to make it certain that the experiment of mating them will sooner or later be tried purposely almost as often as it is now tried accidentally. But mating such couples must clearly not involve marrying them. In conjugation two complementary persons may supply one another's deficiencies: in the domestic partnership of marriage they only feel them and suffer from them. Thus the son of a robust, cheerful, eupeptic British country squire, with the tastes and range of his class, and of a clever, imaginative, intellectual, highly civilized Jewess, might be very superior to both his parents; but it is not likely that the Jewess would find the squire an interesting companion, or his habits, his friends, his place and mode of life congenial to her. Therefore marriage, while it is made an indispensable condition of mating, will delay the advent of the Superman as effectually as Property, and will be modified by the impulse towards him just as effectually.

The practical abrogation of Property and Marriage as they exist at present will occur without being much noticed. To the mass of men, the intelligent abolition of property would mean nothing except an increase in the quantity of food, clothing, housing and comfort at their personal disposal, as well as a greater control over their time and circumstances. Very few persons now make any distinction between virtually complete property and property held on such highly developed public conditions as to place its income on the same footing as that of a propertyless clergyman, officer, or civil servant. A landed proprietor may still drive men and women off his land, demolish their dwellings, and replace them with sheep or deer; and in the unregulated trades the private trader may still sponge on the regulated trades and sacrifice the life and health of the nation as lawlessly as the Manchester cotton manufacturers did at the beginning of last century. But though the Factory Code on the one hand, and Trade Union organization on the other, have, within the lifetime of men still living, converted the old unrestricted property of the cotton manufacturer in his mill and the cotton spinner in his labor into a mere permission to trade or work on stringent public or collective conditions, imposed in the interest of the general welfare without any regard for individual hard cases, people in Lancashire still speak of their "property" in the old terms, meaning nothing more by it than the things a thief can be punished for stealing. The total abolition of property, and the conversion of every citizen into a salaried functionary in the public service, would leave much more than 99 per cent of the nation quite unconscious of any greater change than now takes place when the son of a shipowner goes into the navy. They would still call their watches and umbrellas and back gardens their property.

Marriage also will persist as a name attached to a general custom long after the custom itself will have altered. For example, modern English marriage, as modified by divorce and by Married Women's Property Acts, differs more from early XIX-century marriage than Byron's marriage did from Shakespear's. At the present moment marriage in England differs not only from marriage in France, but also from marriage in Scotland. Marriage as modified by the divorce laws in South Dakota would be called mere promiscuity in Clapham. Yet the Americans, far from taking a profligate and cynical view of marriage, do homage to its ideals with a seriousness that seems old fashioned in Clapham. Neither in England nor America would a proposal to abolish marriage be tolerated for a moment; and yet nothing is more certain than that in both countries the progressive modification of the marriage contract will be continued until it is no more onerous nor irrevocable than any ordinary commercial deed of partnership. Were even this dispensed with, people would still call themselves husbands and wives; describe their companionships as marriages; and be for the most part unconscious that they were any less married than Henry VIII. For though a glance at the legal conditions of marriage in different Christian countries shows that marriage varies legally from frontier to frontier, domesticity varies so little that most people believe their own marriage laws to be universal. Consequently here again, as in the case of Property, the absolute confidence of the public in the stability of the institution's name, makes it all the easier to alter its substance.

However, it cannot be denied that one of the changes in public opinion demanded by the need for the Superman is a very unexpected one. It is nothing less than the dissolution of the present necessary association of marriage with conjugation, which most unmarried people regard as the very diagnostic of marriage. They are wrong, of course: it would be quite as near the truth to say that conjugation is the one purely accidental and incidental condition of marriage. Conjugation is essential to nothing but the propagation of the race; and the moment that paramount need is provided for otherwise than by marriage, conjugation, from Nature's creative point of view, ceases to be essential in marriage. But marriage does not thereupon cease to be so economical, convenient, and comfortable, that the Superman might safely bribe the matrimonomaniacs by offering to revive all the old inhuman stringency and irrevocability of marriage, to abolish divorce, to confirm the horrible bond which still chains decent people to drunkards, criminals and wasters, provided only the complete extrication of conjugation from it were conceded to him. For if people could form domestic companionships on no easier terms than these, they would still marry. The Roman Catholic, forbidden by his Church to avail himself of the divorce laws, marries as freely as the South Dakotan Presbyterians who can change partners with a facility that scandalizes the old world; and were his Church to dare a further step towards Christianity and enjoin celibacy on its laity as well as on its clergy, marriages would still be contracted for the sake of domesticity by perfectly obedient sons and daughters of the Church. One need not further pursue these hypotheses: they are only suggested here to help the reader to analyze marriage into its two functions of regulating conjugation and supplying a form of domesticity. These two functions are quite separable; and domesticity is the only one of the two which is essential to the existence of marriage, because conjugation without domesticity is not marriage at all, whereas domesticity without conjugation is still marriage: in fact it is necessarily the actual condition of all fertile marriages during a great part of their duration, and of some marriages during the whole of it.

Taking it, then, that Property and Marriage, by destroying Equality and thus hampering sexual selection with irrelevant conditions, are hostile to the evolution of the Superman, it is easy to understand why the only generally known modern experiment in breeding the human race took place in a community which discarded both institutions.

III
The Perfectionist Experiment at Oneida Creek

In 1848 the Oneida Community was founded in America to carry out a resolution arrived at by a handful of Perfectionist Communists "that we will devote ourselves exclusively to the establishment of the Kingdom of God." Though the American nation declared that this sort of thing was not to be tolerated in a Christian country, the Oneida Community held its own for over thirty years, during which period it seems to have produced healthier children and done and suffered less evil than any Joint Stock Company on record. It was, however, a highly selected community; for a genuine Communist (roughly definable as an intensely proud person who proposes to enrich the common fund instead of to sponge on it) is superior to an ordinary joint stock capitalist precisely as an ordinary joint stock capitalist is superior to a pirate. Further, the Perfectionists were mightily shepherded by their chief Noyes, one of those chance attempts at the Superman which occur from time to time in spite of the interference of Man's blundering institutions. The existence of Noyes simplified the breeding problem for the Communists, the question as to what sort of man they should strive to breed being settled at once by the obvious desirability of breeding another Noyes.

But an experiment conducted by a handful of people, who, after thirty years of immunity from the unintentional child slaughter that goes on by ignorant parents in private homes, numbered only 300, could do very little except prove that the Communists, under the guidance of a Superman "devoted exclusively to the establishment of the Kingdom of God," and caring no more for property and marriage than a Camberwell minister cares for Hindoo Caste or Suttee, might make a much better job of their lives than ordinary folk under the harrow of both these institutions. Yet their Superman himself admitted that this apparent success was only part of the abnormal phenomenon of his own occurrence; for when he came to the end of his powers through age, he himself guided and organized the voluntary relapse of the communists into marriage, capitalism, and customary private life, thus admitting that the real social solution was not what a casual Superman could persuade a picked company to do for him, but what a whole community of Supermen would do spontaneously. If Noyes had had to organize, not a few dozen Perfectionists, but the whole United States, America would have beaten him as completely as England beat Oliver Cromwell, France Napoleon, or Rome Julius Cæsar. Cromwell learned by bitter experience that God himself cannot raise a people above its own level, and that even though you stir a nation to sacrifice all its appetites to its conscience, the result will still depend wholly on what sort of conscience the nation has got. Napoleon seems to have ended by regarding mankind as a troublesome pack of hounds only worth keeping for the sport of hunting with them. Cæsar's capacity for fighting without hatred or resentment was defeated by the determination of his soldiers to kill their enemies in the field instead of taking them prisoners to be spared by Cæsar; and his civil supremacy was purchased by colossal bribery of the citizens of Rome. What great rulers cannot do, codes and religions cannot do. Man reads his own nature into every ordinance: if you devise a superhuman commandment so cunningly that it cannot be misinterpreted in terms of his will, he will denounce it as seditious blasphemy, or else disregard it as either crazy or totally unintelligible. Parliaments and synods may tinker as much as they please with their codes and creeds as circumstances alter the balance of classes and their interests; and, as a result of the tinkering, there may be an occasional illusion of moral evolution, as when the victory of the commercial caste over the military caste leads to the substitution of social boycotting and pecuniary damages for dueling. At certain moments there may even be a considerable material advance, as when the conquest of political power by the working class produces a better distribution of wealth through the simple action of the selfishness of the new masters; but all this is mere readjustment and reformation: until the heart and mind of the people is changed the very greatest man will no more dare to govern on the assumption that all are as great as he than a drover dare leave his flock to find its way through the streets as he himself would. Until there is an England in which every man is a Cromwell, a France in which every man is a Napoleon, a Rome in which every man is a Cæsar, a Germany in which every man is a Luther plus a Goethe, the world will be no more improved by its heroes than a Brixton villa is improved by the pyramid of Cheops. The production of such nations is the only real change possible to us.

IV

Man's Objection to His Own Improvement

But would such a change be tolerated if Man must rise above himself to desire it? It would, through his misconception of its nature. Man does desire an ideal Superman with such energy as he can spare from his nutrition, and has in every age magnified the best living substitute for it he can find. His least incompetent general is set up as an Alexander; his king is the first gentleman in the world; his Pope is a saint. He is never without an array of human idols who are all nothing but sham Supermen. That the real Superman will snap his superfingers at all Man's present trumpery ideals of right, duty, honor, justice, religion, even decency, and accept moral obligations beyond present human endurance, is a thing that contemporary Man does not foresee: in fact he does not notice it when our casual Supermen do it in his very face. He actually does it himself every day without knowing it. He will therefore make no objection to the production of a race of what he calls Great Men or Heroes, because he will imagine them, not as true Supermen, but as himself endowed with infinite brains, infinite courage, and infinite money.

The most troublesome opposition will arise from the general fear of mankind that any interference with our conjugal customs will be interference with our pleasure and our romance. This fear, by putting on airs of offended morality, has always intimidated people who have not measured its essential weakness; but it will prevail with those degenerates only in whom the instinct of fertility has faded into a mere itching for pleasure. The modern devices for combining pleasure with sterility, now universally known and accessible, enable these persons to weed themselves out of the race, a process already vigorously at work; and the consequent survival of the intelligently fertile means the survival of the partisans of the Superman; for what is proposed is nothing but the replacement of the old unintelligent, inevitable, almost unconscious fertility by an intelligently controlled, conscious fertility, and the elimination of the mere voluptuary from the evolutionary process.[1] Even if this selective agency had not been invented, the purpose of the race would still shatter the opposition of individual instincts. Not only do the bees and the ants satisfy their reproductive and parental instincts vicariously; but marriage itself successfully imposes celibacy on millions of unmarried normal men and women. In short, the individual instinct in this matter, overwhelming as it is thoughtlessly supposed to be, is really a finally negligible one.

[1] The part played in evolution by the voluptuary will be the same as that already played by the glutton. The glutton, as the man with the strongest motive for nourishing himself, will always take more pains than his fellows to get food. When food is so difficult to get that only great exertions can secure a sufficient supply of it, the glutton's appetite develops his cunning and enterprise to the utmost; and he becomes not only the best fed but also the ablest man in the community. But in more hospitable climates, or where the social organization of the food supply makes it easy for a man to overeat, then the glutton eats himself out of health and finally out of existence. All other voluptuaries prosper and perish in the same way; and this is why the survival of the fittest means finally the survival of the self-controlled, because they alone can adapt themselves to the perpetual shifting of conditions produced by industrial progress.

V

The Political Need for the Superman

The need for the Superman is, in its most imperative aspect, a political one. We have been driven to Proletarian Democracy by the failure of all the alternative systems; for these depended on the existence of Supermen acting as despots or oligarchs; and not only were these Supermen not always or even often forthcoming at the right moment and in an eligible social position, but when they were forthcoming they could not, except for a short time and by morally suicidal coercive methods, impose superhumanity on those whom they governed; so, by mere force of "human nature," government by consent of the governed has supplanted the old plan of governing the citizen as a public-schoolboy is governed.

Now, we have yet to see the man who, having any practical experience of Proletarian Democracy, has any belief in its capacity for solving great political problems, or even for doing ordinary parochial work intelligently and economically. Only under despotisms and oligarchies has the Radical faith in "universal suffrage" as a political panacea arisen. It withers the moment it is exposed to practical trial, because Democracy cannot rise above the level of the human material of which its voters are made. Switzerland seems happy in comparison with Russia; but if Russia were as small as Switzerland, and had her social problems simplified in the same way by impregnable natural fortifications and a population educated by the same variety and intimacy of international intercourse, there might be little to choose between them. At all events Australia and Canada, which are virtually protected democratic republics, and France and the United States, which are avowedly independent democratic republics, are neither healthy, wealthy nor wise; and they would be worse instead of better if their popular ministers were not experts in the art of dodging popular enthusiasms and duping popular ignorance. The politician who once had to learn how to flatter Kings has now to learn how to fascinate, amuse, coax, humbug, frighten or otherwise strike the fancy of the electorate; and though in advanced modern States, where the artisan is better educated than the King, it takes a much bigger man to be a successful demagogue than to be a successful courtier, yet he who holds popular convictions with prodigious energy is the man for the mob, while the frailer skeptic who is cautiously feeling his way towards the next century has no chance unless he happens by accident to have the specific artistic talent of the mountebank as well, in which case it is as a mountebank that he catches votes, and not as a meliorist. Consequently the demagogue, though he professes (and fails) to readjust matters in the interests of the majority of the electors, yet stereotypes mediocrity, organizes intolerance, disparages exhibitions of uncommon qualities, and glorifies conspicuous exhibitions of common ones. He manages a small job well: he muddles rhetorically through a large one. When a great political movement takes place, it is not consciously led nor organized: the unconscious self in mankind breaks its way through the problem as an elephant breaks through a jungle; and the politicians make speeches about whatever happens in the process, which, with the best intentions, they do all in their power to prevent. Finally, when social aggregation arrives at a point demanding international organization before the demagogues and electorates have learned how to manage even a country parish properly much less internationalize Constantinople, the whole political business goes to smash; and presently we have Ruins of Empires, New Zealanders sitting on a broken arch of London Bridge, and so forth.

To that recurrent catastrophe we shall certainly come again unless we have a Democracy of Supermen; and the production of such a Democracy is the only change that is now hopeful enough to nerve us to the effort that Revolution demands.

VI

Prudery Explained

Why the bees should pamper their mothers while we pamper only our operatic prima donnas is a question worth reflecting on. Our notion of treating a mother is, not to increase her supply of food, but to cut it off by forbidding her to work in a factory for a month after her confinement. Everything that can make birth a misfortune to the parents as well as a danger to the mother is conscientiously done. When a great French writer, Emile Zola, alarmed at the sterilization of his nation, wrote an eloquent and powerful book to restore the prestige of parentage, it was at once assumed in England that a work of this character, with such a title as Fecundity, was too abominable to be translated, and that any attempt to deal with the relations of the sexes from any other than the voluptuary or romantic point of view must be sternly put down. Now if this assumption were really founded on public opinion, it would indicate an attitude of disgust and resentment towards the Life Force that could only arise in a diseased and moribund community in which Ibsen's Hedda Gabler would be the typical woman. But it has no vital foundation at all. The prudery of the newspapers is, like the prudery of the dinner table, a mere difficulty of education and language. We are not taught to think decently on these subjects, and consequently we have no language for them except indecent language. We therefore have to declare them unfit for public discussion, because the only terms in which we can conduct the discussions are unfit for public use. Physiologists, who have a technical vocabulary at their disposal, find no difficulty; and masters of language who think decently can write popular stories like Zola's Fecundity or Tolstoy's Resurrection without giving the smallest offense to readers who can also think decently. But the ordinary modern journalist, who has never discussed such matters except in ribaldry, cannot write a simple comment on a divorce case without a conscious shamefulness or a furtive facetiousness that makes it impossible to read the comment aloud in company. All this ribaldry and prudery (the two are the same) does not mean that people do not feel decently on the subject: on the contrary, it is just the depth and seriousness of our feeling that makes its desecration by vile language and coarse humor intolerable; so that at last we cannot bear to have it spoken of at all because only one in a thousand can speak of it without wounding our self-respect, especially the self-respect of women. Add to the horrors of popular language the horrors of popular poverty. In crowded populations poverty destroys the possibility of cleanliness; and in the absence of cleanliness many of the natural conditions of life become offensive and noxious, with the result that at last the association of uncleanliness with these natural conditions becomes so overpowering that among civilized people (that is, people massed in the labyrinths of slums we call cities), half their bodily life becomes a guilty secret, unmentionable except to the doctor in emergencies; and Hedda Gabler shoots herself because maternity is so unladylike. In short, popular prudery is only a mere incident of popular squalor: the subjects which it taboos remain the most interesting and earnest of subjects in spite of it.

VII
Progress an Illusion

Unfortunately the earnest people get drawn off the track of evolution by the illusion of progress. Any Socialist can convince us easily that the difference between Man as he is and Man as he might become, without further evolution, under millennial conditions of nutrition, environment, and training, is enormous. He can show that inequality and iniquitous distribution of wealth and allotment of labor have arisen through an unscientific economic system, and that Man, faulty as he is, no more intended to establish any such ordered disorder than a moth intends to be burned when it flies into a candle flame. He can show that the difference between the grace and strength of the acrobat and the bent back of the rheumatic field laborer is a difference produced by conditions, not by nature. He can show that many of the most detestable human vices are not radical, but are mere reactions of our institutions on our very virtues. The Anarchist, the Fabian, the Salvationist, the Vegetarian, the doctor, the lawyer, the parson, the professor of ethics, the gymnast, the soldier, the sportsman, the inventor, the political program-maker, all have some prescription for bettering us; and almost all their remedies are physically possible and aimed at admitted evils. To them the limit of progress is, at worst, the completion of all the suggested reforms and the leveling up of all men to the point attained already by the most highly nourished and cultivated in mind and body.

Here, then, as it seems to them, is an enormous field for the energy of the reformer. Here are many noble goals attainable for many of those paths up the Hill Difficulty along which great spirits love to aspire. Unhappily, the hill will never be climbed by Man as we know him. It need not be denied that if we all struggled bravely to the end of the reformer's paths we should improve the world prodigiously. But there is no more hope in that If than in the equally plausible assurance that if the sky falls we shall all catch larks. We are not going to tread those paths: we have not sufficient energy. We do not desire the end enough: indeed in most cases we do not effectively desire it at all. Ask any man would he like to be a better man; and he will say yes, most piously. Ask him would he like to have a million of money; and he will say yes, most sincerely. But the pious citizen who would like to be a better man goes on behaving just as he did before. And the tramp who would like the million does not take the trouble to earn ten shillings: multitudes of men and women, all eager to accept a legacy of a million, live and die without having ever possessed five pounds at one time, although beggars have died in rags on mattresses stuffed with gold which they accumulated because they desired it enough to nerve them to get it and keep it. The economists who discovered that demand created supply soon had to limit the proposition to "effective demand," which turned out, in the final analysis, to mean nothing more than supply itself; and this holds good in politics, morals, and all other departments as well: the actual supply is the measure of the effective demand; and the mere aspirations and professions produce nothing. No community has ever yet passed beyond the initial phases in which its pugnacity and fanaticism enabled it to found a nation, and its cupidity to establish and develop a commercial civilization. Even these stages have never been attained by public spirit, but always by intolerant willfulness and brute force. Take the Reform Bill of 1832 as an example of a conflict between two sections of educated Englishmen concerning a political measure which was as obviously necessary and inevitable as any political measure has ever been or is ever likely to be. It was not passed until the gentlemen of Birmingham had made arrangements to cut the throats of the gentlemen of St. James's parish in due military form. It would not have been passed to this day if there had been no force behind it except the logic and public conscience of the Utilitarians. A despotic ruler with as much sense as Queen Elizabeth would have done better than the mob of grown-up Eton boys who governed us then by privilege, and who, since the introduction of practically Manhood Suffrage in 1884, now govern us at the request of proletarian Democracy.

At the present time we have, instead of the Utilitarians, the Fabian Society, with its peaceful, constitutional, moral, economical policy of Socialism, which needs nothing for its bloodless and benevolent realization except that the English people shall understand it and approve of it. But why are the Fabians well spoken of in circles where thirty years ago the word Socialist was understood as equivalent to cut-throat and incendiary? Not because the English have the smallest intention of studying or adopting the Fabian policy, but because they believe that the Fabians, by eliminating the element of intimidation from the Socialist agitation, have drawn the teeth of insurgent poverty and saved the existing order from the only method of attack it really fears. Of course, if the nation adopted the Fabian policy, it would be carried out by brute force exactly as our present property system is. It would become the law; and those who resisted it would be fined, sold up, knocked on the head by policemen, thrown into prison, and in the last resort "executed" just as they are when they break the present law. But as our proprietary class has no fear of that conversion taking place, whereas it does fear sporadic cut-throats and gunpowder plots, and strives with all its might to hide the fact that there is no moral difference whatever between the methods by which it enforces its proprietary rights and the method by which the dynamitard asserts his conception of natural human rights, the Fabian Society is patted on the back just as the Christian Social Union is, while the Socialist who says bluntly that a Social revolution can be made only as all other revolutions have been made, by the people who want it killing, coercing and intimidating the people who don't want it, is denounced as a misleader of the people, and imprisoned with hard labor to show him how much sincerity there is in the objection of his captors to physical force.

Are we then to repudiate Fabian methods, and return to those of the barricader, or adopt those of the dynamitard and the assassin? On the contrary, we are to recognize that both are fundamentally futile. It seems easy for the dynamitard to say "Have you not just admitted that nothing is ever conceded except to physical force? Did not Gladstone admit that the Irish Church was disestablished, not by the spirit of Liberalism, but by the explosion which wrecked Clerkenwell prison?" Well, we need not foolishly and timidly deny it. Let it be fully granted. Let us grant, further, that all this lies in the nature of things; that the most ardent Socialist, if he owns property, can by no means do otherwise than Conservative proprietors until property is forcibly abolished by the whole nation; nay, that ballots and parliamentary divisions, in spite of their vain ceremony of discussion, differ from battles only as the bloodless surrender of an outnumbered force in the field differs from Waterloo or Trafalgar. I make a present of all these admissions to the Fenian who collects money from thoughtless Irishmen in America to blow up Dublin Castle; to the detective who persuades foolish young workmen to order bombs from the nearest ironmonger and then delivers them up to penal servitude; to our military and naval commanders who believe, not in preaching, but in an ultimatum backed by plenty of lyddite; and, generally, to all whom it may concern. But of what use is it to substitute the will of reckless and bloodyminded Progressives for cautious and humane ones? Is England any the better for the wreck of Clerkenwell prison, or Ireland for the disestablishment of the Irish Church? Is there the smallest reason to suppose that the nation which sheepishly let Charles and Laud and Strafford coerce it, gained anything because it afterwards, still more sheepishly, let a few strongminded Puritans, inflamed by the masterpieces of Jewish revolutionary literature, cut off the heads of the three? Suppose the Gunpowder plot had succeeded, and a Fawkes dynasty were at present on the throne, would it have made any difference to the present state of the nation? The guillotine was used in France up to the limit of human endurance, both on Girondins and Jacobins. Fouquier Tinville followed Marie Antoinette to the scaffold; and Marie Antoinette might have asked the crowd, just as pointedly as Fouquier did, whether their bread would be any cheaper when her head was off. And what came of it all? The Imperial France of the Rougon Macquart family, and the Republican France of the Panama scandal and the Dreyfus case. Was the difference worth the guillotining of all those unlucky ladies and gentlemen, useless and mischievous as many of them were? Would any sane man guillotine a mouse to bring about such a result? Turn to Republican America. America has no Star Chamber, and no feudal barons. But it has Trusts; and it has millionaires whose factories, fenced in by live electric wires and defended by Pinkerton retainers with magazine rifles, would have made a Radical of Reginald Front de Boeuf. Would Washington or Franklin have lifted a finger in the cause of American Independence if they had foreseen its reality?

No: what Cæsar, Cromwell and Napoleon could not do with all the physical force and moral prestige of the State in their mighty hands, cannot be done by enthusiastic criminals and lunatics. Even the Jews, who, from Moses to Marx and Lassalle, have inspired all the revolutions, have had to confess that, after all, the dog will return to his vomit and the sow that was washed to her wallowing in the mire; and we may as well make up our minds that Man will return to his idols and his cupidities, in spite of all "movements" and all revolutions, until his nature is changed. Until then, his early successes in building commercial civilizations (and such civilizations, Good Heavens!) are but preliminaries to the inevitable later stage, now threatening us, in which the passions which built the civilization become fatal instead of productive, just as the same qualities which make the lion king in the forest insure his destruction when he enters a city. Nothing can save society then except the clear head and the wide purpose: war and competition, potent instruments of selection and evolution in one epoch, become ruinous instruments of degeneration in the next. In the breeding of animals and plants, varieties which have arisen by selection through many generations relapse precipitously into the wild type in a generation or two when selection ceases; and in the same way a civilization in which lusty pugnacity and greed have ceased to act as selective agents and have begun to obstruct and destroy, rushes downwards and backwards with a suddenness that enables an observer to see with consternation the upward steps of many centuries retraced in a single lifetime. This has often occurred even within the period covered by history; and in every instance the turning point has been reached long before the attainment, or even the general advocacy on paper, of the leveling-up of the mass to the highest point attainable by the best nourished and cultivated normal individuals.

We must therefore frankly give up the notion that Man as he exists is capable of net progress. There will always be an illusion of progress, because wherever we are conscious of an evil we remedy it, and therefore always seem to ourselves to be progressing, forgetting that most of the evils we see are the effects, finally become acute, of long-unnoticed retrogressions; that our compromising remedies seldom fully recover the lost ground; above all, that on the lines along which we are degenerating, good has become evil in our eyes, and is being undone in the name of progress precisely as evil is undone and replaced by good on the lines along which we are evolving. This is indeed the Illusion of Illusions; for it gives us infallible and appalling assurance that if our political ruin is to come, it will be effected by ardent reformers and supported by enthusiastic patriots as a series of necessary steps in our progress. Let the Reformer, the Progressive, the Meliorist then reconsider himself and his eternal ifs and ans which never become pots and pans. While Man remains what he is, there can be no progress beyond the point already attained and fallen headlong from at every attempt at civilization; and since even that point is but a pinnacle to which a few people cling in giddy terror above an abyss of squalor, mere progress should no longer charm us.

VIII

The Conceit of Civilization

After all, the progress illusion is not so very subtle. We begin by reading the satires of our fathers' contemporaries; and we conclude (usually quite ignorantly) that the abuses exposed by them are things of the past. We see also that reforms of crying evils are frequently produced by the sectional shifting of political power from oppressors to oppressed. The poor man is given a vote by the Liberals in the hope that he will cast it for his emancipators. The hope is not fulfilled; but the lifelong imprisonment of penniless men for debt ceases; Factory Acts are passed to mitigate sweating; schooling is made free and compulsory; sanitary by-laws are multiplied; public steps are taken to house the masses decently; the bare-footed get boots; rags become rare; and bathrooms and pianos, smart tweeds and starched collars, reach numbers of people who once, as "the unsoaped," played the Jew's harp or the accordion in moleskins and belchers. Some of these changes are gains: some of them are losses. Some of them are not changes at all: all of them are merely the changes that money makes. Still, they produce an illusion of bustling progress; and the reading class infers from them that the abuses of the early Victorian period no longer exist except as amusing pages in the novels of Dickens. But the moment we look for a reform due to character and not to money, to statesmanship and not to interest or mutiny, we are disillusioned. For example, we remembered the maladministration and incompetence revealed by the Crimean War as part of a bygone state of things until the South African War showed that the nation and the War Office, like those poor Bourbons who have been so impudently blamed for a universal characteristic, had learned nothing and forgotten nothing. We had hardly recovered from the fruitless irritation of this discovery when it transpired that the officers' mess of our most select regiment included a flogging club presided over by the senior subaltern. The disclosure provoked some disgust at the details of this schoolboyish debauchery, but no surprise at the apparent absence of any conception of manly honor and virtue, of personal courage and self-respect, in the front rank of our chivalry. In civil affairs we had assumed that the sycophancy and idolatry which encouraged Charles I to undervalue the Puritan revolt of the XVII century had been long outgrown; but it has needed nothing but favorable circumstances to revive, with added abjectness to compensate for its lost piety. We have relapsed into disputes about transubstantiation at the very moment when the discovery of the wide prevalence of theophagy as a tribal custom has deprived us of the last excuse for believing that our official religious rites differ in essentials from those of barbarians. The Christian doctrine of the uselessness of punishment and the wickedness of revenge has not, in spite of its simple common sense, found a single convert among the nations: Christianity means nothing to the masses but a sensational public execution which is made an excuse for other executions. In its name we take ten years of a thief's life minute by minute in the slow misery and degradation of modern reformed imprisonment with as little remorse as Laud and his Star Chamber clipped the ears of Bastwick and Burton. We dug up and mutilated the remains of the Mahdi the other day exactly as we dug up and mutilated the remains of Cromwell two centuries ago. We have demanded the decapitation of the Chinese Boxer princes as any Tartar would have done; and our military and naval expeditions to kill, burn, and destroy tribes and villages for knocking an Englishman on the head are so common a part of our Imperial routine that the last dozen of them has not elicited as much sympathy as can be counted on by any lady criminal. The judicial use of torture to extort confession is supposed to be a relic of darker ages; but while these pages are being written an English judge has sentenced a forger to twenty years penal servitude with an open declaration that the sentence will be carried out in full unless he confesses where he has hidden the notes he forged. And no comment whatever is made either on this or on a telegram from the seat of war in Somaliland mentioning that certain information has been given by a prisoner of war "under punishment." Even if these reports were false, the fact that they are accepted without protest as indicating a natural and proper course of public conduct shows that we are still as ready to resort to torture as Bacon was. As to vindictive cruelty, an incident in the South African War, when the relatives and friends of a prisoner were forced to witness his execution, betrayed a baseness of temper and character which hardly leaves us the right to plume ourselves on our superiority to Edward III at the surrender of Calais. And the democratic American officer indulges in torture in the Philippines just as the aristocratic English officer did in South Africa. The incidents of the white invasion of Africa in search of ivory, gold, diamonds and sport, have proved that the modern European is the same beast of prey that formerly marched to the conquest of new worlds under Alexander, Antony, and Pizarro. Parliaments and vestries are just what they were when Cromwell suppressed them and Dickens ridiculed them. The democratic politician remains exactly as Plato described him; the physician is still the credulous impostor and petulant scientific coxcomb whom Molière ridiculed; the schoolmaster remains at best a pedantic child farmer and at worst a flagellomaniac; arbitrations are more dreaded by honest men than lawsuits; the philanthropist is still a parasite on misery as the doctor is on disease; the miracles of priestcraft are none the less fraudulent and mischievous because they are now called scientific experiments and conducted by professors; witchcraft, in the modern form of patent medicines and prophylactic inoculations, is rampant; the landowner who is no longer powerful enough to set the mantrap of Rhampsinitis improves on it by barbed wire; the modern gentleman who is too lazy to daub his face with vermilion as a symbol of bravery employs a laundress to daub his shirt with starch as a symbol of cleanliness; we shake our heads at the dirt of the middle ages in cities made grimy with soot and foul and disgusting with shameless tobacco smoking; holy water, in its latest form of disinfectant fluid, is more widely used and believed in than ever; public health authorities deliberately go through incantations with burning sulphur (which they know to be useless) because the people believe in it as devoutly as the Italian peasant believes in the liquefaction of the blood of St. Januarius; and straightforward public lying has reached gigantic developments, there being nothing to choose in this respect between the pickpocket at the police station and the minister on the treasury bench, the editor in the newspaper office, the city magnate advertising bicycle tires that do not side-slip, the clergyman subscribing the thirty-nine articles, and the vivisector who pledges his knightly honor that no animal operated on in the physiological laboratory suffers the slightest pain. Hypocrisy is at its worst; for we not only persecute bigotedly but sincerely in the name of the cure-mongering witchcraft we do believe in, but also callously and hypocritically in the name of the Evangelical creed that our rulers privately smile at as the Italian patricians of the fifth century smiled at Jupiter and Venus. Sport is, as it has always been, murderous excitement: the impulse to slaughter is universal; and museums are set up throughout the country to encourage little children and elderly gentlemen to make collections of corpses preserved in alcohol, and to steal birds' eggs and keep them as the red Indian used to keep scalps. Coercion with the lash is as natural to an Englishman as it was to Solomon spoiling Rehoboam; indeed, the comparison is unfair to the Jews in view of the facts that the Mosaic law forbade more than forty lashes in the name of humanity, and that floggings of a thousand lashes were inflicted on English soldiers in the XVIII and XIX centuries, and would be inflicted still but for the change in the balance of political power between the military caste and the commercial classes and the proletariat. In spite of that change, flogging is still an institution in the public school, in the military prison, on the training ship, and in that school of littleness called the home. The lascivious clamor of the flagellomaniac for more of it, constant as the clamor for more insolence, more war, and lower rates, is tolerated and even gratified because, having no moral ends in view, we have sense enough to see that nothing but brute coercion can impose our selfish will on others. Cowardice is universal: patriotism, public opinion, parental duty, discipline, religion, morality, are only fine names for intimidation;

and cruelty, gluttony, and credulity keep cowardice in countenance. We cut the throat of a calf and hang it up by the heels to bleed to death so that our veal cutlet may be white; we nail geese to a board and cram them with food because we like the taste of liver disease; we tear birds to pieces to decorate our women's hats; we mutilate domestic animals for no reason at all except to follow an instinctively cruel fashion; and we connive at the most abominable tortures in the hope of discovering some magical cure for our own diseases by them.

Now please observe that these are not exceptional developments of our admitted vices, deplored and prayed against by all good men. Not a word has been said here of the excesses of our Neros, of whom we have the full usual percentage. With the exception of the few military examples, which are mentioned mainly to show that the education and standing of a gentleman, reinforced by the strongest conventions of honor, *esprit de corps,* publicity and responsibility, afford no better guarantees of conduct than the passions of a mob, the illustrations given above are commonplaces taken from the daily practices of our best citizens, vehemently defended in our newspapers and in our pulpits. The very humanitarians who abhor them are stirred to murder by them: the dagger of Brutus and Ravaillac is still active in the hands of Caserio and Luccheni; and the pistol has come to its aid in the hands of Guiteau and Czolgosz. Our remedies are still limited to endurance or assassination; and the assassin is still judicially assassinated on the principle that two blacks make a white. The only novelty is in our methods: through the discovery of dynamite the overloaded musket of Hamilton of Bothwellhaugh has been superseded by the bomb; but Ravachol's heart burns just as Hamilton's did. The world will not bear thinking of those who know what it is, even with the largest discount for the restraints of poverty on the poor and cowardice on the rich.

All that can be said for us is that people must and do live and let live up to a certain point. Even the horse, with his docked tail and bitted jaw, finds his slavery mitigated by the fact that a total disregard of his need for food and rest would put his master to the expense of buying a new horse every second day; for you cannot work a horse to death and then pick up another one for nothing, as you can a laborer. But this natural check on inconsiderate selfishness is itself checked, partly by our shortsightedness, and partly by deliberate calculation; so that beside the man who, to his own loss, will shorten his horse's life in mere stinginess, we have the tramway company which discovers actuarially that though a horse may live from 24 to 40 years, yet it pays better to work him to death in 4 and then replace him by a fresh victim. And human slavery, which has reached its worst recorded point within our own time in the form of free wage labor, has encountered the same personal and commercial limits to both its aggravation and its mitigation. Now that the freedom of wage labor has produced a scarcity of it, as in South Africa, the leading English newspaper and the leading English weekly review have openly and without apology demanded a return to compulsory labor: that is, to the methods by which, as we believe, the Egyptians built the pyramids. We know now that the crusade against chattel slavery in the XIX century succeeded solely because chattel slavery was neither the most effective nor the least humane method of labor exploitation; and the world is now feeling its way towards a still more effective system which shall abolish the freedom of the worker without again making his exploiter responsible for him as a chattel.

Still, there is always some mitigation: there is the fear of revolt; and there are the effects of kindliness and affection. Let it be repeated therefore that no indictment is here laid against the world on the score of what its criminals and monsters do. The fires of Smithfield and of the Inquisition were lighted by earnestly pious people, who were kind and good as kindness and goodness go. And when a Negro is dipped in kerosene and set on fire in America at the present time, he is not a good man lynched by ruffians: he is a criminal lynched by crowds of respectable, charitable, virtuously indignant, high-minded citizens, who, though they act outside the law, are at least more merciful than the American legislators and judges who not so long ago condemned men to solitary confinement for periods, not of five months, as our own practice is, but of five years and more. The things that our moral monsters do may be left out of account with St. Bartholomew massacres and other momentary outbursts of social disorder. Judge us by the admitted and respected practice of our most reputable circles; and, if you know the facts and are strong enough to look them in the face, you must admit that unless we are replaced by a more highly evolved animal—in short, by the Superman—the world must remain a den of dangerous animals among whom our few accidental supermen, our Shakespeares, Goethes, Shelleys and their like, must live as precariously as lion tamers do, taking the humor of their situation, and the dignity of their superiority, as a set-off to the horror of the one and the loneliness of the other.

IX

The Verdict of History

It may be said that though the wild beast breaks out in Man and casts him back momentarily into barbarism under the excitement of war and crime, yet his normal life is higher than the normal life of his forefathers. This view is very acceptable to Englishmen, who always lean sincerely to virtue's side as long as it costs them nothing either in money or in thought. They feel deeply the injustice of foreigners, who allow them no credit for this conditional highmindedness. But there is no reason to suppose that our ancestors were less capable of it than we are. To all such claims for the existence of a progressive moral evolution operating visibly from grandfather to grandson, there is the conclusive reply that a thousand years of such evolution would have produced enormous social changes, of which the historical evidence would be overwhelming. But not Macaulay himself, the most confident of Whig meliorists, can produce any such evidence that will bear cross-examination. Compare our conduct and our codes with those mentioned contemporarily in such ancient scriptures and classics as have come down to us, and you will find no jot of ground for the belief that any moral progress whatever has been made in historic time, in spite of all the romantic attempts of historians to reconstruct the past on that assumption. Within that time it has happened to nations as to private families and individuals that they have flourished and decayed, repented and hardened their hearts, submitted and protested, acted and reacted, oscillated between natural and artificial sanitation (the oldest house in the world, unearthed the other day in Crete, has quite modern sanitary arrangements), and rung a thousand changes on the different scales of income and pressure of population, firmly believing all the time that mankind was advancing by leaps and bounds because men were constantly busy. And the mere chapter of accidents has left a small accumulation of chance discoveries, such as the wheel, the arch, the safety pin, gunpowder, the magnet, the Voltaic pile and so forth: things which, unlike the gospels and philosophic treatises of the ages, can be usefully understood and applied by common men; so that steam locomotion is possible without a nation of Stephensons, although national Christianity is impossible without a nation of Christs. But does any man seriously believe that the *chauffeur* who drives a motor car from Paris to Berlin is a more highly evolved man than the charioteer of Achilles, or that a modern Prime Minister is a more enlightened ruler than Cæsar because he rides a tricycle, writes his dispatches by the electric light, and instructs his stockbroker through the telephone?

Enough, then, of this goose-cackle about Progress: Man, as he is, never will nor can add a cubit to his stature by any of its quackeries, political, scientific, educational, religious, or artistic. What is likely to happen when this conviction gets into the minds of the men whose present faith in these illusions is the cement of our social system, can be imagined only by those who know how suddenly a civilization which has long ceased to think (or in the old phrase, to watch and pray) can fall to pieces when the vulgar belief in its hypocrisies and impostures can no longer hold out against its failures and scandals. When religious and ethical formulæ become so obsolete that no man of strong mind can believe them, they have also reached the point at which no man of high character will profess them; and from that moment until they are formally disestablished, they stand at the door of every profession and every public office to keep out every able man who is not a sophist or a liar. A nation which revises its parish councils once in three years, but will not revise its articles of religion once in three hundred, even when those articles avowedly began as a political compromise dictated by Mr. Facing-Both-Ways, is a nation that needs remaking.

Our only hope, then, is in evolution. We must replace the Man by the Superman. It is frightful for the citizen, as the years pass him, to see his own contemporaries so exactly reproduced by the younger generation, that his companions of thirty years ago have their counterparts in every city crowd; so that he has to check himself repeatedly in the act of saluting as an old friend some young man to whom he is only an elderly stranger. All hope of advance dies in his bosom as he watches them: he knows that they will do just what their fathers did, and that the few voices which will still, as always before, exhort them to do something else and be something better, might as well spare their breath to cool their porridge (if they can get any). Men like Ruskin and Carlyle will preach to Smith and Brown for the sake of preaching, just as St. Francis preached to the birds and St. Anthony to the fishes. But Smith and Brown, like the fishes and birds, remain as they are; and poets who plan Utopias and prove that nothing is necessary for their realization but that Man should will them, perceive at last, like Richard Wagner, that the fact to be faced is that Man does not effectively will them. And he never will until he becomes Superman.

And so we arrive at the end of the Socialist's dream of "the socialization of the means of production and exchange," of the Positivist's dream of moralizing the capitalist, and of the ethical professor's, legislator's, educator's dream of putting commandments and codes and lessons and examination marks on a man as harness is put on a horse, ermine on a judge, pipeclay on a soldier, or a wig on an actor, and pretending that his nature has been changed. The only fundamental and possible Socialism is the socialization of the selective breeding of Man: in other terms, of human evolution. We must eliminate the Yahoo, or his vote will wreck the commonwealth.

X
The Method

As to the method, what can be said as yet except that where there is a will, there is a way? If there be no will, we are lost. That is a possibility for our crazy little empire, if not for the universe; and as such possibilities are not to be entertained without despair, we must, while we survive, proceed on the assumption that we have still energy enough to not only will to live, but to will to live better. That may mean that we must establish a State Department of Evolution, with a seat in the Cabinet for its chief, and a revenue to defray the cost of direct State experiments and provide inducements to private persons to achieve successful results. It may mean a private society or a chartered company for the improvement of human live stock. But for the present it is far more likely to mean a blatant repudiation of such proposals as indecent and immoral, with, nevertheless, a general secret pushing of the human will in the repudiated direction; so that all sorts of institutions and public authorities will under some pretext or other feel their way furtively towards the Superman. Mr. Graham Wallas has already ventured to suggest, as Chairman of the School Management Committee of the London School Board, that the accepted policy of the Sterilization of the Schoolmistress, however administratively convenient, is open to criticism from the national stock-breeding point of view; and this is as good an example as any of the way in which the drift towards the Superman may operate in spite of all our hypocrisies. One thing at least is clear to begin with. If a woman can, by careful selection of a father, and nourishment of herself, produce a citizen with efficient senses, sound organs and a good digestion, she should clearly be secured a sufficient reward for that natural service to make her willing to undertake and repeat it. Whether she be financed in the undertaking by herself, or by the father, or by a speculative capitalist, or by a new department of, say, the Royal Dublin Society, or (as a present) by the War Office maintaining her "on the strength" and authorizing a particular soldier to marry her, or by a local authority under a by-law directing that women may under certain circumstances have a year's leave of absence on full salary, or by the central government, does not matter provided the result be satisfactory.

It is a melancholy fact that as the vast majority of women and their husbands have, under existing circumstances, not enough nourishment, no capital, no credit, and no knowledge of science or business, they would, if the State would pay for birth as it now pays for death, be exploited by joint stock companies for dividends, just as they are in ordinary industries. Even a joint stock human stud farm (piously disguised as a reformed Foundling Hospital or something of that sort) might well, under proper inspection and regulation, produce better results than our present reliance on promiscuous marriage. It may be objected that when an ordinary contractor produces stores for sale to the Government, and the Government rejects them as not up to the required standard, the condemned goods are either sold for what they will fetch or else scrapped: that is, treated as waste material; whereas if the goods consisted of human beings, all that could be done would be to let them loose or send them to the nearest workhouse. But there is nothing new in private enterprise throwing its human refuse on the cheap labor market and the workhouse; and the refuse of the new industry would presumably be better bred than the staple product of ordinary poverty. In our present happy-go-lucky industrial disorder, all the human products, successful or not, would have to be thrown on the labor market; but the unsuccessful ones would not entitle the company to a bounty and so would be a dead loss to it. The practical commercial difficulty would be the uncertainty and the cost in time and money of the first experiments. Purely commercial capital would not touch such heroic operations during the experimental stage; and in any case the strength of mind needed for so momentous a new departure could not be fairly expected from the Stock Exchange. It will have to be handled by statesmen with character enough to tell our democracy and plutocracy that statecraft does not consist in flattering their follies or applying their suburban standards of propriety to the affairs of four continents. The matter must be taken up either by the State or by some organization strong enough to impose respect upon the State.

The novelty of any such experiment, however, is only in the scale of it. In one conspicuous case, that of royalty, the State does already select the parents on purely political grounds; and in the peerage, though the heir to a dukedom is legally free to marry a dairymaid, yet the social pressure on him to confine his choice to politically and socially eligible mates is so overwhelming that he is really no more free to marry the dairymaid than George IV was to marry Mrs. Fitzherbert; and such a marriage could only occur as a result of extraordinary strength of character on the part of the duke. Let those who think the whole conception of intelligent breeding absurd and scandalous ask themselves why George IV was not allowed to choose his own wife while any tinker could marry whom he pleased? Simply because it did not matter a rap politically whom the tinker married, whereas it mattered very much whom the king married. The way in which all considerations of the king's personal rights, of the claims of the heart, of the sanctity of the marriage oath, and of romantic morality crumpled up before this political need shows how negligible all these apparently irresistible prejudices are when they come into conflict with the demand for quality in our rulers. We learn the same lesson from the case of the soldier, whose marriage, when it is permitted at all, is despotically controlled with a view solely to military efficiency.

Well, nowadays it is not the King that rules, but the tinker. Dynastic wars are no longer feared, dynastic alliances no longer valued. Marriages in royal families are becoming rapidly less political, and more popular, domestic and romantic. If all the kings in Europe were made as free tomorrow as King Cophetua, nobody but their aunts and chamberlains would feel a moment's anxiety as to the consequences. On the other hand a sense of the social importance of the tinker's marriage has been steadily growing. We have made a public matter of his wife's health in the month after her confinement. We have taken the minds of his children out of his hands and put them into those of our State schoolmaster. We shall presently make their bodily nourishment independent of him. But they are still riff-raff; and to hand the country over to riff-raff is national suicide, since riff-raff can neither govern nor will let anyone else govern except the highest bidder of bread and circuses. There is no public enthusiast alive of twenty years practical democratic experience who believes in the political adequacy of the electorate or of the bodies it elects. The overthrow of the aristocrat has created the necessity for the Superman.

Englishmen hate Liberty and Equality too much to understand them. But every Englishman loves and desires a pedigree. And in that he is right. King Demos must be bred like all other Kings; and with Must there is no arguing. It is idle for an individual writer to carry so great a matter further in a pamphlet. A conference on the subject is the next step needed. It will be attended by men and women who, no longer believing that they can live forever, are seeking for some immortal work into which they can build the best of themselves before their refuse is thrown into that arch dust destructor, the cremation furnace.

MAXIMS FOR REVOLUTIONISTS

The Golden Rule

Do not do unto others as you would that they should do unto you. Their tastes may not be the same.

Never resist temptation: prove all things: hold fast that which is good.

Do not love your neighbor as yourself. If you are on good terms with yourself it is an impertinence: if on bad, an injury.

The golden rule is that there are no golden rules.

Idolatry

The art of government is the organization of idolatry.

The bureaucracy consists of functionaries; the aristocracy, of idols; the democracy, of idolaters.

The populace cannot understand the bureaucracy: it can only worship the national idols.

The savage bows down to idols of wood and stone: the civilized man to idols of flesh and blood.

A limited monarchy is a device for combining the inertia of a wooden idol with the credibility of a flesh and blood one.

When the wooden idol does not answer the peasant's prayer, he beats it: when the flesh and blood idol does not satisfy the civilized man, he cuts its head off.

He who slays a king and he who dies for him are alike idolaters.

Royalty

Kings are not born: they are made by artificial hallucination. When the process is interrupted by adversity at a critical age, as in the case of Charles II, the subject becomes sane and never completely recovers his kingliness.

The Court is the servant's hall of the sovereign.

Vulgarity in a king flatters the majority of the nation.

The flunkeyism propagated by the throne is the price we pay for its political convenience.

Democracy

If the lesser mind could measure the greater as a footrule can measure a pyramid, there would be finality in universal suffrage. As it is, the political problem remains unsolved.

Democracy substitutes election by the incompetent many for appointment by the corrupt few.

Democratic republics can no more dispense with national idols than monarchies with public functionaries.

Government presents only one problem: the discovery of a trustworthy anthropometric method.

Imperialism

Excess of insularity makes a Briton an Imperialist.

Excess of local self-assertion makes a colonist an Imperialist.

A colonial Imperialist is one who raises colonial troops, equips a colonial squadron, claims a Federal Parliament sending its measures to the Throne instead of to the Colonial Office, and, being finally brought by this means into insoluble conflict with the insular British Imperialist, "cuts the painter" and breaks up the Empire.

Liberty and Equality

He who confuses political liberty with freedom and political equality with similarity has never thought for five minutes about either.

Nothing can be unconditioned: consequently nothing can be free.

Liberty means responsibility. That is why most men dread it.

The duke inquires contemptuously whether his gamekeeper is the equal of the Astronomer Royal; but he insists that they shall both be hanged equally if they murder him.

The notion that the colonel need be a better man than the private is as confused as the notion that the keystone need be stronger than the coping stone.

Where equality is undisputed, so also is subordination.

Equality is fundamental in every department of social organization.

The relation of superior to inferior excludes good manners.

Education

When a man teaches something he does not know to somebody else who has no aptitude for it, and gives him a certificate of proficiency, the latter has completed the education of a gentleman.

A fool's brain digests philosophy into folly, science into superstition, and art into pedantry. Hence University education.

The best brought-up children are those who have seen their parents as they are. Hypocrisy is not the parent's first duty.

The vilest abortionist is he who attempts to mold a child's character.

At the University every great treatise is postponed until its author attains impartial judgment and perfect knowledge. If a horse could wait as long for its shoes and would pay for them in advance, our blacksmiths would all be college dons.

He who can, does. He who cannot, teaches.

A learned man is an idler who kills time with study. Beware of his false knowledge: it is more dangerous than ignorance.

Activity is the only road to knowledge.

Every fool believes what his teachers tell him, and calls his credulity science or morality as confidently as his father called it divine revelation.

No man fully capable of his own language ever masters another.

No man can be a pure specialist without being in the strict sense an idiot.

Do not give your children moral and religious instruction unless you are quite sure they will not take it too seriously. Better be the mother of Henri Quatre and Nell Gwynne than of Robespierre and Queen Mary Tudor.

Marriage

Marriage is popular because it combines the maximum of temptation with the maximum of opportunity.

Marriage is the only legal contract which abrogates as between the parties all the laws that safeguard the particular relation to which it refers.

The essential function of marriage is the continuance of the race, as stated in the Book of Common Prayer.

The accidental function of marriage is the gratification of the amoristic sentiment of mankind.

The artificial sterilization of marriage makes it possible for marriage to fulfill its accidental function while neglecting its essential one.

The most revolutionary invention of the XIX century was the artificial sterilization of marriage.

Any marriage system which condemns

a majority of the population to celibacy will be violently wrecked on the pretext that it outrages morality.

Polygamy, when tried under modern democratic conditions, as by the Mormons, is wrecked by the revolt of the mass of inferior men who are condemned to celibacy by it; for the maternal instinct leads a woman to prefer a tenth share in a first-rate man to the exclusive possession of a third-rate one. Polyandry has not been tried under these conditions.

The minimum of national celibacy (ascertained by dividing the number of males in the community by the number of females, and taking the quotient as the number of wives or husbands permitted to each person) is secured in England (where the quotient is 1) by the institution of monogamy.

The modern sentimental term for the national minimum of celibacy is Purity.

Marriage, or any other form of promiscuous amoristic monogamy, is fatal to large States because it puts its ban on the deliberate breeding of man as a political animal.

Crime and Punishment

All scoundrelism is summed up in the phrase "Que Messieurs les Assassins commencent!"

The man who has graduated from the flogging block at Eton to the bench from which he sentences the garotter to be flogged is the same social product as the garotter who has been kicked by his father and cuffed by his mother until he has grown strong enough to throttle and rob the rich citizen whose money he desires.

Imprisonment is as irrevocable as death.

Criminals do not die by the hand of the law. They die by the hands of other men.

The assassin Czolgosz made President McKinley a hero by assassinating him. The United States of America made Czolgosz a hero by the same process.

Assassination on the scaffold is the worst form of assassination, because there it is invested with the approval of society.

It is the deed that teaches, not the name we give it. Murder and capital punishment are not opposites that cancel one another, but similars that breed their kind.

Crime is only the retail department of what, in wholesale, we call penal law.

When a man wants to murder a tiger he calls it sport: when the tiger wants to murder him he calls it ferocity. The distinction between Crime and Justice is no greater.

While we have prisons it matters little which of us occupy the cells.

The most anxious man in a prison is the governor.

It is not necessary to replace a guillotined criminal: it is necessary to replace a guillotined social system.

Titles

Titles distinguish the mediocre, embarrass the superior, and are disgraced by the inferior.

Great men refuse titles because they are jealous of them.

Honor

There are no perfectly honorable men; but every true man has one main point of honor and a few minor ones.

You cannot believe in honor until you have achieved it. Better keep yourself clean and bright: you are the window through which you must see the world.

Your word can never be as good as

your bond, because your memory can never be as trustworthy as your honor.

Property

Property, said Proudhon, is theft. This is the only perfect truism that has been uttered on the subject.

Servants

When domestic servants are treated as human beings it is not worth while to keep them.

The relation of master and servant is advantageous only to masters who do not scruple to abuse their authority, and to servants who do not scruple to abuse their trust.

The perfect servant, when his master makes humane advances to him, feels that his existence is threatened, and hastens to change his place.

Masters and servants are both tyrannical; but the masters are the more dependent of the two.

A man enjoys what he uses, not what his servants use.

Man is the only animal which esteems itself rich in proportion to the number and voracity of its parasites.

Ladies and gentlemen are permitted to have friends in the kennel, but not in the kitchen.

Domestic servants, by making spoiled children of their masters, are forced to intimidate them in order to be able to live with them.

In a slave state, the slaves rule: in Mayfair, the tradesman rules.

How to Beat Children

If you strike a child, take care that you strike it in anger, even at the risk of maiming it for life. A blow in cold blood neither can nor should be forgiven.

If you beat children for pleasure, avow your object frankly, and play the game according to the rules, as a foxhunter does; and you will do comparatively little harm. No foxhunter is such a cad as to pretend that he hunts the fox to teach it not to steal chickens, or that he suffers more acutely than the fox at the death. Remember that even in childbearing there is the sportsman's way and the cad's way.

Religion

Beware of the man whose god is in the skies.

What a man believes may be ascertained, not from his creed, but from the assumptions on which he habitually acts.

Virtues and Vices

No specific virtue or vice in a man implies the existence of any other specific virtue or vice in him, however closely the imagination may associate them.

Virtue consists, not in abstaining from vice, but in not desiring it.

Self-denial is not a virtue: it is only the effect of prudence on rascality.

Obedience simulates subordination as fear of the police simulates honesty.

Disobedience, the rarest and most courageous of the virtues, is seldom distinguished from neglect, the laziest and commonest of the vices.

Vice is waste of life. Poverty, obedience and celibacy are the canonical vices.

Economy is the art of making the most of life.

The love of economy is the root of all virtue.

Fairplay

The love of fairplay is a spectator's virtue, not a principal's.

Greatness

Greatness is only one of the sensations of littleness.

In heaven an angel is nobody in particular.

Greatness is the secular name for Divinity: both mean simply what lies beyond us.

If a great man could make us understand him, we should hang him.

We admit that when the divinity we worshiped made itself visible and comprehensible we crucified it.

To a mathematician the eleventh means only a single unit: to the bushman who cannot count further than his ten fingers it is an incalculable myriad.

The difference between the shallowest routineer and the deepest thinker appears, to the latter, trifling; to the former, infinite.

In a stupid nation the man of genius becomes a god: everybody worships him and nobody does his will.

Beauty and Happiness, Art and Riches

Happiness and Beauty are by-products.

Folly is the direct pursuit of Happiness and Beauty.

Riches and Art are spurious receipts for the production of Happiness and Beauty.

He who desires a lifetime of happiness with a beautiful woman desires to enjoy the taste of wine by keeping his mouth always full of it.

The most intolerable pain is produced by prolonging the keenest pleasure.

The man with toothache thinks everyone happy whose teeth are sound. The poverty stricken man makes the same mistake about the rich man.

The more a man possesses over and above what he uses, the more careworn he becomes.

The tyranny that forbids you to make the road with pick and shovel is worse than that which prevents you from lolling along it in a carriage and pair.

In an ugly and unhappy world the richest man can purchase nothing but ugliness and unhappiness.

In his efforts to escape from ugliness and unhappiness the rich man intensifies both. Every new yard of West End creates a new acre of East End.

The XIX century was the Age of Faith in Fine Art. The results are before us.

The Perfect Gentleman

The fatal reservation of the gentleman is that he sacrifices everything to his honor except his gentility.

A gentleman of our days is one who has money enough to do what every fool would do if he could afford it: that is, consume without producing.

The true diagnostic of modern gentility is parasitism.

No elaboration of physical or moral accomplishment can atone for the sin of parasitism.

A modern gentleman is necessarily the enemy of his country. Even in war he does not fight to defend it, but to prevent his power of preying on it from passing to a foreigner. Such combatants are patriots in the same sense as two dogs fighting for a bone are lovers of animals.

The North American Indian was a type of the sportsman warrior gentleman. The Periclean Athenian was a type of the intellectually and artistically cultivated gentleman. Both were political failures. The modern gentleman, without the hardihood of the one or the culture of the other, has the appetite of both put together. He will not succeed where they failed.

He who believes in education, criminal

law, and sport, needs only property to make him a perfect modern gentleman.

Moderation

Moderation is never applauded for its own sake.

A moderately honest man with a moderately faithful wife, moderate drinkers both, in a moderately healthy house: that is the true middle class unit.

The Unconscious Self

The unconscious self is the real genius. Your breathing goes wrong the moment your conscious self meddles with it.

Except during the nine months before he draws his first breath, no man manages his affairs as well as a tree does.

Reason

The reasonable man adapts himself to the world: the unreasonable one persists in trying to adapt the world to himself. Therefore all progress depends on the unreasonable man.

The man who listens to Reason is lost: Reason enslaves all whose minds are not strong enough to master her.

Decency

Decency is Indecency's Conspiracy of Silence.

Experience

Men are wise in proportion, not to their experience, but to their capacity for experience.

If we could learn from mere experience, the stones of London would be wiser than its wisest men.

Time's Revenges

Those whom we called brutes had their revenge when Darwin showed us that they were our cousins.

The thieves had their revenge when Marx convicted the bourgeoisie of theft.

Good Intentions

Hell is paved with good intentions, not with bad ones.

All men mean well.

Natural Rights

The Master of Arts, by proving that no man has any natural rights, compels himself to take his own for granted.

The right to live is abused whenever it is not constantly challenged.

Faute de Mieux

In my childhood I demurred to the description of a certain young lady as "the pretty Miss So and So." My aunt rebuked me by saying "Remember always that the least homely sister is the family beauty."

No age or condition is without its heroes. The least incapable general in a nation is its Cæsar, the least imbecile statesman its Solon, the least confused thinker its Socrates, the least commonplace poet its Shakespeare.

Charity

Charity is the most mischievous sort of pruriency.

Those who minister to poverty and disease are accomplices in the two worst of all the crimes.

He who gives money he has not earned is generous with other people's labor.

Every genuinely benevolent person loathes almsgiving and mendicity.

Fame

Life levels all men: death reveals the eminent.

Discipline

Mutiny Acts are needed only by officers who command without authority. Divine right needs no whip.

Women in the Home

Home is the girl's prison and the woman's workhouse.

Civilization

Civilization is a disease produced by the practice of building societies with rotten material.

Those who admire modern civilization usually identify it with the steam engine and the electric telegraph.

Those who understand the steam engine and the electric telegraph spend their lives in trying to replace them with something better.

The imagination cannot conceive a viler criminal than he who should build London like the present one, nor a greater benefactor than he who should destroy it.

Gambling

The most popular method of distributing wealth is the method of the roulette table.

The roulette table pays nobody except him who keeps it. Nevertheless a passion for gaming is common, though a passion for keeping roulette tables is unknown.

Gambling promises the poor what Property performs for the rich: that is why the bishops dare not denounce it fundamentally.

The Social Question

Do not waste your time on Social Questions. What is the matter with the poor is Poverty: what is the matter with the Rich is Uselessness.

Stray Sayings

We are told that when Jehovah created the world he saw that it was good. What would he say now?

The conversion of a savage to Christianity is the conversion of Christianity to savagery.

No man dares say so much of what he thinks as to appear to himself an extremist.

Mens sana in corpore sano is a foolish saying. The sound body is a product of the sound mind.

Decadence can find agents only when it wears the mask of progress.

In moments of progress the noble succeed, because things are going their way: in moments of decadence the base succeed for the same reason: hence the world is never without the exhilaration of contemporary success.

The reformer for whom the world is not good enough finds himself shoulder to shoulder with him that is not good enough for the world.

Every man over forty is a scoundrel.

Youth, which is forgiven everything, forgives itself nothing: age, which forgives itself everything, is forgiven nothing.

When we learn to sing that Britons never will be masters we shall make an end of slavery.

Do not mistake your objection to defeat for an objection to fighting, your objection to being a slave for an objection to slavery, your objection to not being as rich as your neighbor for an objection to poverty. The cowardly, the insubordinate, and the envious share your objections.

Take care to get what you like or you will be forced to like what you get. Where there is no ventilation fresh air is declared unwholesome. Where there is no religion hypocrisy becomes good taste. Where there is no knowledge ignorance calls itself science.

If the wicked flourish and the fittest survive, Nature must be the God of rascals.

If history repeats itself, and the unexpected always happens, how incapable must Man be of learning from experience!

Compassion is the fellow-feeling of the unsound.

Those who understand evil pardon it: those who resent it destroy it.

Acquired notions of propriety are stronger than natural instincts. It is easier to recruit for monasteries and convents than to induce an Arab woman to uncover her mouth in public, or a British officer to walk through Bond Street in a golfing cap on an afternoon in May.

It is dangerous to be sincere unless you are also stupid.

The Chinese tame fowls by clipping their wings, and women by deforming their feet. A petticoat round the ankles serves equally well.

Political Economy and Social Economy are amusing intellectual games; but Vital Economy is the Philosopher's Stone.

When a heretic wishes to avoid martyrdom he speaks of "Orthodoxy, True and False" and demonstrates that the True is his heresy.

Beware of the man who does not return your blow: he neither forgives you nor allows you to forgive yourself.

If you injure your neighbor, better not do it by halves.

Sentimentality is the error of supposing that quarter can be given or taken in moral conflicts.

Two starving men cannot be twice as hungry as one; but two rascals can be ten times as vicious as one.

Make your cross your crutch; but when you see another man do it, beware of him.

Self-Sacrifice

Self-sacrifice enables us to sacrifice other people without blushing.

If you begin by sacrificing yourself to those you love, you will end by hating those to whom you have sacrificed yourself.

THE LIFE AND WORKS OF GEORGE BERNARD SHAW

By IVOR BROWN

It is a curious fact that since the time of Shakespeare, the writers of the best English comedies—Congreve, Sheridan, Goldsmith, Oscar Wilde, Bernard Shaw, and Sean O'Casey—all had Irish boyhoods and four of them were born in the city of Dublin. There George Bernard Shaw was born on July 26, 1856.

In Southern Ireland there has long been a divided society. The wealthy and powerful class, once known as "the Ascendancy," might be called Anglo-Irish; their religion has been Protestant as a rule. The poorer classes in the towns as well as the peasantry are Roman Catholic and Irish of native descent. The Shaw family were of the former class, but they were far from wealthy and it was at a Protestant school of the Wesleyan Sect that young George had most of his brief education. Of this schooling he afterward wrote with contempt, but he may have been taught more than he was ready to admit.

Throughout his life Shaw looked with anger upon Ireland and its capital. His home life was an unhappy one, not only because there was little money but also because the parents were incompatible. Shaw's father for awhile held a sinecure in the law courts; after that he went into the corn-milling business where he did poorly. He was gay, careless, and drank too much. His mother was by nature cold and severe, and the hard times she endured naturally did not soften her. She was not actually unkind, but she was never sympathetic to her son or his two sisters. Music was her consolation and Shaw lived in a home which, however poor in finance, had a rich musical culture. This he could enjoy and later profit by, since it was as a musical critic that he made his first success in journalism. He managed to educate himself by reading, especially the great English novelists, and by visits to the theaters and to the Dublin Picture Gallery.

At fifteen he went into the office of a land agency and quickly learned the business of collecting rents and keeping accounts. He was never exactly a dreamy literary boy, with no head for figures or no interest in his work, and he was quickly promoted to cashier. All his life he retained a keen appreciation of money and skill in its management, acting as his own agent and publisher instead of employing others to make his contracts and look after his affairs.

Dublin, however, must have seemed a small world to him, and at twenty he moved to London. His mother had gone there four years earlier, leaving the husband whose company she could no longer tolerate and setting up as a teacher of music. Her son joined her at a house in the suburb of Fulham and afterwards in Fitzroy Square in the center of the town.

He now intended to live by his pen, but he made a faulty start by setting out to write novels. Between the ages of twenty-three and twenty-seven he wrote four of these, *The Irrational Knot,* whose title refers to marriage (1880), *Love among the Artists* (1881), *Cashel Byron's Profession* (1882) about a prize boxer, and *An Unsocial Socialist* (1883). These he sent to many publishing houses, but they were rejected—not without reason. Shaw was not a natural writer and his work lacked an urgent narrative quality. He had read Charles Dickens closely, but he lacked Dickens' gift, and he could not leap into fame as a ready-made novelist at the age of twenty-three. In later life he frankly confessed that his storytelling met the neglect which it deserved. It was even with some hesitation that he allowed those books to be published after he had won fame as a dramatist.

Shaw was never ashamed to say, indeed he even enjoyed saying, that he had lived on his mother's earnings during those years, but it was a very thin living. Much of his energy was devoted to the study and advocacy of socialism. He had been much impressed by Henry George's book *Progress and Poverty* and he had studied the work of Karl Marx, but he did not become a Marxist. His attachment to socialism was mainly through a group of middle-class reformers who formed the small but soon influential body called the Fabian Society. They took their title from the Roman general Fabius Cunctator, who, in his wars with Hannibal, advised delay before striking a hard blow. There was nothing revolutionary about the Fabians: they studied social conditions closely and pleaded in their pamphlets for collective ownership of the means of production. They aimed chiefly at reaching men of other parties with their ideas and were unlikely ever to strike the hard blow of which the Roman Fabius had talked as the sequel to careful preparation.

For the Fabians Shaw wrote some pamphlets and also a short book on municipal socialism. He also did what his fellow-Fabians did not do. He spoke on street corners and at all kinds of public meetings, overcoming his natural shyness and making himself into a first-class speaker and lecturer. But these were gratuitous services to a cause, and a living still had to be earned.

Novel writing had failed him because he was not equipped for it. But with his clear, trenchant style and his exceptional speed of mind, he was admirably fitted for journalism. His early devotion to music and painting could now be made to bear some slightly rewarding fruit. He became music critic for a lively evening paper, *The Star,* where he wrote from 1888 to 1890 with the pseudonym of Corno di Bassotto. Later he was art critic for *The World.* Finally, and most important, he was drama critic for *The Saturday Review* where he wrote brilliantly about the theater from January, 1895, to May, 1898. His articles were later collected and issued in two volumes of *Dramatic Opinions.* They remain as lively and challenging as when they were written.

His interest in the theater was stimulated very early by the visits to Dublin of some great actors of the day, notably Barry Sullivan and Sir Henry Irving. Of the latter's lavish methods of producing Shakespeare, Shaw was soon to be sharply critical, for he had become a disciple of the simplicity and realism of the Free Theater movement led by Antoine in Paris and rapidly spreading in Europe. He was especially attracted by the work of Henrik Ibsen. Five years before his own professional entry to dramatic criticism, he had written *The Quintessence of Ibsenism* (1891), a book in which he analyzed and keenly appreciated the work of the Norwegian master. In this, by the vigor of his arguments in Ibsen's defense, he showed that the man who had failed as a novelist could amply succeed as a critic and a publicist.

Shaw made several attempts to find his métier as a dramatist before he drew public attention as the most vigorous and readable of the dramatic critics. His first piece, *Widowers' Houses,* an attack on slum landlords, was written in 1892. It was followed in 1894 by *Arms and the Man,* a gaily satirical attack on those who romanticize the grim actualities of war. About the same time (1893) he had also investigated the problem of prostitution and the procuress in *Mrs. Warren's Profession.* He amused himself by laughing at the Ibsenites in *The Philanderer.* But his work was, for the present, unrewarding and the most Shaw could hope for was an occasional and out-of-the-way performance: it was a long time before he had a play continuously and profitably performed for a long run in the center of London.

The English theater at the end of the last century had no fresh life in it. It was the home of conventional stories with conventional situations and shallow, romantic conclusions; in a phrase of George Meredith's, "romance fiddles harmonics on the strings of sensuality." With this definition, Shaw, an intellectual Puritan, strongly agreed. The popular plays of his time, especially the musical comedies, as he saw them, were providing escape for voluptuaries into a world of facile eroticism where carnal desires were dignified with the name of love and projected at the public with the allure of expensively vulgar decoration, glamorous personalities, and the charm of sensuous waltz-time music.

The nonmusical side of the English stage, and indeed of most of the European stage at that period, which he had first watched as a youth and later analyzed as a critic, sickened Shaw with its romanticism about sex. This he regarded as a mere fabrication of lies. The audiences were told over and over again what they wanted to believe: that woman was a delicate flower waiting passively to be plucked in matrimony by the active and conquering male, as handsome as the woman was beautiful. After that, all would be bliss. The plays were thought to end happily if the wedding bells brought down the curtain. The belief that if woman were womanly and man manly, marriage was the perfect solution and the gate to unbroken felicity, Shaw knew to be nonsense. So probably did many who dreamily accepted it as they enjoyed their trivial entertainments. But they were happy with the pleasant pretense. Shaw was not happy and he was determined to ridicule that nonsense and to substitute what he believed to be the truth of the matter. He first asserted that the happy English home was a romantic myth and then proceeded to put forward his own conception of woman as an extremely active huntress in the jungle of sex relations. This is the line taken in *Man and Superman* (1903) and its long, diverting preface.

In reviewing this stale theater of make believe and in describing his own invasion of it as a dramatist, he paid full tribute to his master. "Ibsen," he wrote, "was the point of the new departure." Ibsen had shown the snug home of the romantics to be a most unhappy doll's house. Ibsen had created in Rebecca West the unwomanly woman who was not waiting in a flower bed for the plucking by a masculine hand: she knew what she wanted and where she was going. Ibsen had taken the romantic illusions of the nineteenth century one by one and exposed the lies underlying them; he had shown the rottenness of commerce in *The Pillars of Society,* of democracy in *The Enemy of the People,* and of bourgeois domesticity in *Ghosts* and *A Doll's House.* But Ibsen had only reached the English playgoers in occasional performances of plays which the critics, romantics to a man, had assailed as sordid libels on society. Shaw, the Ibsenite, would carry on the necessary social service of smashing the old idols. So he went to work, ridiculing the idea of war as a glorious demonstration of courage, examining the economics of vice instead of dismissing its victims as deplorably vicious and deserving all they got, and peering through the windows of the happy home so dear to the romantics in order to discover the frustrations and distresses within.

It was in New York, not in London, that a play of his first earned him a considerable reward. This was *The Devil's Disciple* (1896), in which the American actor Richard Mansfield scored a great success as the young sinner who becomes a self-sacrificing hero in the hour of crisis. The play was performed in 1898, when Shaw was afflicted with an injury to his leg: the royalties from this enabled him to rest and to give up a regular journalism.

In 1898, he published his first seven plays in two volumes called *Plays Pleasant* and *Plays Unpleasant.* He included full descriptions of the characters and scenes which made the plays more easily readable by the numerous people who had not seen them on the stage. He attached explanatory prefaces, a custom that he was to continue throughout his life. In this writing of introductions his brilliance in exposition, argument, and sometimes invective revealed him as a superb master of both explanatory and combative prose. Sometimes the preface was better than the play which it introduced. This, however, could not be said of two first-rate comedies, *Candida* (1894) and *You Never Can Tell* (1895).

A happy partnership was to follow with a young actor, writer, and director of plays, Granville Barker (who later preferred to be known as Harley Granville-Barker). At the Court Theater in Sloane Square there were seasons of matinee performances in which this clever man of the theater provided some finely schooled acting in the presentation of Shaw's new work.

Shaw married in June of 1898 Charlotte Payne-Townshend, a member of a wealthy Anglo-Irish family. She was six months younger than he was. By that time he was earning enough to avoid suspicion that he was marrying for money, a sneer which would have given him great pain. She met him when he was overworked and ill, limping on crutches owing to the decay of a bone in his foot. She took him in hand as a devoted friend, who could ease his way of life, and defend him from tiring visitors. She had a horror of sexual relations and insisted on a marriage without them. But it proved to be a long and happy partnership with no interruption, although Shaw was an obvious target for feminine admirers. Charlotte encouraged her husband to travel in order to escape from his work, but even on their farthest journeys he kept up his habit of prolific letter writing. Shaw's immense vitality was shown in the energy with which he kept up a long and typically lively correspondence with all manner of people, some of whom were not socially or professionally important.

Among the principal plays to emerge

in the early years of the twentieth century was *Man and Superman* (1903), in which Shaw's theory of woman as the aggressive and possessive sex was strongly stated. *John Bull's Other Island* (1904), about the present and future of Ireland, was written in the same year that Shaw was defeated as candidate for London County Council. *Major Barbara* was written in 1905, the year he went back to Ireland for the first time since he had left; at the same time he bought a house there at Ayot St. Lawrence. *The Doctor's Dilemma* and *Our Theatres in the Nineties* were written in 1906, followed by *Getting Married* (1908) and *Misalliance* and *The Showing-up of Blanco Posnet* (both 1909).

It was in *Doctor's Dilemma* that another of the common worships was examined, that of science, especially medical science. Shaw had no faith in doctors, especially the wealthy and titled leaders of the profession who flourished fashionably and prospered financially in the Harley Street area of London and his ridicule of their follies and pretensions in this play is devastating. His lampoon of the surgeon profiting by expensive and unnecessary operations and of the other medical men could not be dismissed as merely a piece of irresponsible impishness and a manifestation of Shaw the shameless jester. It was founded on fact.

But still he was not what is called in London "a West End dramatist." He became so finally in 1911, with a light piece, *Fanny's First Play,* and he was in a position to supply a piece for Sir Herbert Beerbohm-Tree, then the leading actor-manager and a prominent figure in London life. This piece was *Pygmalion,* whose story of a Cockney flower-girl taught by a professor of euphonics to speak correct English and pass as a lady has been made familiar to the world by the musical version called *My Fair Lady.* The rehearsals of the orginal play were a battle between the author and the actor-manager and the atmosphere was made even stormier by the presence in the flower-girl's part of Mrs. Patrick Campbell, a powerful actress who amused herself by pursuing Shaw with her fascinations and making mischief where she could. At the time, the play had only a moderate success. A year later, in 1912, Shaw finished work on *Androcles and the Lion,* and included a preface in which he set forth his views on Christianity.

During World War II Shaw wrote some one-act plays but he spent his time mainly in planning *Heartbreak House,* which he described as Chekhovian in manner. It expressed a deep pessimism about the future of man. It was finished in 1919 and produced in 1921, by which time Shaw had written his cycle of five plays, *Back to Methuselah* (1920). Here he argued that men died before they had learned wisdom, and could, if they had the will to do so, achieve the longevity necessary to sagacity. Beginning in the Garden of Eden and ending with the vision of a world properly ruled by immensely aged men, it was largely a play of prolonged conversations and has been seldom performed.

In 1923 came what many think his finest work, the chronicle play of *Saint Joan,* with its finely written trial scene in which the Church is given a remarkable persuasive statement of its case against heresy to counter the pleas of the Saint herself. In this piece Shaw's capacity for staging an argument was employed on an immensely moving story: those who said that he lacked humanity could make the accusation no longer. The run was a long one and revivals have been frequent. Certainly it has been the play most favored by the general public, appealing to thousands who said that they did not go to the theater to get a socialist lecture.

It was in *Saint Joan* that the contradiction in Shaw's attitude to personal liberty is most apparent. The Maid of Orléans appealed to him because of her insistence that the Divine Voices which she heard and by which she was guided were of stronger authority in deciding her conduct than the orders and disciplines of the Church. She would not accept the view that only through the Church and its hierarchy could the individual have contact and communion with God. She claimed a direct approach and the right to make private decisions. Shaw wrote in his preface that "the supremacy of private judgment for the individual is the quintessence of Protestantism." So he is in fact claiming Joan as the companion of Hus, Wycliffe, and finally Luther in asserting the claims of the private person against the supposed infallible wisdom of the Church. Shaw pointed out that many great Catholics, some of them later canonized, had been at one time in conflict with the Church, but Joan, herself canonized five hundred years ago, appealed to him as rebel and a Protestant.

After *Saint Joan,* however, Shaw became increasingly doctrinaire and contemptuous of theatrical storytelling. He had said that the stage was his pulpit and he began to write a series of plays in which the preacher's argument was much and the action very little. Possibly the best of these was *The Apple Cart* (1929), a discussion of the technique of government. His last contribution to the stage was *Buoyant Millions,* which appeared in 1947, and soon disappeared, when the author was ninety-one years of age.

Shaw was distraught after the death of his wife in 1943 and his health and extraordinary vitality rapidly diminished thereafter. When he himself died on November 2, 1950, at the age of ninety-four years and fourteen weeks, his ashes were mingled with those of his wife in the garden at Ayot St. Lawrence.

Shaw's theatrical skill, remarkable personality and delicious wit have left their mark on the twentieth century, as has his philosophical thought. For himself and for all speakers and writers he demanded the liberty to be the critics of societies and governments, challenging authority without stint, just as he asserted the right of the Maid of Orleans to be her own communicant with God. The notion of government of the people, by the people, and for the people Shaw regarded as dangerous claptrap. He believed that government was a task for people trained and skilled: the philosopher-kings imagined by Plato in ancient Athens were his ideal. He liked the idea of socialism only because he favored equality, but he knew that man, if wholly free, would never choose or achieve equality because the abler and more active would seize the greater share of riches and power. So the idea of political freedom was regarded as illusory and even dangerous. All liberal opinion is on Shaw's side in this, but no liberal opinion was on his side when he defended the dictatorships whose treatment of protesting and dissident people was a complete denial of personal rights. While Shaw saw that political democracy could be, and often was, incompetent and even corrupt, he could not see that at least it admitted more personal freedom than did the authoritarian states in which his own life would have been impossible.

It is curious that Shaw should have so completely failed to realize that the liberty of speech which he wanted for himself would not have been granted to him by any dictator and that he would have been sent to Siberia or a concentration camp, if he still had his head on his shoulders, by any of the autocrats to whose contempt of parliamentary democracy he was sympathetic. He had long raged against the censorship of stage plays in England, a battle he eventually won, yet he never hurled the thunderbolts of his anger and his wit against men who were imposing a drastic censorship on news and views of every kind.

That the human will is free and can triumph was a principle belief of his later years. He rebelled strongly against the Darwinian theory of evolution by natural selection. Shaw maintained that it was not a lucky chance which made survival and growth possible: it was the determination to differ and advance. Thus he held that giraffes had not got long necks because those who happened to be born with longer necks fared better by reaching up to more of the foliage that was their food. In his view, some giraffe had willed and striven to reach further and so altered their own physique, passing on that alteration to their progeny. Evolution, for him, was a constant victory for effort and it was the duty of man to exercise his willpower in pursuit of betterment. He too could reach higher and higher, if he chose.

There was little comfort in Shaw's philosophy for "the average sensual man." But for that creature Shaw never had much sympathy, at least in theory. In the practice of his life, however, he did not always live by his bleak philosophy that would entangle the spirit of man from his body. He had his compassion for human weakness, and, above all, he had his laughter. He could not have been the world-winning dramatist that he became without a sense of humor. He was both a preacher and a master of comedy. He won his vast audience with the latter and he could not have done so if his mind had been only "the pure intelligence" of one of his own characters. He was a man happier and in some ways wiser than his creed.

Ivor Brown is a well-known English drama critic and journalist.

THE 1925 PRIZE

By GUNNAR AHLSTRÖM

No NOBEL PRIZE for Literature was given in 1925; it was postponed to the following year, when two awards were given. And in 1926, international politics replaced the Prize for Literature in the limelight since the 1925 and 1926 Prizes for Peace were shared by four candidates —Chamberlain and Dawes, Briand and Streseman. But finally, the literary Prize returned to the public eye in one of the most extraordinary cases in the Nobel annals.

When the Swedish Academy finally made its decision to award the Prize for Literature to George Bernard Shaw on November 11, 1926, the secretary sent the customary cable to the laureate. The first reaction came out in an interview of questionable authenticity in the form of an epigram circulated by Reuters. "To me it's a puzzle," Shaw was quoted as saying, "I suppose I got the Prize because this year I haven't written anything at all." In the next few days various rumors made headlines. "Bernard Shaw refuses Nobel Prize" or "Shaw amazes world by declining Nobel Prize." "What is this golden bell which they hang around the neck of illustrious old men?" Shaw asked.

Who could resist applauding the reaction of this Irish humorist who refused to take part in the nonsense? All his life, Shaw had resisted honors of any kind. In every offer of an honorary degree, decoration, or title he had seen a threat to his personal integrity. From this point of view, the Nobel Prize itself was also a kind of humiliating prostitution.

George Bernard Shaw was one of a group of veteran candidates for the Nobel Prize whose name had been proposed again and again and whose literary production had been considered, discounted, and reconsidered time and again. After all, he had been born in 1856 and had thus had ample time to become a leading character on the literary stage long before his work came to the attention of the Nobel Committee and the Swedish Academy

Shaw was one of the candidates nominated in 1911. The nomination was made by Gilbert Murray of Oxford, a member of the Academic Committee of the Royal Society of Literature. On this occasion, Shaw's work was reviewed in a highly favorable study prepared by Erik Axel Karlfeldt, who was not only a great rustic poet in his own right but also a fine critic of English literature. However, the Academy was still ruled by Dr. af Wirsén, the permanent secretary; for him Bernard Shaw had the reputation of being "too paradoxical, too brutal, too inartistic." The Prize went to Maurice Maeterlinck.

The long war years followed, marked

in part by Shaw's tempestuous pacifism and his vacillating reputation. *Heartbreak House* was published but not produced; *Back to Methusaleh* was considered a rather insipid curiosity, nothing more. But in 1924 *Saint Joan* came out, bringing instant celebrity and unchallenged prestige to its author. The shepherdess of Domrémy was a box-office hit, creating the glory of Sybil Thorndike in London, of Elizabeth Bergner in Berlin, of Ludmilla Pitoëff in Paris. Once more the world listened to a man of genius speaking a universal language. The fact did not go unheeded in Stockholm.

Shaw was nominated in vain by his Swedish supporters in 1921. The Nobel Committee's expert, Per Hallström, was on guard, ready to launch his critical arrows, and he put Shaw's name third, below H. G. Wells and John Galsworthy. In 1924, Shaw reappeared as a candidate, nominated this time by a new member of the Swedish Academy who for many years had served as director of the National Dramatic Theater. In the discussions the next year, the Shavian party found a powerful ally in the Archbishop of Uppsala, Nathan Söderblom, who marshaled the full power of the ecclesiastical eloquence to call the dramatic grandeur of the Maid of Orléans to the public's attention. The play had been produced in Stockholm, and its purely literary qualities succeeded in conquering Hallström's reluctance. This change of opinion is clearly evident in the presentation address in which he apostrophized the absent laureate and in which his previous reservations were converted into ringing praise.

England was keenly interested in the Nobel Prize. Of course the interest was solely due to the effort of George Bernard Shaw. No other writer had sought publicity—both written and photographic—with such enthusiasm. He was also a most respectful prostitute in regard to the press, but only as part of his struggle to rally men's minds to his cause.

The press showed Shaw no mercy on the score of the Nobel Prize when the old rebel finally accepted. The symbolic crown of laurels, however, was accompanied by a more tangible reward in the form of a sizeable amount of money. It was well known that in the field of economics Shaw suffered from weird phobias—and these were immediately triggered by the awarding of the Prize. He differed from Tolstoy in that he did not detest money in itself. Quite the contrary, he considered money to be a necessary and beneficent antidote against poverty, the fatal plague of modern society, the mortal sin of our age, the source of all vice.

As his own earnings increased over the years, Shaw felt freer and enjoyed being able to escape from the humiliating considerations which he claimed were imposed by capitalism. In his eyes, however, the one thing which threatened the sovereignty of his genius was the existence of the tax collector. On this point Shaw was intractable to an exaggerated degree. His secretary, Blanche Patch, tells in her memoirs of the periodical obsession which overcame him in his old age about the magnitude of his income. He was convinced that the more he earned the more monstrous was the tax upon it. His capital, he maintained, would ineluctably be changed into deficit in a few years. If he earned 100 pounds, his tax would be 147 pounds. Neither logic nor calculation could change his mind. "I maintain my figure of 147 pounds, which is the easiest to remember."

This complicated psychology explains the mental block, the succession of wild reactions caused by the telegram from the Swedish Academy and the series of incoherent statements which were forthcoming during the next few days while newsmen were vainly looking for him. On principle, Shaw detested public honors, and he also saw a threat in this check for 6,500 pounds sterling. A bomb in the cellar of his house could not have frightened him more.

For a few days, the Swedish minister in London did not have an easy life. He did everything he could to avoid the scandal, and he found a valuable ally in the tact of Shaw's Swedish translator, Lady Low, née Ebba Byström, who was also a good friend of the playwright. She has told me of the eloquence which she was forced to muster in an effort to convince the laureate that he could not toss away this Prize, like a pebble, onto the shores of the Baltic. "My dear Bernard, it isn't done. Sweden has tried to honor you, and you reply by insulting them." These wise counsels finally resulted in Shaw's change of heart and he decided to accept the award, but not the Prize money. He elected to use the money to set up an Anglo-Swedish fund for culture. This arrangement seemed to satisfy the various factions, and everyone could rejoice in the happy ending.

In the Academy's view, Shaw had accepted the money de facto, after which he was free to use it for any purpose he chose. Mistral had done something similar, as had Paul Heyse and Romain Rolland. As it happened, the award became the basis for an official body, The Anglo-Swedish Literary Foundation, with a headquarters, a corporate seal, and a board of trustees in London. It survived the vicissitudes of postwar inflation, eventually developing into an efficient instrument for realizing the generous intentions of its founder. It was largely thanks to Shaw's foundation that Swedish paper was not used mostly for wrapping Australian apples, and it facilitated the publication of English translations of several important works of Strindberg; later it was to provide a substantial number of Swedish writers with a pulpit from which to reach an international public.

The impenitent patriarch thus attained a certain satisfaction when he saw how his Nobel money, acquired in so paradoxical a manner, was used. When he finally retired to his country estate at Ayot St. Lawrence, his visitors could see the famous diploma framed and hanging in a corner. On it they could read the motivation for awarding the Prize to the master of Ayot St. Lawrence, "for his work which is marked both by idealism and humanity, its stimulating satire often being infused with a singular poetic beauty."

Translated by Dale McAdoo.

Frans Eemil Sillanpää

1939

"For his deep comprehension and exquisite art in painting the nature of his country and the life of its peasants in their mutual relations"

Illustrated by MAURICE FRANTZ POINTEAU

PRESENTATION ADDRESS

By PER HALLSTRÖM

PERMANENT SECRETARY
OF THE SWEDISH ACADEMY

THE DIPLOMA of a Nobel Prize has just been given to you and you have heard the reasons which led the Swedish Academy to accord this distinction to your literary work. These reasons are very briefly stated on this parchment, but you have been deprived of the many homages which would have been paid you at the ceremony of the distribution of the Nobel Prizes.

These homages you will find equally in our company, in the simplicity characteristic of our gatherings, but with the same warmth as that which you would have received in the festival room on the day of the ceremony. None of us knows your Finnish language; we have been able to appreciate your works only in translations, but no doubt exists about your mastery as a writer. This mastery is so great that it appears clearly even in a foreign attire. Simple, brief, objective, without the least affectation, your language flows with the clarity of a spring and reflects what your artist's eye has seized. You have chosen your motifs with the greatest delicacy and, one could almost say, with a sort of timidity before what is immediately beautiful. You wish to create beauty from what exists in everyday nature, and the manner in which you can do it often remains your secret. It is not at the writer's desk that one sees you work but before the easel of the watercolorist, and, over your shoulder, one often accustoms one's eye to see in a new manner. Sometimes, when painting spaces and clouds in the light of a summer day, you forget the fear that you have of a too favorable motif and you then employ the musical art with the hand of a master. This characteristic trait, your fondness for the simple and the typical, you show also in your description of man. This description takes pleasure in rendering the everyday life of the peasants, strongly attached to the earth from which it draws its strength. When it is a question of deeds, you show an equal mastery, and the effect is produced only with the simplest means.

Concerning your most celebrated work, you have said some words which no one else could have found: "Everything that touches Silja is generally of a magnificent insignificance." No artist can go farther in the desire to remain respectfully faithful to the reality of things. Thus you have represented your people, without the least finery.

At the present moment, even the name of your country is significant everywhere. As simple as you see them, your people find themselves a prey to fateful powers, heroically great in their indomitable courage, faithful to their duty to the very end, to the death which they confront without trembling. In our thanks for what you have given, our thoughts go still further; they go, with all our admiration and the emotion which grips us, to your people, to your nation.

There was no formal Acceptance Speech by Sillanpää.

THE MAID SILJA

THE HISTORY OF THE LAST OFFSHOOT OF AN OLD FAMILY TREE

By F. E. SILLANPÄÄ

Translated from the Finnish by Alexander Matson

[Excerpt]

Fallen Asleep While Young

Death came to Silja, a young and beautiful country girl, a week or so after Midsummer Day, when summer is still fresh and new. In view of her station in life, she died a fairly decent death. For although she was but a fatherless and motherless farm-maid, with no other relatives either, to whom she could turn for aid, and although she had had to be cared for by others for some time, at least she had not been dependent on charity. Thus her life escaped even that slight tinge of ugliness. On the Kierikka farm, where she was then in service, a tiny room adjoined the bath-house. There she was allowed to take up her quarters and thither her food was brought, the scantiness of which was well justified in that she never ate it all. This humane treatment was in no way due to any special love for their fellow-men on the part of the Kierikka family, but rather to a kind of shiftlessness; the farm was in general not very well managed. Perhaps they had Silja's savings in mind. At any rate she had plenty of good clothes, which of course became the perquisite of the person who nursed her. The mistress had already shown a tendency to borrow Silja's clothes.

Silja, taking after her father in this, was particularly neat in her habits; she made that wretched hovel quite pretty. From it emerged the faint coughing that sounded through the ramshackle window as far as the grass of the yard, where the drab-faced Kierikka children spent their days. It was one of the little things that, with the grass and flowers, went to the making of life that summer in the Kierikka farmyard.

There, towards the end of her days, the girl was able to taste the incomparable joy of solitude. As her mood, according to the wont of consumptives, remained light to the end, this spring solitude was an admirable balm for her somewhat excited love. She was solitary only so far as human beings were concerned; sympathetic company, speechless, it is true, but all the more devoted, she had in abundance. The relative sunniness of the room and the twittering of the swallows nesting in the bath-house eaves gave her finer instincts admirable material for the creation of bright and happy fancies. Dread visions of death kept away until the end; indeed she hardly realized that it was the death so often heard of in life that now came to her. Death itself came at a moment when the speechless delights of her surroundings were at their tenderest and strongest. It came in the morning, just before five, the crowning moment of the sun and the swallows. The newborn day further chanced to be a Sunday, and at that hour there was nothing in the surroundings to spoil it.

Seen from the moment of death, the life of Man is like a brief, petrified vision, a kind of symbol evoking melancholy. Thus, Silja was twenty-two years old; she was born yonder, a score or so miles to the north, and during her life she moved ever farther southward. From the incorporeal image that death always conjures forth as it were in the air near the scene of its presence, from that picture all inessential features are shed, until one might almost declare all patterns of human fate, in the light of that moment, to be pretty much of like value. In the after-death image of this maiden, which, to be sure, there was no one to absorb with his consciousness so early that Sunday, there was not much to shed. From its secret timeless beginning onward, the whole of her being, as life went by, had grown harmoniously together. A pure unbroken skin held it with elastic bonds in its own dark fastnesses, whence, to the close-held ear of a lover, had carried the beating of a heart, and his seeking eye caught a reflected glance. During her life she had not had time to be much more than a human being who smilingly fulfilled her fate. All that concerns Silja, now lying dead in the Kierikka bathhouse, is for the most part ravishingly insignificant.

True, in the distance represented by the time around her birth, events are dimly discernible in which natural Fate moves on a bolder scale, having to set the luck of this dying breed on a new foundation for its closing phase. For Silja, be it remarked, was the last of her family. The extinction of such breeds of small fame is indeed observed of none; yet in the process are repeated the same melancholy main features as in cases of greater consequence.

The Father

1

The summer-morning death of Silja, that lonely figure left to her own resources, may thus be seen as the end of a long chain of events that we can regard as beginning thirty years earlier, when Silja's father Kustaa inherited the Salmelus farm. It was not a big estate, but the family had held it beyond all memory, at any rate since 1749, the year from which the parish register began; that was a known fact. The reputation of the early masters had of course been forgotten, but probably most of them were the best of the dwellers in the tiny community. The finest strength of the family flourished at its highest during the rule of Kustaa's father. Its growth was imperceptible: rumor knew of no specific acts, either good or bad; yet to humbler toilers the gable windows of Salmelus spoke the language of an ever prouder dignity. There was something peculiarly dignified even in the fact that only one son was born to him, which sole child seemed nevertheless to thrive. During the whole of his childhood he was allowed to live as he liked. He looked on the entire farm as a big playground, where he sauntered, humming and smiling, into boyhood. "The young master of Salmelus" and many another such phrase caressed his ear and mind, little as he pondered over their meaning. The unvarying dignity of his parents educated him in a manner unperceived; hardly anyone had ever heard the master or mistress counsel, let alone punish him. So he grew into a big, smiling youth, who had inherited his slightly beaked nose from his father and the color and expressions of his eyes and hair from his mother.

Doubtless the parents nurtured many silent hopes in regard to their son, but they could not, of course, speak to him of them. The mother was sometimes inclined, when the talk turned to the rest of the world, to explain her own views to the boy, but these attempts ended in a mild argufying and joking, which revealed as in a flash the strong ties of natural affection. The mother was left with the feeling that the boy was what she was, and the father's heart warmed in secret when he saw this. Two centers formed in the boy's mind, around which the incidents of his character settled: one was a kind of unconscious honorableness, honesty, a word he was unaccustomed to hear, the other a strong feeling that Salmelus was something eternally lasting and independent of people, something in which all that happened was as natural as breathing, something that led people instead of being guided by them.

Growing up in this way young Kustaa experienced the funeral, first of his mother, and very soon afterwards of his father. His mother died in the spring while the ice was breaking up, his father in the autumn of the same year.

Immediately after his mother's death, Kustaa sensed that life at Salmelus had been badly shaken for the first time in his experience, that it had taken a new course, from which it was hardly likely to return. Nor could he have said whether the turn was for the better or the worse; the reviving glory of the spring mingled with the gravity of death and a change in life that might lead whither? Clearly something more had happened than the departure of a single person; those who remained were not as before even in the beautiful sunlight.

It was a strange summer. Kustaa returned from taking the horses to pasture. In the midst of the familiar evening glow he shuddered unpleasantly: looking affectionately at the house, he had forgotten that his father lived, was still alive. As though loneliness personified had come to meet him as he stood there at the pasturage gate . . . Hilma, the young kitchenmaid, sat on the porch steps gazing with dreamy eyes at the horizon. An incident usual in the extreme: the farmhands were at supper and the girl was there to help if anything ran short at table. A hundred bright summer evenings may be superficially as alike as the tickets in a lottery. But in one is the great prize; solemnly exciting, as the threat of thunder at bedtime. Kustaa was compelled from a fairly long distance to approach the sitting girl straight across the yard. The girl might have risen and slowly, in perfectly normal fashion, gone in. But she did not do so. She sat there, calmly letting her face reflect her beautiful melancholy mood, her half-swooning glance seeming to demand the familiar young man's recognition of it. To a young man who had lost his mother the mood and glance of the girl were very sweet. He had to place the reins on the wall of the porch where the girl sat. He stretched out over her shoulder to hang them up. . . . There, on that summer evening, were Hilma and Kustaa, coming companions in fate, parents of jointly begotten children. There was no getting rid of that evening by ignoring it.

On the contrary, the consequences of that moment led far and, from the very beginning, in different directions too. It was not long before the old master noticed how matters stood. He tried his best not to see it, but young love that has not yet led to any act fills the whole house with its peculiar throbbing. It issues from each movement and speech of the lovers, even from their silence. In this respect the note of a soft and very modest humming has all the force of a mighty roaring. Impossible, however, for the master of Salmelus to think clearly and simply of matters which his nature abjured. Thus, he now pondered chiefly on the extent to which the death of the mistress had altered the life and atmosphere of the farm, on how much of the loss was inevitably absolute or strove to be compensated in strange forms. . . . The master of Salmelus felt an unpleasant twinge when he found that his meditations had brought him up at the most distasteful of all distasteful minor details: that the girl was a poor servant. "Not that, I didn't mean that," and it seemed to him that this fact, on the contrary, gave to the girl a trait of some alien nobility. Yet the old man sensed in those tiny, ever more frequent incidents something else, the first faint grins of a coming mockery. All unconsciously an old familiar path had been lost, the ground underfoot was now plainly unreliable. And at this rate it would be night before the path was found—if it ever was found again.

The old master was suddenly aware that nothing had been arranged on the farm after the death of the mistress. How had it been possible to go in this fashion? Why, it was as though she who had been escorted away in the spring had not been needed. The master meditated in his room and felt at the same time what he did not desire to feel: how somewhere at that very moment some mocking force of nature was causing two hearts to palpitate, both of them really guiltless. So much the harder, then, this germinating fate, seeing that both were so innocent. The master pondered and gazed at the dark August alders and the cut fields. Martta would have to be invited here. Perhaps she could slightly remedy the change by a new change.

He wrote a letter to his sister and set off that same evening to post it. At the post office he was given a letter containing an invitation to a wedding, three parishes away. He came home at dusk and, speaking of the wedding, said to Kustaa: "I suppose you will have to go there, I don't feel strong enough."

Kustaa consented, in reality blissfully. It was a light task for him now to set out on such a convivial journey. On his departure eyes gave solemn assurances on both sides, and at his destination Kustaa Salmelus was a bright and handsome wedding guest.

He felt greatly refreshed by the wedding. Happiness, accumulated during absence, had not evaporated; it now flooded his being, and all through the last stage of his return journey he was visited by the most delicious moods. Happiness led him a downhill track; even at a distance no difficulties loomed. His luck was indeed good, for at a bend in the road a woman came artlessly from a cottage by the roadside and even more artlessly entered into conversation with him. Kustaa learned one thing and another from her without any show of curiosity on his part, for what more natural than that he should be in no hurry on his home-coming from a wedding that fine evening. The master's sister had come to Salmelus to take charge of the household, and had said at once that no two women were needed in the house if she was to be mistress, and that very day she picked a quarrel with Hilma, whereupon the master had gently told Hilma to look for a new situation. So that Hilma was now back at her home in the backwoods.

"Was that so? Well, goodbye then. Goodbye, goodbye."

Kustaa did not even think of what he

had learned until he was out of sight of the cottage. Neither did he look behind him and see the cottar's little girl creep cautiously after him, and, seeing him turn off along the backwoods track, speed off home again. Not until he was on the track leading to the cabin where Hilma lived did he sit down at the roadside to rest and savor his mood, which had greatly expanded these last few days and now seemed to be turning really bright. All he saw was the trees of the forest, and nothing was farther from his mind than the rule of a household, present or future. To the after-languor of a wedding visit joined easily the light atmosphere of childhood, which in reality had never faded from his mind. He had known Hilma ever since he was a child—actually he was coming home from distances far remoter than the scene of the wedding. The calm warm weather lent to the falling evening a sense of fullness and absence of haste. Long, long hours would pass before he, some time that night, would go to Salmelus, to his own room. As to the mind of a child, the hours before him loomed long and delightful. The private room of a young man is dear to him because of its willingness to wait.

The fullness of life almost oppressed him at the moment when the cabin came into view. Was it not a weekday in summer and had not so much occurred latterly; and was it usual for the heir to Salmelus to walk there as he was doing, dressed in his Sunday clothes? The road and gate-posts seemed to view the approaching visitor with surprise, but the face of the mistress of the cabin revealed some anticipated joy; in it was the same gleam as in the eyes of that old woman by the roadside. Luckily, Hilma was not in the cabin.

"I heard as I was going home that Hilma had left us, so I came to see her."

"There's no room for two mistresses in the same house, we do know." Hilma's mother fussed softly with coffee for the visitor.

"It looks as though Hilma isn't at home."

"Aye, what if your trouble was for nothing?"

"She's out yonder, in the bakery chamber," burst from the youngest sister. Kustaa had the sensation of having called at an envious neighbor's as he came down the steps and smiling, with calm footsteps, crossed the yard to the bakery.

The chamber was a tiny old room with no other view from its windows than the hop-poles and between them a glimpse of field and lake; of the rest of the homestead no sign. There, in the greenish twilight of that low-ceilinged room, he found Hilma. The same girl as on the porch steps at Salmelus, yet not the same. Here the girl was in her own atmosphere, her bosom beat unoppressed by fear, the faint ransom of shame was here a delight. Their love, which hitherto had known neither word nor act, knew both that night.

Kustaa Salmelus—afterwards Silja's father—walked every path of his life with smiling eyes.

Since then years have passed by the dozen, enough for such matters to be forgotten, especially as it was much later that events occurred at Salmelus which here as elsewhere are the real things, things concerning the farm and property.

Yet that autumn was enough to set tingling the minds of the lowly people who, in their confined circumstances, are so greatly in love with the customary. And what, to tell the truth, was there unusual in this event if not its background and the property and chattels involved. The women of the cabins almost suffered from their lack of proper words to describe it. It was an unpleasant, unsettling disturbance of the subconscious foundations of their existence. If a roistering farmer's son had tried to reach the bed of a cottar's daughter by night and been admitted, that would have been a refreshing event in the life of the backwoods. Nothing to worry about for her who could sue a farmer for the support of a child. If all went well, a farmer could pay quite an enormous sum to keep the matter relatively dark. But that was not Kustaa's way, the instinct of the women was annoyingly clear on that point. This phase of the matter, however, faded from memory long ago. The chattering wives have been borne long ago, all admirably silent, from the backwoods to the village church and lie, thoroughly forgotten, in the grassy lines of the common graves. Someone may still know enough to say that the dead wife of that dead master of Salmelus who moved away was born in the cabin yonder, but no one is left who could make a right good tale of it.

The old master of Salmelus lay awake that night until Kustaa came home. It was about two in the morning when he arrived. The boy came on dancing feet, and the father needed to hear or see no more than that to know everything.

The man who arrived at the old house in the moonlight scarcely thought at that moment of the important changes his father and aunt had carried out there. The old master understood it perfectly. He grasped that if the boy had thought at all of such remote matters, he would certainly have been grateful to them. He heard Kustaa getting ready for bed; although the sounds carried faintly, he seemed to read from them the happy state of mind of the mover. When no further sound came, the old master felt himself finally alone, alone with the utter vacuity of his recent arrangements. Though not even to himself would he admit that he had tried to arrange matters with an ultimate motive.

When an old man stays awake in the small hours thinking such thoughts, it is apt to go ill with him, particularly if he can reach no strong redeeming decision. His grip on life relaxes, and in the same degree feels the clutch of death. In the silence of the waning night the master of Salmelus remembered his wife in a specially serious fashion. Up to then his instinct had been that there were two to remember her, and everything had been easier, more loving. Now, suddenly, the inner meaning of things had changed. A spasm shot through the left side of his breast with such pain that the pipe nearly fell out of his hand. He put it quickly from him and began hastily undressing himself that he might be ready in bed, if haply—his sleep were to be long.

Three had formed a whole; when one was torn away, the others fell away lifeless. Continuity was no longer possible; even the farm became a thing unsubstantial to the man aware of the proximity of death. All that still had being was the picture of the dead mistress and the memory of her with those solemn traits that are and remain in every case the living core between husband and wife and become evident to them only at moments of great gravity. Whether he would see another day was of no importance. In a deeper sense, no morrow could ever dawn for him again. His defeat was complete, although no battle could be said to have been waged.

After that night the old master was graver than ever and extremely reticent. He moved about as before, but spoke so little that the men sometimes found it difficult to guess what they were supposed to do, as Kustaa too was inclined to a similar silence. Everyone knew quite well what was happening, but strangely enough the closest spectators found little to say about it. Even Kustaa's excursions were known, but how to tease him about them was somehow a problem.

Once a cottar happened to explain his errand to the master while Kustaa and a few other men were near. The old master said hardly a word, only smiled very faintly and looked at Kustaa. "What do you think?"

Kustaa blushed and smiled, but simultaneously a look of helpless pain came into his face. "What have I . . . ?" He walked away and nearly cried.

Later that evening in Hilma's room, he aroused the girl's attention by his passionate caresses and silence.

"What's the matter with you?" she asked.

The man only stared before him and his jaw quivered.

"Tell me, it will make it easier," went on the girl.

"Father is getting so weak."

These were Kustaa's words and the girl found no other answer than silence and a lapse into non-existent thought. Kustaa laid his head on one side of her breast as a tired child leans on its mother. There he liked to linger, in the mood and the attitude in which the repose of a child and the oblivion of a man are at their deepest.

The master's room at Salmelus and Hilma's room at the cabin. These were the poles of Kustaa's life, between which he moved, in his mind a vague majestic sense of waiting. When he arrived at the one, the other faded entirely. At home he sometimes found himself longing for his mother. On such occasions a soft melancholy drew down his male mind to the safe level of a child's mind.

So wore on the fine weather of the late summer. The weather grew damper, threshing-barns smoked. One morning the master of Salmelus was seen to go to the barn, as usual. From the woodstack he took an armful of split cordwood, threw it over the threshold into the barn and after what looked like a pause, moved clumsily in himself. Martta, his sister, saw this, and as by chance she had happened to watch Vihtori's entry into the barn, so, without thinking of the matter, she continued to stare in the same direction for some time. The morning was colorless and insipid: one of those stray moments of life when even a busy person may suddenly, startled, become aware of the dread weight of time. This happened to Martta, who became conscious at the same time that she had been staring a long time with wide-open eyes at the barn. But no smoke came from the barn, nor did Vihtori reappear through the door. Not the slightest sound came from any part of the farm. Martta rose and looked around her: the clock showed an unexpected hour. Where was everyone?

She went out and stood on the kitchen steps. The opening of the barn gazed at her, black and relentless, seeming to prolong this strange moment of time. What had happened to the world? It would be foolish to walk over to the barn; nevertheless she went. "I came to see what you were dawdling here for," she thought of saying to Vihtori. No sound came from the barn, not even when she was near it. And when she peered over the threshold, she saw Vihtori, dearest of her brothers, lying on the floor with his arms straight along his sides.

Thus that day began with the morning and throughout its course seemed to thicken as evening drew nigh. Usually a sense of relief attaches to the death of an old person, but it was not so in this case. Kustaa had not had a downright talk with his father since he was a child—a childhood that had continued until his mother's death. Now his father had silently drawn away from him, leaving unsaid what he might have had to say to the man. And he who thus withdraws in silence, withdraws a victor.

That evening Kustaa set out rather early for the backwoods.

"What kind of a man are you? Your father still warm and you after women. Do you know, boy, why your father died?"

"I'm thinking Hilma will have to be told," Kustaa answered his aunt.

"I suppose you mean to bring that person here, now that—"

"I don't know. It was you who drove her away."

"I did not drive her away, but I do know that she will not come here so long as the one who drove her away is aboveground."

Kustaa knew exactly how matters stood, yet the conversation made an unpleasant impression on him. If his father's silence had been effective, neither were the words of his father's sister ineffective. Kustaa lacked one quality: he did not know how to be ruthless. There lay the key to his fate, even later, when material misfortunes befell him. He was susceptible to poison.

Hilma was to him what she was, irrevocably all that a wife, good or bad, is to a man; yet the words of this old unmarried woman had their intended effect.

It was not Hilma's fault that she did not know how to approach her sweetheart in these matters, that she was compelled to stop at silence, and affected meditation. Nor did she sin by so doing. She was indeed Kustaa's bride now, but otherwise she was only Hilma, a young and childish backwoods girl, who had been in service at Salmelus—and in her own way had been more skillful than any other. She had known enough to look a man in the eye on that distant summer evening and hold her ground when he bent over her to hang up his reins. By that act she had arrived then at Kustaa's side and remained there. She had confirmed her act by the manner in which she received Kustaa when he came to her room on his return from the wedding. During the whole of that long evening and night all that had happened had been a further growth and confirmation, sufficient to all eternity, of what had already begun.

So that to kill what had then been born was more than any poison could now do.

Hilma did not come to Salmelus while the old master was above-ground. Not until the third day after the funeral, after the last guests had gone, did she come, faintly shy, yet quite sure of herself and not in the slightest afraid of old Martta. A young maiden, who was however in secret already a wife, as such Kustaa saw her now in the old farmhouse, which at that moment began to live again in the rays of a powerful and, now, calm love. Kustaa had not invited Hilma to come, she had been guided by her own sure instinct. Such a coming is more precious than the most precious assurances.

Martta was silent in the kitchen when Kustaa went there, and gave no answer when he asked for some refreshment for the visitor. Kustaa began foraging for himself, but as Anna, the dairymaid, happened to come in at that moment, he asked her to continue. At that Martta burst into an angry weeping in the middle of some small task. Anna made no move, only stared angrily, she too. Kustaa said to her, smiling, but gravely: "Will you do it, Anna?"

Without a word in reply the girl set wrathfully about obeying him.

Kustaa insisted on keeping Hilma overnight. He made the bed for her in the guest-room with his own hands. Hilma smiled her calm smile, rather shy of the familiar imposing interiors and even of Kustaa, who was the master of all this and as such inevitably strange in some ways.

Far away in the distance was the summer day of Hilma's departure, a fair memory with its delicious excitements. Now it was late autumn when Hilma a little clumsily said goodnight to Kustaa on the threshold of the dignified old room. She understood why Kustaa did not follow her into the room. Sleep was slow in coming, but it was good and peaceful in the dark silence, which in a matter-of-fact tone, as though to itself, seemed to be recounting the events that had occurred on this farm, all unfamiliar to her, but pleasant to see in nightly visions like these. She vaguely awaited Kustaa about midnight, but did not feel disappointed at being left alone until daybreak.

During the morning Hilma stayed in the inner rooms, but in the kitchen old Martta angrily prepared to leave the house. When Kustaa saw his aunt's swollen eyelids, he felt a distasteful pity for her. It was as though the old and spiteful woman were not alone, beside her seemed to stand something invisible, something old and harsh, against which one wanted to rebel, although instinct said that it had the weight of generations behind it.

Kustaa inquired as tactfully as he knew how, whether there had been any arrangement about wages.

"I have never been a paid servant in all my life, and am not now."

After this slight thrust Kustaa began to feel that the victory was his when he went to the back room, where Hilma sat in her Sunday clothes and smiled. He had the upper hand of Martta, but even then the day was a strange mixture of Sunday and weekday, happiness and something else. He ought to be picturing to himself how Hilma would soon be moving in here, to become—the mistress. Soon this childish sweet maiden, to whom all oppression of mind was an alien as sin to an angel, would be his altogether; in these rooms, with nothing to be ashamed of, without Martta, without anyone . . . He had not gone to Hilma in the night . . . all this was somehow too gentle, crushing in its softness.

The stable-hand came to ask whether he could be spared to escort Aunt Martta, as she had asked him and was waiting. Even the stable-hand looked bad-tempered and downhearted, as though he too had an angry retort ready for an opportunity to use it. When, a little later, the couple drove out of the gate, with Kustaa and Hilma looking on from the window, Kustaa had a feeling that there was something shameless in that moment into which he, and still more the backwoods girl beside him, had been drawn. The house was definitely emptied of something that had always been there, but was scarcely likely to return. Something of which departing Aunt Martta was only a vague, tiresome relic. It had gone now, but in the walls of the house remained a spirit of permanent bliss. Kustaa felt clearly that that evening, the color of life just then, would henceforward continue. To this he had come with Hilma, who understood nothing of it all; who, like a faithful dumb animal, went where he went, awaiting his sign to give him everything she, a woman, had to give. More than at any other moment Kustaa would have liked to lean his head against Hilma's breast in the deepest oblivion of all. But it ought to happen in the tiny dark bakery-chamber at Hilma's home, with all that this deserted home stood for forgotten—though here the house was, it too like some helpless being that not even a stranger would coldly ignore.

Kustaa was perhaps born to take leave of things, but was unable to leave them. He hardly noticed the crossroads before him: that a path would have led him away from the broad flat road to deep, peaceful, homelike lands. He set off along the broad road, taking with him the weaker of the two.

The dairymaid came to ask what was to be cooked for supper, and who was to cook it. She had no time.

This question of supper made the first steps along the new road deceptively delightful. Hilma had to take her old place in the kitchen, but in a new frame of mind. Again the girl beamed her brightest rays. She enjoyed enormously the contact with familiar things. Here and there alterations had been made since her departure in the summer; now it was all the more pleasant to wipe out this alien touch from some shelf of the cupboard. Supper was prepared, the farm-folk came to eat. A merry cottar took the edge off the atmosphere of self-consciousness by cracking a few hearty jokes about the new mistress, whom he avowed he had missed.

Among the rest of the eaters, especially among the women, a different mood reigned. There were glassy stares and a continued sullenness. And when the same cottar, after resting a few minutes on top of his supper, took his dinner-bag and remarked: "Suppose I too had better go and give my missus a hug," no one made any answer.

Hilma saw nothing of these moods around her. Her womanhood throbbed at its strongest. It was beautiful to have such a very good reason now to stay here another night—why, she had been here since daytime yesterday. And she was more than convinced that her darling beloved man would not leave her to spend the whole night alone.

She went of her own accord to make her bed, again in the guest-room. Was it not evening?

When Kustaa went into the kitchen the next morning, while Hilma still slept, Hilma's mother sat there. With fawning mien she inquired about her daughter—surely the old aunt hadn't eaten her, as she had not come home. And hearing that Hilma was still in bed, which she had of course already heard from the maids, she began playfully insisting that it wasn't for a mistress to dawdle like that in the morning; the farm would soon be sold up. The maids would have a fine lot to say about her.

"I'm not going there until she's gone. What business had she to come here?" said Hilma from her bed to Kustaa.

She got up, however, and went into the kitchen, but Kustaa did not show himself again to Hilma's mother.

In the afternoon Hilma said: "I suppose I'd better go and fetch some of my clothes. Are you coming with me?"

"Perhaps it's just as well that you go alone. The boy can drive you there."

It was twilight before Hilma returned and began setting out a few small objects in the guest-room. With unconscious feminine unscrupulousness she took permanent possession of the room. Kustaa had to come there to visit her, as he had done in her bakery-chamber. And from that day onward she stayed at Salmelus—until her departure eight years later, with Silja, the only child left to her, on her arm. But before that much had time to happen.

True, it was only slowly and by small stages that everything happened. The big clock marched steadily and gravely across the hours of life, minute by minute, holidays and weekdays, through calm and storm. Seen from the clock they look fairly much alike, but if one moves away from the clock and begins to live them, one discovers that they have other dimensions than mere length. Each of them, however, has to be lived by those still in life, and for each minute account must be rendered at least in that the following minute begins from it. It does not begin from emptiness, nor can one elect to begin it from some pleasant past minute.

Thus the young couple at Salmelus

lived their life. As they became accustomed to what had been set going, it became, imperceptibly, as the clock marched ever onward, the fundamental color of life. There was no reason in the beginning to picture the onward flow of years, that was a capacity they had exchanged, during that summer and autumn of wonders, for the glow of the moment.

The wedding was held in all privacy. Hilma's mother came indeed twice to Salmelus to persuade the young couple to celebrate their wedding at Plihtari, at the bride's home, according to custom. But on neither occasion would Kustaa allow himself to be drawn into a conversation with her, and Hilma on her part said that Kustaa could do as he liked.

"People will begin to think the marriage was before the wedding," grumbled Tilta, Hilma's mother.

"It was," said Hilma with a provoking smile.

"Well, then, it doesn't matter where a couple like that is married, if anywhere —perhaps there won't be any wedding."

The mother-in-law's visit ended drily; even the coffee seemed to stick in the woman's throat, and her goodbye was said in a queer whinnying tone. Three weeks, however, had elapsed since the banns were read in church, so that something final had to be done about it. The following morning, while still in bed, Hilma seized Kustaa's hand and said:

"Listen, we shall simply have to see a parson. My clothes are beginning to feel tight."

"Let's go then," said Kustaa, and jerked his hand away with playful ferocity.

A little while later he returned to the room and said:

"Aren't you ready? The trap is waiting."

Hilma had only reached the stage of combing her hair, but she hugely enjoyed this early joke. The comb stopped at first, then began to move at a busier rate.

"Am I to be married today?"

"Aye, and I too, I suppose," Kustaa said playfully.

In spite of everything the day denoted an extaordinarily blissful rise to Hilma. Although the banns had already been read, it was impossible for Hilma to regard herself as other than a girl, whose fate had been what it had been, but whose life was nevertheless sweet and sheltered in the protection of yonder reticent, smiling man. Now she was to be a wedded wife. A wife—Hilma pondered over the word as though it was the first time she had heard it.

Behind a black horse with tinkling bells they drove to the Rectory. On their return later in the day the master soon found an opportunity of saying to the maid: "Ask the mistress."

The supper was richer than usual. There was a white cloth on the table and a few glasses of spirits were served, as the custom had been on festive occasions when the old master was alive. And during the next few days the cottars' and laborers' wives who came to the house were received with more ceremony than usual until all of them had shared in the festivity. The cottars' women returned home on different days by their own paths, thinking of the new and rather strange conditions on Salmelus Farm.

The early winter then passed quietly and peacefully. No one disturbed the young couple; in the absence of other heirs no division of the estate had been necessary. The young mistress went about her tasks on the wintry paths of the yard. An old man from the backwoods would chance to pass the house. Seeing the mistress he would stop, stare with his eyes and bedraggled mouth, and then go on his way, to tell those at home all he had seen on his travels. The blessed state of the mistress of Salmelus was obvious even from the road.

"Ah now, there's a girl who knew her way. How the Plihtari crowd will riot there! Tilta knows what she's about. Funny how some people have all the luck. . . ."

Kustaa was sometimes treated to the sight of the ill-mannered pause of such ancients, and guessed its import. He heard remarks too. One evening, when the stable chaff-boxes were found to be breaking up, the master said good-humoredly, without further thought:

"We'll have to ask old Plihtari to mend them."

He felt as though he had said a good word for his wife in the hearing of all these men. One old cottar, however, flashed out, as though airing some secret fury:

"Devil take it, we don't need any master-worker from Plihtari for that." And as he lifted the box into the manger he swore at the horse.

"Is Vuorenmaa angry with Plihtari about anything?" Kustaa asked the other men.

"It's not worth anybody's while to be angry with a rag like him," muttered Vuorenmaa, who had heard the question.

Kustaa hammered a shade too loudly at the tub beside him, but said no more. The men finished their tasks and hurried away. Vuorenmaa was last and absent-mindedly made as though to blow out the lamp.

"I'm stopping," said Kustaa, and struck the tub a loud blow.

"Stop, damn you, for the rest of your life, if you like," hissed the old man and bounced out of the stable.

Kustaa put out the lamp and followed him.

In the kitchen the men were already at supper and Hilma, too, was busy there, to Kustaa's eye very much as she had used to be while in service. The present kitchenmaid Loviisa, Vuorenmaa's daughter, had seated herself beside her father, the mistress was alone beside the range.

"What are you standing there for? Loviisa can do the waiting," said Kustaa in a strange voice and went past them into the inner rooms.

The hands went on eating without a word, and Hilma remained where she was. A tense atmosphere could be felt in the farmhouse that evening, though no one knew whence it spread.

When the men had risen from their meal and gone out, the cottars to their homes and hired men to their quarters, Kustaa came into the kitchen again, where Hilma still was, now alone with Loviisa. The girl was clearing the table and the mistress seemed to be waiting for an answer to some recent remark.

"Old Vuorenmaa was in a great temper. What's happened to him?" said Hilma as Loviisa went on with her work.

Kustaa looked at the girl's back and then at his wife.

"I don't know what it was about—the old man snapped at me too. Doesn't Loviisa know?"

Kustaa went out, moved about the yard for a while and returned to the kitchen.

"His daughter Eeva's in the family way, I hear. That's what he was full of, I suppose," said Hilma.

"Yes, and it's Iivari Plihtari's doing," said Loviisa and jerked at some object with unnecessary violence.

The married life of Hilma and Kustaa moved steadily onward. Their conversation that evening, after they had withdrawn to their own room, did not lack serious turns and long silences. The Plihtari crowd, Hilma's family, grew in significance each day that passed. Kustaa no longer had the feeling of being alone with Hilma, not even in these late loving hours. The farm and its inhabitants, cottars with their daughters, Plihtari, and Hilma, Plihtari's daughter, were all here now. At one moment Kustaa would be shocked at the run of his thoughts: was he alone among all that? And since when? Perhaps since that evening in the little room at Plihtari, when Hilma had not known what to say to him. . . . Were the two evening hours, then, all there had been to it: one here on the kitchen porch and the other there, on his return from the wedding?

Yes, there was something else. In the movements of the woman with him in the room was none of the shyness of the slender cottage girl, nor need there be. That swollen waist held something untouched by these other things. Kustaa looked and looked as though he was only just now aware of his wife's state; a warm passion unknown to him before filled his blood and spirit. The loss of all that had been at Salmelus before denoted only an emptiness, the weight of which had again been heavy this evening. But from this winter would emerge the spring and then summer! living did not stop, it only had to be sheltered. The moment began to take on nearly the same color as once before on a summer evening on the porch. Hilma's soft sobbing had stopped, the last repartee had been forgotten. Driven by his awakened strong passion, Kustaa crossed over to his wife and hugged her. Hilma's eyes were still bright with moisture as she said:

"Not so hard—you might hurt the boy."

At such moments only the walls of the little room and familiar objects, some of them from Plihtari, from Hilma's former room, encompassed them. They slept like unconscious children, but in the morning, when they awoke, the farm with its workers, the cottars with their daughters, the Plihtaris, were with them.

In the kitchen might be Tilta Plihtari, looking marvelously modestly and humbly at Kustaa as he went by. It would then come out that they were short of money, at home. Hilma would say the words. And when, later in the day, a worker happened to ask for his wages, the master would be a bit short of money—in hand, of course, for there was plenty loaned out during the old master's time. On such days it was as though the traces of Tilta Plihtari's morning call still remained in the house. Kustaa's countenance changed as he spoke to the worker who had come for his wages: red of cheek he looked at Hilma, who ought to know and understand. But on Hilma's face was that special absent air that Kustaa had sometimes seen on it before. Now for the first time he saw it at a moment when they were not alone.

Money, aye, what was to be done about money? He would have to call in a few loans. Kustaa spoke as though to himself, but both the worker and Hilma were permitted to hear. And it was not long after that a debtor came of his own accord and paid back a loan.

"I heard that you were thinking of giving me notice about that loan, and hurried to repay it."

"I've never said a word about you."

"Ville Kivistoja said that the master had threatened to give Korkeemäki notice to repay, one day when he hadn't the money to pay for the woodcutting. But he's such a rattle that there's no trusting what he says."

This event, too, gave rise to a nocturnal conversation between the couple. There was money, however, in the cashbox now, and it was not to be loaned out again. The five hundred marks that Iivari Plihtari got from them before Christmas could hardly be called a loan. The master of Salmelus did not even dream he would ever get it back. Unpleasant, however, the whole matter.

It began to occur ever oftener that when one of them, Kustaa or Hilma, accidentally mentioned the Plihtaris, the conversation led sooner or later to a minor discord. Kustaa showed with increasing clarity that he did not like his mother-in-law's visits; when she sat, honey-sweet, in the kitchen and with obvious pleasure addressed her son-in-law in the presence of the servants, Kustaa would say something, as though in answer, to the dairymaid who drank her coffee apart from the rest. Nor did Kustaa show any special regard for Hilma in this matter. Whoever liked could see the shuddering rise of the man's gorge at such moments, and the young dairymaid would be disconcerted by the needless favor shown by the master. As though she—and this chance kitchen company, on whose side even the mistress appeared to be on those occasions—had unwittingly, by her mere presence, been a source of irritation to something that ought not to be irritated.

In the field and sheds Kustaa would occasionally come on the men in the middle of some coarse tale, which they would break off with a couple of mysterious remarks on his arrival, as though to spite him. "Who said that—or did that?" asked the master openly to get into contact with the spirit of the gathering.

"The girl in the story," the answer might be; or: "the boy when he came home from market." And no other explanation followed, until the master happened to be standing apart from the others with an old cottar, who told him in a fawning tone that it was Iivari Plihtari's adventures that they were joking about.

After such experiences Kustaa would be silent as he laid himself down beside his wife. Hilma sought and pressed his hand, but there was no answering pressure, only the lifeless calluses of palm and fingers, to her touch. The dark silence grew heavier, and under the common quilt both tried to prevent their breathing from being heard. The wife found it harder; her state made her breath come quickly, and agitation made her pant softly. When she turned, a quivering sigh broke from her, and suddenly she seized her husband's arm and amid her passionate sobs a whisper could be made out that tended irresistibly to become a cry.

"Why are you always so sulky? You knew well enough where I came from when you took me. And there's no need for you to see my folks here if you don't want. I haven't asked mother to come here. I'll tell her to keep away. And none of the others have been here."

"They haven't, but their fame has," answered Kustaa harshly.

Hilma seemed not to have heard his remark. She continued to cry and to press ever closer to her husband. Finally Kustaa could not help trying to make some comforting gesture with one hand. But at that the sobbing woman broke into full lamentation.

"Oh, why has it come to this? Why has my life got to be spoiled for such things, when I've never done or been like that?"

Her woman's body felt as though warmer than before and slightly clumsy as she nestled under her husband's shoulder. Realization of this softened the man's temper as it had sometimes done before. Her last sentence, too, claimed his attention: the thought had never entered his mind that Hilma, Plihtari's daughter, might have had her adventures before she came to Salmelus. By Hilma's remark he knew now that on that point at least he need fear nothing: Hilma seemed entirely unconscious of what had happened between them: and that was the surest of all guarantees. Tenderness gained the upper hand in his mind, and he caressed his wife as he had used to do when she was unwed.

Followed hours of silent and loving rest, but in the morning they awoke earlier than usual. The look in their eyes seemed to remind the other of something, and then, in low tones, they began to converse.

Hilma now spoke to her husband for the first time in earnest about her brother Iivari, with whose very latest doings she seemed to be well acquainted. Eeva Vuorenmaa had probably been delivered of a child by now, and the child was Iivari's, there could hardly be any getting away from that. The Vuorenmaas, however, were said to have let it get about that if Iivari would definitely agree and was able to pay Eeva five hundred marks, they would not go to law. But it would have to be done before Christmas, or else he would get the writ as a Christmas present. But how could Iivari be expected to own such a sum—unless he could borrow it somewhere and work off the loan little by little with odd jobs.

Kustaa acted as though Hilma had put a direct question to him or appealed to him outright.

"You ought really to go there today and get all the facts straight," Kustaa said as he got up to dress, and by the gentleness of his voice he let her know that he would not mind her resting awhile yet. And Hilma remained in bed, warmed by his attention, though she had no need of rest. It was good, anyhow, to think over the weeks still before her and her preparations, those done and those still ahead.

The earth was frozen, but the winter's snow had not come yet. The road from Salmelus to Plihtari was in good condition even for a bad walker, so that it was only with faint protests that Kustaa allowed Hilma to set out on foot. It was nice to watch her move along the road, away from the house, on a known errand. Hilma walked rather heavily, but still with so much elasticity that the sight warmed the heart of her husband. To Hilma herself the journey brought a powerful joy unexperienced by her before: it was only now that she had the feeling of approaching her former home as the established mistress of a farm.

The air that rushed to meet her as she opened the cabin door felt unfamiliar too for the first time, and for one moment a feeling flashed into her mind that she was on an unnecessary and badly planned errand. Her mother had paused in a strange attitude in the middle of the floor and was looking at her daughter as at some mysterious intruder, taking in with bold directness and at great length the swelled contours of her body before saying:

"Been sacked by some old aunt again?"

"What makes you think that?" It was all the daughter could say.

"I was only thinking that the mistress of a farm as big as yours would have had no need to walk all that way in your state."

"And I thought that it would be nice walking on a dry road, as I was in no hurry. Old Granny Tonttila told me that a fair amount of walking would be good for me."

"Is it Granny Tonttila's advice you're following these days? Well, she's known how to advise her own, as two of them have brats for no other known reason than that self-same advice."

"Soon there'll be two of yours as well off as hers. One's got his squalling already, I hear, and the other's not far off, as you can see."

It was no more than might have been expected of Tilta, yet the very air of the cabin seemed more disgusting this time than ever before. It gave, however, an easy lead for the errand on which she had come. Iivari himself was not at home, probably after squirrels with his gun.

"No, he's not at Kyntöhuhta hearing the prices at market, so's he can send his squirrel-skins," said the youngest sister irritably.

"Aye, then there'll be something for Vuorenmaa's daughter to lay her hands on," grumbled the mother, this time at her son.

Not until old Plihtari, the father, came on the scene, hooked his ax on a peg, threw his mittens on a rafter and got the necessary hold of the subject, did the talk lose its edge. Old Vuorenmaa had personally told him that they would be content with five hundred marks; he had objected that it was rather a lot, but the old chap had started harping on rich sons-in-law and all kinds of things.

Hilma's little sister listened with her high forehead drawn into deep wrinkles as the grown-ups arranged the matter.

"Kustaa can lend it well enough," said Hilma in a thin adult voice and so that all of them could note her use of that Christian name. "But Iivari'll have to pay it back."

"I'm sure he wouldn't take it as a gift. Who knows whether he'll consent to borrow it?" said the father amicably.

Hilma was really grown-up as she discussed the matter in brief phrases. Even the mother let fall a gracious remark, and when at last old Plihtari set out with his horse, no less, and rattling cart to take his daughter to Salmelus, there reigned at the moment of departure a real clannish spirit in the house, of the kind that comes seldom, but when it does come is exceedingly familiar to all, warm, like a nourishing breath. It remained hovering over the mother, sister, and the air of the cabin and accompanied the married sister as she sat beside her father behind the familiar small horse. Only when Salmelus came into view did Hilma lose her confidence. The gable windows of Salmelus were like a seeing eye, and Hilma felt as though in some way she was there, behind those windows, and had never gone from there, though she was now sitting beside her father. To enter Salmelus now gave her almost the same feeling that entering the Plihtari cabin had given that morning. The blissful happiness she had known a moment ago made the place seem strange to her. With painful effort Plihtari's little mare, driven by the old man, drew its load up from the storehouse hollow to the kitchen steps.

The master and mistress debated this time with old Plihtari in the inner rooms. The farm-hands might think and say what they liked. They had plenty to say. Some of them passed fairly straight hints to old Vuorenmaa. Eeva's chances of getting her baby its due, one of them said, were very good, judging by the big pile of cakes that had gathered below the old mare's hindquarters at her hitching-post.

"The Devil and all," said old Vuorenmaa, spitting angrily.

Kustaa knew well enough that the clearest and surest way would be for him to give the money to Vuorenmaa; and if it had not been for the recent incident in the stable he might have done so. It was impossible now. He gave the notes to his flushed and voluble father-in-law, knowing as he gave them that they were gone forever and doubting the outcome.

During Plihtari's slow leavetaking Kustaa vanished and did not reappear in the house until he heard the rattle of the departing cart. He understood Hilma's festive mood, which on that cold day of early winter illumined the whole house, but could not help being irritated by it. Somehow it made him feel more alone than ever, in spite of his wife's evident efforts to draw nearer to him. Hilma tried by her gestures and glances to reveal that there was no need for Kustaa to bother about that, or about anything else. And she succeeded. That evening they could still forget their worries of the day.

The Plihtari family then kept away from Salmelus until, on the day before Christmas Eve, Hilma's young sister appeared, with an invitation to Kustaa and Hilma to come to Plihtari some time during the holidays. The invitation was reasonable enough, as the young couple had not once been together to the wife's former home. When Kustaa, on his way to work in the morning, saw his sister-in-law on the bench in the kitchen where his mother-in-law usually sat, he nodded affably and even shook hands. And when Hilma told him her sister's errand in the girl's hearing, he answered in the same mood: "Yes, let's go during the holidays. But, have you got anything in the way of a Christmas gift to take there?"

But at the same moment an unpleasant memory awoke in his mind: the words Christmas gift reminded him of Vuorenmaa and of the "Christmas gift" Vuorenmaa had threatened to give the Plihtaris, of whom there were again two in the kitchen. Let one of them into the house and at once there were two.

Kustaa went into the cattle-yard and hoped that when he returned, his wife's sister would have gone.

Vuorenmaa happened to be working there just then at some little winter-day job set for him by the master. Faintly sullen in appearance, as usual, he glanced now and then towards the kitchen door, as though expecting someone. When the Plihtari girl finally appeared, he left his work without hesitation and went to talk to her. The conversation did not last long. Vuorenmaa came back to his work, to where the master was still standing.

"I asked the girl what young Plihtari means to do about his child, but she didn't know. Christmas is near enough now, so that perhaps it's best to set the sheriff on the job."

The master said nothing, and Vuorenmaa went on with his work. When at last he cast a side glance at the master he saw the familiar threatening flush on his cheeks. For all his age Vuorenmaa was still a man, and in his prime no one had dared to lay hands on him. With the young master of Salmelus, however, it had happened to him more than once that against his will he had had to speed up his work while the master stood beside him, gripping him, or so it felt, by the neck. Or else he had to get quickly out of the way, as on that day in the stable. Something like that was in the air now, so long as the master remained silent.

"Hasn't Iivari been to see you about some agreement?" came at last the master's voice as though from somewhere behind his throat.

"He—has—not." Vuorenmaa let the words come one after the other as a winning card-player plays his last cards. Obviously the man knew everything.

The master turned away as though to search for something in his pocket. He turned back again and asked in an ever thinner voice:

"Will five hundred be enough for Eeva?" Not until he had uttered the words did he see how much deeper he had sunk: he had never even discussed the matter before with Vuorenmaa, or the sum.

Vuorenmaa gave a harshly worded assent, and the master turned away again. When he turned once more to speak, he had to clear his throat, first softly, then loudly.

"You can leave your work early

enough for you to get to the sheriff's in your working time, to hear what he has to say."

The master then went his way in earnest. At any rate, his last word had been an order to his cottar. But how alone he was.

From this began the first act done by Kustaa without the knowledge of his wife; perhaps it was also the beginning of his outward misfortune. But, as we have hinted before, order had to be made out of disorder, whether by the course of life itself or by its humble agent is a matter of indifference, if one takes the wide view. Kustaa may have thought, who knows, that he only wanted to spare Hilma a distressing agitation, her pregnancy being nearly at its end. Somewhere, however, at the back of his thoughts was the feeling that he was punishing somebody; certainly also himself.

It was easy for Kustaa to get away to the village, what with Christmas preparations in the air. He found so much to do that the time passed almost unnoticed to late evening. When he left home Hilma submissively suggested that he might bring something for the Plihtaris. To this Kustaa said nothing. At the village he was seen to go first of all to the sheriff's; from there he called at the tanner's and then went to the shop, where, very slowly, he made his purchases. The horse stood for hours on end at the hitching-post, and the clumsy scrolls of the embroidered date on the Salmelus sleigh rug hung over the back of his sleigh. As it was rare for Kustaa to leave his farm, one and another of the customers at the shop came to shake hands with him. He saw old Vuorenmaa approach the shop—look at the old fellow, coming right to the village in his resiny working clothes. The master of Salmelus began to make his departure and reached the shadow of the doorway just as the cottar entered. There were those in the shop whose eyes took on a new gleam, especially after Vuorenmaa had paid for his purchases out of a fairly big wad of notes, which anyone could see had not been long in the old man's pocket.

Half an hour later the sheriff and his wife gazed on the young farmer who, for the second time that day, was setting out from their yard. They admired the fine flush on his cheeks, his slightly arched nose and his valuable rug. They spoke, too, of the matter that the master of Salmelus had arranged that day through the sheriff. The matter had resulted in a document now in Kustaa's pocket, attesting that: "I Kaarle son of Sefania Vuorenmaa, on behalf of my daughter Eeva, a minor . . . received . . . undertake full responsibility that no money in respect of the child will hereafter be sued for from Iivari Plihtari . . . event of death her assigns shall not be required to repay . . ."

This document Kustaa Salmelus thus kept secret from his wife. For all that on his return home he was calm and gave a a full account of his purchases to his wife. True, he had not known what to buy the Plihtaris, but perhaps Hilma would find something suitable at home. And if Kustaa henceforward was rather inclined to absent himself, there was nothing in that to awaken Hilma's surprise; it was inevitable that in their intimate relations, for the time being, Kustaa would gradually have to draw aside.

They paid their Christmas holiday visit to Plihtari, although Kustaa knew as they set out that the journey would not end well. And as Kustaa is as central a figure in this story as his future daughter, towards whom the story is shaping, and as this visit denoted a decisive turn on the path to which this last male descendant of his family had been brought, the visit should be described in full.

2

Plihtari was an old homestead on the edge of a sparsely-populated backwood settlement; a characteristic winding forest road led to it, marked in summer by the raised roots of trees and the cow-tracks that thickened into muddy patches with greeny-yellow pools at the halts formed by gates; in winter by the deep ruts of wood-loads and bunches of hay accumulated at the gates. A generation ago it had been a prosperous homestead, but the present Heikki had allowed it gradually to deteriorate. To some extent this was due to the expiration of the former lease; the tenant having fattened, the owner naturally made the terms of the new lease harder, and as Heikki Plihtari was a simple, good-natured fellow, he was incapable of leaving the place, but agreed to a curtailment of his usufruct rather than have his rent raised. But just as much it was due to something wrong in the way the household was ruled. Heikki had married, or had been snatched by, Tilta, one of the notorious Karjaharju girls and the handling of one of these would have been task enough for a harder man. Along with her there came into the house a certain unrest and commotion, a groping, grasping spirit. Whatever was gained thereby, Tilta regarded as her work and especially as redounding to her honor; what was lost, of that Heikki heard sufficient. Tilta bore three children, of whom the oldest, Hilma, although taking more after her father, mild and silent, succeeded after all so marvelously in becoming mistress of the old and respected Salmelus estate; quite as though there never had been a half-ruined Plihtari and the girl had burst into bloom there out of the air.

And now in answer to an invitation, she drove beside her husband along the wintry road. The day was a Sunday between Christmas and New Year's Day. Hilma was in a rather inspired mood, for they had even been together to church that day, as on some pleasure trip. The smile of the man too sitting beside her was more expressive than usual, as though his wielding of the reins was some jolly task, the import of which would be revealed later. A pretty visiting load in every way.

At their destination, the Plihtari cabin, they were expected, but the moment never comes there when everything would be ready to receive anyone. During these Christmas holidays quarrels have been even more frequent in the cabin than usual, and now the old man in particular fumes and grumbles, without really knowing at whom. He it was who took the money and in some measure he is guilty of its shrinkage, though he never intended as big a hole in it as that. All he had wanted was a new bell for his horse-collar and a set of winter harness, and he was sure that at a pinch Vuorenmaa would have agreed to wait for that bit even until after Christmas. But then Tilta took her share and finally Iivari himself took some, and in the end the sum was not big enough to be worth while taking to Vuorenmaa. Iivari and Tilta side with each other; with her connivance the son has been at the barrel of strong ale that was not to be tapped until the Salmelus couple came, and now he mocks at the whole matter.

"Stop that jawing, you scoundrel," roared the old man at his son with really astonishing vehemence. The son stood up and began, cursing, to explain that he had never begged anything from the master of Salmelus, and God help him, never would; if a man like me isn't good enough to be his wife's brother, he can do without, and I'm not going to feed any brats of Vuorenmaa's daughter. At that, however, paternal instincts began to awaken in good-natured Heikki. He roared louder, but the son only seemed to brace himself up, and the mother was about to intervene—when all at once the tinkle of an unfamiliar sleigh-bell sounded from the stable corner, the arched neck of a bay filly came into view, followed by two familiar faces at the back of a sleigh. A moment later Heikki was already holding the reins; Iivari had slipped round the porch and out of sight.

He was allowed to go in peace, even to stop and listen how humbly Tilta and Heikki received their visitors; no one took any notice of him, Iivari. His self-confidence swelled as he trod the narrow path through the snow towards the cellar. From the cellar door he sank into the dank mild depths, smelling of damp stone, fumbled through a series of familiar actions, until the friendly noise of strong ale running into a can answered from the darkness.

"Yonder in the little room there's our old man now, father—hm—and then that young Salmelus, who's like a father even to father—ah—and then our sister, stuck up, she too—Ah-h—" So ran Iivari Plihtari's thoughts as in the darkness of the cellar he sipped the drink that had been strictly decreed was to be saved for the master of Salmelus. And the more he drank, the sicker he became alike of Plihtari and Salmelus and Vuorenmaa, each in his own sphere, and he decided to go somewhere else, to the neighboring villages, not to return until the visitors could be expected to have gone. He made sure the tap of the barrel was closed, locked the cellar door and, without thinking of what he was doing, put the big key in his pocket. His temper ran high, yet for the length of a furrow he advanced half running.

Inside, the visitors had been led into the little room, newly heated, and Tilta was to bring coffee and cake there while Heikki mulled ale. It was not long, therefore, before the loss of the key was discovered, and the fact that Iivari, too, had disappeared, though no one thought at first of connecting the two. Fierce, whispered quarreling, bustling and the sound of searching carried through the wall, whereupon Hilma went to see what was the matter. The drive to Plihtari had flushed her slightly thinned face to real beauty, and she wore a new dress, straight and ample, made especially for her, as for gentlewomen in her state. She was a fairly imposing sight as with her arms behind her back she stepped into the empty center of the living-room floor, like any other guest from a guest-chamber.

It was Hilma, too, who first began to suspect that the key might be in Iivari's possession. And after a few ejaculations and a protracted aimless searching, the hosts were ready, as though defeated in their efforts to keep Iivari out of it, to accept the theory. Hilma begged that the door might be left alone until the boy came, surely he would not be long; but when Tilta firmly declared her intention of having the potatoes for soup out of there within an hour, Heikki went off without a word to the cellar and broke open the door. Soon ale foamed in the tankard and old Heikki was able to lead the talk with his son-in-law in the direction he wanted. An old man like him didn't need much before both his voice and his speech grew soft. Heikki described matters, and the mother and daughters delivered the side-remarks demanded by the fashion of the family. The old man's account stretched over the whole evening and only ended in the living-room bed, into which he collapsed in a noisy slumber at nine, fully clad. By that time it had been clearly explained how it would actually have been foolish to thrust all that money on the Vuorenmaa crowd, when it wasn't even said that the child was Iivari's.

"Yes he is its father," broke in the fourteen-year-old sister at this point.

"You shut up," roared the mother in answer and then went on to say that they hadn't taken out a writ after all, in spite of their threats to have it served as a Christmas present, and that was why Iivari was now so joyful that he'd taken the key.

"If he took it," interjected the youngest of the family.

"Yes, perhaps it was you," whinnied the father in an attempt at a joke.

Kustaa, too, had sampled the excellent ale with a relish—Tilta Plihtari was so skillful at brewing that she was often fetched to brew guest-ale on the big estates. In honor of her son-in-law she had now brewed according to her reputation, for which purpose she had had to make a new breach in the notes obtained from Kustaa, and Iivari had not had time to draw more than a couple of quarts from the cask. The fine flush on the cheeks of the master of Salmelus gradually turned into a dull red, and at last he too was delivering a similar endless, though rather vaguer, speech to that of his father-in-law. He related to Hilma's mother Tilta how he had been thinking over that matter of Iivari's and come to the conclusion that if his father and mother had been alive to advise him, he, though the matter did not concern him, Kustaa, or his wife, the slightest bit, he would have had to do something for the sake of the family name, and so in the end he had paid up after all. To this the mother-in-law did her best to explain that even if the money they got had not been put to that purpose, it had not been wasted, not much of it. Anyone would feel ashamed to visit a son-in-law like him with old tattered harness like theirs had been—folk might have taken them for a pack of gypsies—and so on, beyond Kustaa's understanding just now.

And so matters became no clearer until Iivari, returning home, made them plain. His manner of explanation was such as to bring the newly-formed bonds between the parties to their final and irremediable strain. Snap they might, but only after a series of deaths.

Old Heikki was thus already speechless in his bed at nine, and Tilta's meal, for which the potatoes had been brought through the same broken door as the ale, was at last ready for Hilma and Kustaa to enjoy. They ate in solitude in the little room, and by now Kustaa was explaining to Hilma all that about the advice his father and mother would have given him. Then the first sounds of the brawling of approaching drunkards were heard, soon to resolve themselves into a babble of speech, after which the noise of Iivari groping clumsily into the cellar could be heard even in the room. He did not stay there long; soon doors banged, first the porch-door, then the living-room door, where arose the commotion that might have been expected.

Tilta's reproachful whispers alternated with Iivari's ever louder opinions. "Our ale isn't going to be drunk by that Salmelus lot. It's surely Kustaa Salmelus's own brat, as he's paid both me and Vuorenmaa's girl now—ho-ho-hoo—oh God save us—is that parrot-beak still here with his woman?"

Even Heikki could be heard awakening in his bed and trying to yell some command, but he was soon silent again. Then Hilma rose from table and rushed into the living-room. Kustaa stayed where he was, but cocked his ears, and soon he heard something that made him get up and go into the living-room.

He came at the right moment to see, and experience, an event that remained the only one of its quality in his whole life. Was that well-dressed pregnant woman really his wife, and the drunken man who at that same moment pushed the woman so that she staggered helplessly against the corner of the stove, was it his wife's relative, her brother? Whatever they were, Kustaa Salmelus, for the first and last time in his life, now did violence to another man. A dreadful nausea gripped the whole of his being as he felt his fingers twist into the collar of that—Iivari, was that his name?—so that the side of his forefinger lay along the man's flesh. They were bent somehow over the oven-side bench, some brand-new harness dangled between them, and Kustaa came to his senses to find two women shrieking prayers into his ear. His grip relaxed on a man whose face was dark-blue and from whose one hand a big iron key, from the other the tap of a barrel, had fallen to the floor. He saw old Plihtari standing behind him in solemn anger, as though the old man had just quelled him. Somewhat confused, Kustaa laughed aloud and said: "Now the Salmelus family is going." He saw Tilta and Hilma trying to revive their still unconscious Iivari, and dashed hatless towards his sleigh.

Kustaa did not properly awake until on his homeward journey in the sleigh, while skillfully avoiding a bad stump he had noted on his arrival, he saw his wife sitting beside him as though half-asleep, looking slightly bored. Before them shone the moon, newly risen. Kustaa remembered everything, and refrained from opening his mouth. He was again midway between Salmelus and Plihtari. Was his father still alive there where he was bound? No: not even alive. Matters were bad.

In the yard Hilma got out of the sleigh and went, she too wordless, inside. Kustaa settled the horse in the stable, and when he arrived at the bedside, Hilma lay there turned away and seemed to sleep. A long quivering sigh, however, showed that she lay awake.

3

When people say that so-and-so lost his farm, they are not as a rule referring to any specific event that was directly responsible for the loss, unless the question is expressly of the hauls made towards the end of the 'sixties. In those years of helpless famine many a resouceful farmer laid the foundations of the material prosperity which enables his son even today to walk idle and rich, especially if the "old man" had the sense to eject his chief tenants before newfangled protective legislation came into force. In those years, towards the end of the famine, farms were sometimes sold by the provincial authorities for unpaid taxes of no great size, and if one of these far-sighted farmers had the coin, naturally he went and bid for the threatened estate rather than lend the money to his oppressed neighbor, who was unable to do more, perhaps, than read a few chapters of Luther before trying to sleep.

And sometimes a fever wiped out the folk on a farm so well as to leave no importunate supplicants for help, beyond perhaps a half-witted old pensioner. The tale might be embroidered to any length —recalling off-hand phases of it as one views the half-educated landowners who pry even today for the chance of a good bargain in land and then turn one's gaze to some taciturn, wizened old laborer in whose features one seems to descry a certain dignity, only to hear that he is the former master of such and such a farm.

These matters are in a class by themselves and link up with the history of the country, with the great joint trials of the nation.

The everyday, less noticeable cases, however, are sometimes much more mysterious in their hidden causes. On many farms sickness can strike down the cattle, children, the wife, twice in succession; an April wind can wipe the tender rye-shoots off the soil and an August frost freeze the sap in the half-ripe ears of summer corn; fires can occur or a neighbor for whom the master has entered into security fail; and still the farmer remains on his land. But the next generation, son or son-in-law, can be swept away, though nothing of the kind befall again. On the contrary, in the 'nineties, the time with which we are concerned just now—the rule of Kustaa and Hilma at Salmelus lasted fairly exactly that decade through —it might happen that the first symptom of decay was an outwardly swift rise in wealth and consequence. The results of the forest sales of those times are well known; it is easy to imagine that type of old rustic swaggering with his money in some town tavern. Now that the debris of those fellings has rotted where it lay and new trees await their fate at the forester's hands, the sole relics of those sudden accessions to wealth are a few stone granaries on insecure foundations and those raw-looking "best room" windows with two bare upright panes and a third laid crosswise over them, which remind one especially of the leather money-case of a forest-buyer of the period. A pot of money obtained by the drawing of a crow's-foot tempted the farmer to show himself modern, and that none might fail to see it, he altered the old dignified six-pane windows of his best room to the kind in his brother's home in the suburb of a town, that same brother who made a definite pauper of his country brother, and so on. . . .

The last hereditary master of Salmelus sold no forest and did not change the old greenish window-panes of his house. And although to Kustaa, on his return from that Christmas-tide visit, the instinct of centuries of landowners whispered that his life and situation were not what they should have been, his straightforward nature, in which, to be sure, was also a strain of high-minded obstinacy, was wholly unable to grasp that he was the master who was to lose Salmelus. Even afterwards, when the enormous bulk of the master of Roimala already grunted its satisfied appreciation of the Salmelus lands, Kustaa could not have named any specific act by which he or his wife could have occasioned the loss.

In the morning Kustaa awoke first, lit the lamp and then looked at his wife, beside whom he had slept this as other nights. Hilma seemed to be sleeping more heavily than usual; her face was half turned away, and its lifeless expression was directed elsewhere, as though to some other life, as one gazing at it from afar, well able to understand its meaning. The quick breathing of the sleeper seemed to affirm its entire innocence of what the face revealed. The heavy womb discernible under the counterpane was like the touching relic of some catastrophe.

A strange blight lay on the man's awakening consciousness. Why should he feel like this, growing worse as moment by moment memory returned. We were at Plihtari, with the sleigh . . . didn't I stable the horse . . . ale and food . . . well, now I made the trip we spoke about . . . and there's the daughter who still followed me from there . . . aye, I am fastened to her, she is mine, mine . . . aye, what can rightly be the matter with me. . . .

Kustaa remembered how old Heikki Plihtari, that loose-kneed ancient, had been the last to stand on the cabin floor, as though he had vanquished them all, even Kustaa, his son-in-law. . . . Why, it was as though he had become the old man's son. . . . Was that what his relations with Plihtari had become. . . . Plihtari's worthless old tenant still fathering it over him here, in this early morning hour, in this old room at Salmelus, all through that daughter of his sleeping there who . . . was firmly anchored here and . . . It was the same room as before, although for long now its atmosphere had not resembled that of the former guest-room; sweated and breathed to exhaustion as the air was. Nor was there any longer the familiar coughing of his father beyond the door . . . I live on the farm alone now, with no one to support me . . . and there sleeps that . . .

Hilma did not awaken even now. Perhaps, while the night wore on and her husband slept, her own agitation had continued, until but a while ago she fell asleep. Kustaa dressed himself slowly; it had to be done, seeing that it was morning, and early winter working morning. On such mornings a farmer rises on awakening, no matter what his night was like. If he is undisturbed in mind, no gazing on a wife for him, for his wife will have risen before him and awakened the maids, whose sleep never ends of itself. A happy farmer has no thoughts as he draws near to his stable in the morning twilight and hears the familiar whinny of his own hack. The men follow him and know their work.

But at Salmelus on that particular morning neither maid nor mistress was yet awake, and there was no sign of the men; and the master tried to think as he trod the stable-path.

He went into the stable and carried out his usual tasks: lit a lamp, shoveled out dung and curried his horse. Then he put the harness on its back. As he busied himself it seemed to him as though some other person was following through his eyes what he did, trying to guess his intention. As a matter of fact he had no intentions, but—he had to go somewhere. The men's soiled sleighs stood outside the stable where they had been left the last weekday; they would be driven off again after day had broken on their old tracks, no master needed for that. Or really—a good deal was needed, but now the master was off to the distant back-meadows to fetch hay. That too was a man's job and very suitable for a master between holidays. The best time to set off would be a couple of hours later. But an early bird . . .

As he drew fast the collar of his horse, Kustaa paused a little, as though thinking together with his horse. The morning was a silent moistish winter morning, so still that the rumbling in the horse's stomach sounded clear and sharp, and when the horse shook off the last vestiges of stable warmth, the clatter of harness and the shafts made a great noise.

Just then the maid Loviisa went past near enough to see what the master was about; she saw the cage for the hay and would thus be able to tell the mistress where he had gone. From the porch she still looked back, then went shivering inside and could be seen lighting the fire. The master felt that he could set off. Unnecessary to go in again to say anything.

Kustaa let the horse take its own pace. It was still so early that he would reach the meadows before dawn. Standing in the sleigh a man could well sink into thought of any depth. The road wound on, a deep furrow across fields, pasturage, forests. A single pair of tracks; the space between them gave the width acquired by an ordinary farm sleigh through the centuries. His son's sleigh would fit, if one might say so, the ruts left by his father's.

Kustaa thought of what he would now do. He had a general feeling that he had to get rid of something. What it was he could not discover, it only felt good to drive off into the wilds. The snow-embedded forest made a man forget the worries he had acquired with his fields. Such moments of oblivion were to be had here at any time, although the thoughts attached to the cleared land always won in the end and took up their everlasting round.

To escape, and never see again or need to remember at least that male being whose throat his hands had recently crushed and for whom he could not, at that moment, think of a name. But as he imagined, standing in the sleigh, such an escape, at once there rolled up so much else that seemed to depend on that male being. The Plihtari homestead and its inhabitants, the daughter now probably awakening in the room at Salmelus, with no companion beside her for the first time since she became mistress of the house. Aye, and Salmelus too, the whole farm, even those who had bequeathed it to him: mother and father, all became joined to that dim idea of escape, in the end even he himself, as though he would have had to escape from himself too. And then that which would soon be born. For the first time Kustaa now thought of that too, directly and bluntly. But even from that, thought led straight to the same sore point, irresistibly. Kustaa's gorge rose: that male being was just dashing Hilma against the corner of the stove when he intervened. Or, his intervention came too late; had not he seen his wife's body fly against the stove. And now afterwards he had the feeling that he had not received proper restitution from that being, and never would. Such things had to be avenged on the instant.

The image of Iivari Plihtari continued to grow in Kustaa's consciousness; powerless the snow-clad forest to help him any longer. As the morning advanced that too became shorn of charm. Iivari Plihtari, that drunken brutal clod, had laid hands on his wife heavy with child, his wife, who was also—oh!—a sister, its sister. More and more entangled everything; ever greater the disgust that swelled in his breast. Kustaa was unable and ashamed to think the matter out, but somewhere at the bottom of his mind he felt that that man had attacked his unborn child too and not only his wife. By his act the man had in some way thrust him, Kustaa, from his strange throne, vaguely envisaged as yet, of fatherhood. He was almost aghast at his own state. Even to fare in this direction seemed vain; the road seemed to be saying: you can drive along me for all I care, but that's all the help you'll get from me. You'll have to turn back anyhow.

Kustaa's road led past Vuorenmaa's cabin, a matter he had not thought of when he set out. The road went rather steeply downhill just there, so that he drove past at a trot. But on his return with the load the horse walked all the slower. For that matter, the young master of Salmelus no longer found any particular grudge in his mind against Vuorenmaa. On the contrary, something new and refreshing seemed to attach to the man at that moment. Old Vuorenmaa was indeed a man and had always been one. He had always been on good terms with Kustaa's father too.

On the return journey the horse stopped of its own accord at Vuorenmaa's well. Kustaa drew water for it, and seeing faces at the window he deemed it the right thing to go in. He was very thirsty.

The old man stood in the middle of the floor, looking as though he was just about to depart, and cast a sharp, somewhat doubtful eye on Kustaa. It turned out that he was just going up to the farm, was he maybe very late, seeing that the master had already done so much? No hurry at all, these holiday times. Vuorenmaa could have a seat on the load, with the master. Easier for an old man to travel lying down than upright.—Aye, that's right, one had to lie down anyway when the end came.

From the adjoining room came the sound of a cradle rocking; the cradle was moved at intervals, after which the sound was fainter for a time. Then it stopped altogether, and Eeva came into the living-room, pale and with her clothes thrown on anyhow. Kustaa asked for something to drink. The mother asked Eeva to fetch it. But it would have to be mulled first.

The ale came; the visitor noted that it had fermented to perfection. Short sentences were exchanged, words that sought for openings and were charged with hidden meanings, until at last it was possible to speak outright. And once that point was reached, there was much to say. Even old Vuorenmaa gave his idea of matters at great length, as he saw them, and he was not to be misled, poor as he was. Finally he spoke standing up and then began firmly demanding that they should go to Salmelus; he, anyhow, had to go, the master could do as he liked. And he pulled on his gauntlets ostentatiously, crossing his thumbs loudly.

Kustaa did not leave. His horse stood at the gate all that winter afternoon. Someone who went past recognized it, and marveled, recalling the relations between Vuorenmaa and Kustaa. Hard words were being exchanged there, he would wager. The matter was wonderful enough, however, to make a detour to Salmelus necessary, to mention the news in the kitchen. And an hour later an old woman's jaw was wagging there: "It was the master of Salmelus all right, I know his horse, I do, and Vuorenmaa's woman was fetching in ale from the cellar. Easy for them to brew ale now, after all the money Eeva got. And the master of Salmelus is the right man to offer a head-full of it to . . ."

Hilma too heard. Without a word she went back into the inner rooms. It was growing dark. Meanwhile Kustaa felt at home in the Vuorenmaa cabin. Warmed by the ale, he talked with the women, with Eeva too, for hours; old Vuorenmaa had carried out his threat and disappeared. Eeva, the daughter who had had a child, sat quite primly alone with the master of Salmelus while her mother was out on some necessary task, sat and conversed patiently, though firmly, skillfully keeping the master's rather slowly advancing argument on the right track. No reason why there should be any quarrel between these two, the master and Eeva, two people, if one might say so, in a similar relation to Plihtari. Kustaa offered the wife payment for the ale, but the woman refused it. "We keep no tavern here and no other loose life either, even if that girl yonder did happen out for a bit of bad luck. . . . Is it true what people are saying, that master had already given the money once to Plihtari and that they spent it on themselves, so that master had to pay it twice over? To be sure, it was only Iivari who had said so, but he was shouting it yesterday all over the village and then bragging about all kinds of things. . . ."

At this point Kustaa seemed to wake up. He stared at the tankard a moment or two, then swallowed its contents and said goodbye, but no more. With composed features he went out of the door, fumbled a little over the unfamiliar steps, gave his horse more water and then climbed on to the load. The midwinter day was over in the backwoods.

It was over also at Salmelus.

"Has this farm any meadows so far away that it takes a whole day to get there?" Hilma asked her husband when he came into the house. It was the first time Hilma used this tone. During the day one thing and another had occurred on the farm which the master ought to have attended to, and the mistress had

had to act and worry over them to the best of her ability. Money too had been needed, and Hilma had not been able to find enough.

As the woman did not cease complaining, Kustaa said in a tired voice:

"Are there any new children to pay for at Plihtari?"

This too was probably the cruelest word ever spoken by the man to his wife.

"Who knows," answered Hilma. "This last one may well be part yours, as your time passes so quickly with that bitch."

Kustaa's expression grew suddenly sharp; he seemed to attack her with his glance. But in the wife's eye was a faint mockery. She was not alarmed, but stood sure of herself and arrogant behind the shelter of her unborn child. Kustaa saw the two of them as though arrayed against him. He was aghast. In his own house he was living as in the house of an enemy.

From such a situation there is never a complete escape. Sad that love should always begin at its highest, purest level, so that often its only course can be downward. Between man and wife it is like an organism of whose veins and tissues some, once broken, can never heal again. The wisest course would be to keep it outwardly rugged and bare from the very beginning. And for a man the very wisest thing would be to seek a wife beyond three forests and seven lakes.

Already during that winter one and another neighbor had his attention drawn to matters in the management of the Salmelus farm that had been done differently during the reign of former masters. Repairs that ought to have been done, a fallen board from the outer lining of the house, a sloping gatepost, were left undone for ever longer periods. In the fields work that ought to have been done in the autumn was left to the spring. Even ditches were left undug. All this became apparent during the succeeding years; no need to recount single details.

Nor was Fate very promising in regard to the continuation of the family line.

In its own way the day when Hilma lay down on her first childbed was a high point in Kustaa's life. The mistress had risen in the morning as usual and sat beside the kitchen table, weakly guiding the household work as well as she could, mostly giving way when the maid offered a contrary suggestion. "Do as you like, I haven't the strength and don't know enough." And by a gesture that had become customary she slightly raised the hem of her dress to observe once more how swollen her ankles and even her calves were.

Suddenly her glance seemed to dissolve, she stood up, but remained leaning on the edge of the table. Loviisa saw her fingers clench. "Mistress, what's the matter with you? Shall I fetch master?"

When the master came, the mistress had already gone into the bedroom and stood in a strange half-leaning posture at the door. Since that Monday their relations had been what one might expect them to be. They had been kept private, however, and no dispute of any consequence had taken place in the presence of others. No one from Plihtari had been to Salmelus. Kustaa had kept mostly to the fields and yard, and even in the evenings little had been said. The nearer Hilma's time came, of which she herself had only a vague idea, the more insignificant Kustaa felt himself beside her, whatever her behavior. Gradually, too, the memory of that moment at the Plihtari stove faded, though sometimes, when they lay silent in their common bed, there came over him that loathsome feeling that someone of such and such name had as it were violated his secretest fatherhood. Kustaa no longer awaited his heir, as one might have expected, knowing his strong male feeling at the time from which his expectations might properly date. Now he merely existed in a situation created for him, unconsciously fending off certain dreadful flashes from his mind. Lest they should crystallize into definite hopes.

Now, as he entered that room of many memories, he felt a new warmth gush through his being. It flowed towards the wife, who in her strange posture seemed to be appealing to the protective instinct of the male. He went across to his wife and without noticing it put his hand on her shoulder and asked her some trifling question. She turned her face to him, and the man was astonished at her expression. Her face had the appearance of some part of her skin that it was impermissible for him to be looking on in such fashion.

"Will you go and tell Granny Tonttila that I sent for her. Tell her to try to come without the whole village noticing it at once, and there's no need to send any word to Plihtari. Go now—oh!"

This was the day, then, that had been ordained, this day was to be the day of days, a day the old farm had not experienced since the birth of its master. Outwardly the news of the beginning pangs of the mistress weighed down the atmosphere of the house, but inwardly it aroused a solemn excitement. The young maids, girl-children of their mothers, felt as though their worth had been increased that day by the state of their mistress. Supreme power over the household was wielded by Granny Tonttila, who gave directions and commands, and who, although usually a good-natured person, would now look no one in the eye, but said her say as it were off-hand. As the day wore on her expression became graver.

The master kept to outdoor work, trying to arrange that there would always be something that he could do alone, now in the woodshed, now in the storehouses, now in the barns. Even to the latter place his feet led him, although once he was there he could not remember what it was he was supposed to be fetching. He opened the door—and there before him was the place where his father had been found, stricken by death. The son stood calmly, with vague eyes. Was it for this he had walked as far as the barns? His brain projected a realistic vision of his father on the right spot on the floor, but the ghost seemed to be sleeping its own sleep before the fireplace and had nothing to say to the son. At least it did not blame him for anything.

Kustaa sat down on the threshold of the barn, half outside of the building; it was as though he felt most at home here after all. He had a clear view of the house from where he sat, even of the window behind which was Hilma, Hilma, whom he had brought here and made. Kustaa had a very vague idea of the process of birth, but he suspected that to it attached, besides pain, blood and other matters that had to be decently spirited away. In it all was something that aroused a man's loathing . . . and to it all joined again . . . again all that of a little while ago, foremost Iivari. The picture of Iivari seemed to float somewhere nearer to the bedroom, its expression saying that if it came to that, he didn't mind being mixed up in this either, but he wasn't going to bow down to Kustaa's topboots. . . . And beside it was the mother . . . and then the drive to fetch hay . . . and over there was now being born that which had become mixed up . . ah . . . The dreadful thing, kin to a hope, was again trying to rise right to the level of conscious thought. Kustaa wailed in spirit, cast himself wholly into the barn and without thinking of what he was doing took his stand in the middle of the space where his father's body had lain. He stood there as though listening to something. Slowly his mind resolved into a state resembling that of a little boy, and so he started off towards the house again.

A search had already been made for him. Everywhere in the house an unfamiliar petrified stillness. The maid Loviisa came out of the bedroom with deliberate slowness and an attempt at silence. "Would the master go in," she said queerly. The master went.

Granny Tonttila's face was in a curious sensitive twist. She seemed to be crying without tears. These few days Kustaa had felt himself a stranger in his own rooms; at that moment the feeling was at its strongest. Everything in the room was different from what it had been. The bed had been moved to form a passage between it and the wall, and it was there that Granny Tonttila stood. Hilma lay in the bed, pale, with eyes listlessly shut, nor did she open them as Kustaa drew near. The finest acts of affection and the meetest words of love of which that weak and humble woman had been capable, now came into the man's mind in one general impression that included them all. At such a moment the measure of affection left in a man for his wife is shown to him, shown every bit as exactly as if he were to go to a cupboard and count the money in his box.

"No human aid could help thee, and never will unless God helps too," said Granny Tonttila faintly.

And as she spoke the old woman turned her gaze to a bundle placed across the foot of the bed. Kustaa too looked, emptiness in his eyes, for he sought nothing. In the opening of the bundle the purple, lifeless head of an infant was visible.

Kustaa could not indeed think of it as a child, still less his child, nor that it was lifeless. When he finally understood, a curious mood descended on him. No despair, not an inkling of sorrow. Even Granny Tonttila's attention was awakened, so that her own mind withdrew for a time from its agitation. She noted for the first time that Kustaa resembled his father, who never showed any agitation in any circumstances. Granny Tonttila had helped to bring Kustaa into the world and since then had regarded him as her boy. Now, before her eyes, this Salmelus boy took on the apparition of staid middle-age, as in certain weather one can follow the growth and development of a cloud against a wall of sky.

But, even in the innermost depths of Kustaa's mind, neither despair nor sorrow could have been found at that moment. His face showed that which moved invisible within him, but its nature was unguessable. He felt a quite special sense of liberation that had begun out there on the barn floor and now reached its height. Actually his expression as he looked upon his dead child resembled the expression one can imagine dwells on the face of a victorious duelist at the moment when his opponent's seconds tend a collapsing body.

Kustaa turned once more towards Hilma, who had revived so much that she was conscious of her husband's presence. A very faint red had risen to her cheeks; Kustaa took note of it as a sleepless person waiting for morning notes the first reddish rays in the air of his room. And now Granny Tonttila witnessed something she had never seen before among country people in her professional capacity. The husband bent down towards his wife and pressed his cheek against the woman's brow. It was Kustaa's own individual caress that he had earlier often bestowed on Hilma. He did it now in the presence of a third person, that moderately good old woman. He felt his cheek warm Hilma's icy forehead.

Something returned—not to what it had been, yet to some measure of permanence, and thereafter remained in the main unaltered. It was repeated years later in outwardly similar circumstances when Hilma, once more recumbent in weakness, was giving up her own spirit to death. The marriage of Kustaa and Hilma was now what it was.

To many other things the day and the moment brought a certain stability. Husband and wife were thereafter more alone together than before; the rest of the world withdrew to its natural distance. During the next few years some flickering touch of feeling at odd moments could recall the first period of Hilma's wifehood, the time when she, though unmarried, was already Kustaa's wife, so distinctly that even Hilma observed it and told her observation to Kustaa.

The Plihtari family of course still existed, Iivari, the old man and the others, and sometimes showed a tendency to make family calls at Salmelus. But since that first still-born child, Hilma's attitude towards them was in some way more passive than before. If she happened to hear of their doings, she no longer drew them into as close connection as before with her own family life. Iivari spent, as a matter of fact, a good deal of time in lumber camps outside of the parish during those years, and did not consequently come into direct contact with Kustaa. And since that moment of mutual recognition at Hilma's childbed, Kustaa perceived a change in his own mental attitude towards his wife's scapegrace brother. Now and then he dreamed indeed a dream that set his spirit on edge even after he had awakened: seeing that dead child of his in a dream he invariably identified it in some way with Iivari, in the fainting state in which Iivari emerged from his hands on that occasion in the Plihtari cabin.

4

So far as this story is concerned, the next few years could be passed over briefly and the reader brought straight to Silja, the youngest child of the marriage and the only one to live for any length of time. The married life of Kustaa and Hilma had now become settled, but it no longer brought them the cheerful strength needed to run the farm. Hilma had not had much of it to begin with, child as she was of a feckless backwoods cabin, with no heritage of such strength in her blood. It was as though the status of Salmelus had dropped a rung lower during the first conflicts of their married life, and as the years went by it began to resemble one of those medium-sized farms with a large family, the master of which only just manages to scrape through with his children and taxes. Even from this level, however, the couple managed to descend another rung outwardly to about the one from which Hilma had come.

Something had come back beside that unhappy childbed, but—much was gone forever. However well everything had turned out and even if that unhappy visit to Plihtari had never been made, much would in any case have altered. Hilma was no longer the fair young girl who had set Kustaa's mind on fire and provided him with the highest flowering festival weeks of his youth. What then now, after all those calamities! There were all kinds of after-rites that left behind them an impression which this simple woman was unable to efface from her husband's mind quickly enough by her own efforts. The man went his way, wondering at the events thrown in his way by life, and struggled. . . . Struggled without thinking of help from his wife in this battle.

About two years later, without any

special fuss, a boy was born to them, who was christened Taavetti, which had been the first Christian name of Kustaa's father. Two years later came a girl whom they named Laura, that too an old Salmelus name.

Two sentences suffice to relate these events, but the years in question contained much more. Never in all his life-struggle was Kustaa Salmelus at a lower ebb than during the time between the births of these two children and the years that followed. His characteristic smile often vanished altogether during those years, without any compensating flashes of manly anger as had been the case when he was younger, during his years of level strength when surrender was not even to be contemplated. Now there was much that it was vain to quarrel with, that slowly bore him down without arousing him to open opposition. In some curious fashion everything in the household grew slacker and thinner, and a day came when the master of Salmelus signed a note of hand in the room of the master of Roimala, as during his childhood many a homespun-clad topbooted farmer in difficulties had done in Kustaa's father's room. He well remembered those old cabin-dwellers and backwoods farmers, red with embarrassment and nervously restless, on whom his father enjoined the importance of paying their interest regularly. It had been one continued recollection of his father and his boyhood, the gradual calling-in of these loans. Now the master of Roimala, a prosperous stout man, one of the leaders of the parish, stroked his side-whiskers and warned Kustaa that he wanted his interest on the appointed day. He then made a rumbling noise in his throat and nose and began to speak of the approaching election of Electors for the Farmers' Estate of the Diet, strongly recommending a certain Elector—who was later elected and helped to send the master of Roimala to the Diet. For that matter, without the support of the Salmelus vote.

The master of Roimala was elected to the Diet, and once there he sponsored a proposal for draining a lake in the parish, or for a government subsidy towards the cost of the work. His bill passed. Now the Roimala estate and another farm recently bought by Roimala gave largely on the lake, so that it was only natural that their owner should go to some trouble to secure the support of the gentlemen of the Diet for his plan. But the matter also concerned the interests of other farms; certain lands belonging to Salmelus faced the lake too. And the owners of these farms were now called upon to contribute a certain sum towards the amount needed over and above the subsidy. Roimala was the guiding spirit of the plan and everyone grasped that it would be carried out as he wanted it to be and also that someone would benefit by it—at any rate Roimala himself.

Kustaa's domestic life was just then at its lowest. The children were ailing, often really ill, and had to be rocked in the cradle most of the night. The guest-room at Salmelus, where a cool unbreathed air had once greeted the visitor and which by the merest chance had become the bedroom of the twain, although a more homely room, the old master's, was available beside it—the guest-room was now filled day and night with the smell of babies and drying cloths. It was no pleasure to a man to go there in the evening, especially when his wife was constantly bewailing some pain or cough.

Kustaa never bought drink for the house, except for some celebration, and these were rare at Salmelus. During those years, however, it happened fairly often that Kustaa would drink to intoxication while out in the village; somehow he always happened to be there where liquor was flowing, the worse matters were at home the oftener. Once he drank himself nearly into a helpless condition. This was after the meeting at which the shareholders agreed about the cost of draining the lake and paid their shares. The meeting was held in Roimala. Salmelus and another farmer with very little land lacked cash and regretted their inability to pay, whereupon the master of Roimala offered to lend them the money. Notes of hand were written, and Roimala gave an acknowledgment that the lake-money had been received; no money changed hands. While drinks were being handed round an old farmer who had been a good friend of Kustaa's father took Kustaa aside and said a few words of warning with regard to Roimala. "You ought rather to have sold some of your timber," the old farmer said.

"I'm not going to start selling forest; my father was always against it," said Kustaa.

"Your father may have been that, seeing that these notes of hand were the other way round with him to what happened to you just now."

When Kustaa awoke in the morning he had no clear impression of how he had come home. But this he remembered, that in Roimala's desk there were now two notes of hand written by him, Kustaa. Hilma was still in bed, not asleep, though she did not move even when she saw Kustaa dressing; she had the air of one pondering over some painful matter. One of the children lay beside her, the other could be heard crying in the kitchen. The maid was trying to soothe it, the hour was therefore late enough for the maids to be up, though both master and mistress were still in bed. Kustaa was so out of countenance that he was unable to make up his mind what to do. He hardly answered old Vuorenmaa's civil question.

Such was the life of the twain in their prime. It began to look as though after the two children now alive, no third child was to come to Salmelus. But the time came for that too—and it was Silja, the only one to reach maturity, who was then born. The origin of the girl's existence is related to an event that was one of the happiest in the now fairly joyless life of Hilma and Kustaa. The mood of the two on that occasion resembled in surprising degree the first period of Hilma's wifehood, the time when a love out of the ordinary so bravely expelled the old traditional spirit from the guestroom at Salmelus. Hilma and Kustaa were invited to a wedding on the same farm where Kustaa had been when Hilma was driven away from Salmelus. The farm was three parishes away and they had to spend the night there; ultimately they spent two nights. Both were marvelously rejuvenated during the days and nights they were away from Salmelus. For that matter they had hardly slept a night together elsewhere since the nights in the bakery room at Plihtari during their first summer. The wedding was a grand one and the festivities lasted three days; between meals there was dancing and ale. Even Kustaa Salmelus danced. On the night of the wedding he could not persuade Hilma to more than a square dance, but the next day Hilma too dared polkas and mazurkas. It was an unusually merry wedding. In the big house were many rooms, one apiece for couples from a distance, while the young people slept on large common beds on the floors of the company rooms. Skylarking and giggling could be heard from these rooms up to dawn, but it did not disturb the married couples in the bedrooms, some of whom, inspired by the spirit of jollity, slept in the first close embrace for long.

Even after their return to Salmelus the festive mood of Hilma and Kustaa continued. Hilma in particular had shed years; she whispered the fact in her husband's ear on their first night again in their everyday bed. "It's just like old times, do you remember? We'll see whether it ends in the same as then."

As the sun sometimes looks backward, gilding the tops of the forest with a sudden beam before setting, so for Hilma and Kustaa the wedding formed a break in their life that was like a gleam from better days. The workaday life of the farm with its difficulties soon withered the brief after-love of the two, but there was one thing it could not stop. The union of two living human cells, growing apace and acquiring at the right periods certain shapes, began more and more to resemble a human being. No one saw it, for it was hidden in the womb of the woman, bound to her by a throbbing cord.

And birth came again to Salmelus, for the fourth and last time. At a certain unpredicted moment the embryo, that had eagerly moved its limbs for some months, began a new series of movements. It turned its head in the direction it was to take, then its shoulders and finally its trunk and limbs—until it had wholly emerged into the light of day; the umbilical cord snapped and a girl-child began its life, of which at that moment no one could say with certainty more than that which applies to all life: that it would end in death.

Just then, to be sure, no one thought of death. The birth had been an easy one, and although Hilma was very tired, she was calm and happy when Kustaa came to her bedside. Curiously enough, the family atmosphere resembled that attending a first birth, one that has turned out happily. It was an evening in spring, and the sunbeams awakened an illusion of happiness in the old room as Granny Tonttila fetched the coffee specially brewed by her for this occasion. It was strong and clear, intended to refresh the exhausted mother. The child had already been bathed and slept peacefully in its fresh-smelling basket when Kustaa bent down to examine it. The father's smile was at its brightest. Even the pale older children seemed nearer to him that day.

After a few hours the child awoke. It was put to its mother's breast and at once began suckling fiercely. It lived. The father gazed at it and forgot his cares.

Cares he had in abundance. He had been compelled more than once to ask Roimala for a small additional loan to pay his interest. Roimala did not refuse. Sharp-sighted neighbors began to guess whither relations between Roimala and Salmelus were tending.

"The best thing Kustaa could do indeed would be to sell his farm and buy a smaller one, the distaff side of his family being weak-like—he'll lose it to Roimala anyhow in the end, so it's no use Kustaa's beggaring himself for Roimala's benefit." So spoke certain staid farmers among themselves, and sometimes, over a glass, even to Kustaa.

Poor, indeed, was the living on the farm, as in any big household whose mistress is growing weaker. It sapped Kustaa's energy too; if it had not been for that darling youngest child, it is very likely that Kustaa would have done the trick and sold his farm. But the girl, christened Cecilia but called Silja, grew and prospered and knew nothing of adversity. She had large gentle eyes with beautiful eyelashes. The color of her eyes, almost black at first, turned gradually into a pure brown. In her features was a hint of her father, and certain old people declared that she resembled in quite special degree Kustaa's mother in her youth. Strange how the two older children were outshone by the youngest, whom everyone addressed and treated as Kustaa had been treated when he, an only child, was the apple of the eye of the dignified master and mistress of Salmelus.

As it turned out, the life of the two other children, Taave and Laura, never came to denote much, to anyone. They moved about together hand in hand, silent and slightly timid, as though each saw his or her main support in the other. Until the time came for them to depart, when, after lying ill side by side in the same bed, they died, one a couple of days before the other. Their sickness was an extremely infectious epidemic that laid low a very large number of the parish children within a few weeks and is sometimes mentioned even now, after the elapse of decades.

Silja did not fall ill, though she had been allowed to move freely in the sickroom. More than one of the people on the farm and its visitors remarked that one would see what happened to that youngest. Kustaa was reticent, but his soft smile began to reappear. As adversity grew until it finally reached its present exceptional stage, the man, now past middle age, began to divine, somewhere at the bottom of his consciousness, that in all this he had been carrying out some preordained task. It seemed almost as though past generations nodded to him as he moved in such thoughts and by their gesture wished to say that to be sure the farm, the inheritance, would have been good to keep and increase, but as matters have turned out you must remember that there is something in a man, the retention and increase of which is more. And as though to seal the matter, that invisible nod seemed to include in its circle the girl-child who by that time had begun to seek the hand of her father in her toddles.

Difficulties on the farm increased. Most of the hay made in the previous summer had rotted. First it had been gathered in too fresh, and self-combustion had begun, so that it had to be carted out anew to dry. Then, just as the hay was ready to be stored in the sheds, a sudden rain made it wetter than it had been while growing. The master was not at home, and so— A master ought not to have too many errands outside of his farm. The part of the hay that was finally dried was not worth much. Good oat-straw, it was said, would be better, which is true. But that year more straw had to be used than usual, and the result was that during the most critical period of the spring, just when the children too lay ill, the state of the Salmelus cattle became serious; the cows began to develop softness of bone and the horses grew thin. Kustaa had done his best to economize with grain, but now the dairymaid threatened to go unless she was given something to feed the cattle. Cows, however, cannot be fed on grain alone, but must have some green fodder.

Thus there was distress on both sides of the yard-fence. Kustaa moved about like a sleepwalker. Hilma took to her bed ever oftener, and her face and the way her clothes hung on her showed that she was not doing it without good cause. An expert stranger could have concluded with entire confidence that not many more cuckoos would fall to the lot of the mistress of Salmelus to hear. Even Kustaa sensed that for Hilma and him there would be no more weddings like that one a while ago, three parishes away.

Kustaa went one day to see the old farmer who had been a great friend of his father's and who had once warned him. "Can you lend me some money, seeing that you warned me about getting mixed up with Roimala," Kustaa said openly.

But the farmer explained that much as he regretted it, it was impossible, so willingly as he would have helped Vihtori Salmelus's son. "You see, I'm an old man and according to the laws of dust my time is short. It's no good me moving even an inch from the road I have trodden in the days of my strength, the road your father too trod, or I'd soon be walking about on the same errand that brings you here. I am not rich, but I have my living, and in the hardest times God has helped me, as I have helped myself. You are caught so tight in Roimala's net that even for that reason it wouldn't be right for me to meddle in your affairs. You, dear boy, have done certain deeds on the path of your life that it isn't for me to judge, and for that matter I haven't heard anything of you that would be unbecoming in a man—on the contrary I have caught a glimpse of your father in your doings. But"—and here the aged farmer nodded his white head—"your father was a sturdy farmer who knew his job, and at your best you're only middling good. There's something gentleman-like in you that comes from your mother's side, well I know it, and I am quite sure that even if it goes ill with you in this world, your eternal welfare is in order."

He spoke as he had often had to speak, during his many years as an alderman, to some young inexperienced judge on his first circuit. As an old man he had to end up by dwelling on the future life. Not that he was grown sentimental, for he knew what practical advice to give his friend's son. He now repeated his advice about selling timber, but Kustaa explained that Roimala had a mortgage on the farm and that the agreement was that even if Kustaa were to sell a single tree the money would have to be given to Roimala in payment of his debt. The debt was now so large that a good deal of forest would have to be cut before there would be enough left over to help Kustaa out of his present fix, and that was something he was not prepared to do, and even that would not bring in anything at once.

"Aye, aye, aye, aye," said the old alderman. "I see, I see everything. He's got his eye on the sawmill, it's in a bad fix just now, soon ripe for harvesting, that blade too, aye, aye . . ."

Kustaa hardly heard the old man's conclusions, so rapt he was in the critical position of his own farm. Not until the old fellow began talking again of Kustaa's affairs did he wake up and take an interest in the conversation. "So much I do know about your affairs that you are not quite a pauper even now. The question is, do you know how to sell your farm to the best advantage? Aye, there's no need for you to start, for as you are now placed and even with an eye to the future I can't see any other way out. Roimala means to get it, everything shows that, but—let us see whether that czar is going to get it for nothing. I know your farm well, both the lands and the forest, and I tell you—I've been thinking over the matter before this—if Roimala does not pay you—so and so much, well—I will."

The last words came with conscious weight and were followed by a dignified snort, as though the old man had been standing up to deliver a speech and then sat down.

This valuation of his farm was the only benefit Kustaa gained by his visit. He was in sore need of money—the cattle were crying for fodder and the farm-hands for wages. All that was left to him was—to drive to Roimala.

Even Roimala, however, was unwilling to lend this time, but began, he too, enumerating the mistakes Kustaa had committed during his life, doing it in a much coarser manner than the old alderman. Roimala emitted mighty grunts and had a coarse name for everything connected with Kustaa's youthful visits to Plihtari. "The only heir to a farm as big as yours gets out of such matters by paying—even boys from worthless backwoods cabins manage that sometimes, so

I hear—ha-ha—as you well know. . . ."

Up to this point Kustaa had blushed. Now he paled and his teeth met. This was the moment of his deepest degradation, and what was he to do? He stood up; Roimala too was silent and slowly hoisted his mighty carcass into its well-known backward curve. Again Kustaa felt himself entirely alone. At that moment the only thing near to him was his own male spirit. The shadow of that big-bodied man seemed already to lie over Salmelus; what Kustaa had to do was to try to save what he could from that shadow as quickly as possible, his wife, two sick and one healthy child, servants, cattle. It was not worth while losing one's temper over the man, who was again stroking those side-whiskers of his, a man too old and helpless for anyone to lay hands on him. Kustaa laughed, he too, with one corner of his mouth, a gesture he had never made before. Then he said:

"Take the whole farm, for that is what you want."

Roimala's eyebrows rose, as they sometimes did in church when the parson, forced thereto by his text, had to say something touching the destruction of soul so easily brought about by earthly mammon. Well, well, so the man was already offering his farm.

"Yes, it may well be that you are not the right man, as you are now fixed anyhow, to manage a farm, and I'm well able to buy it and manage it too. . . . But—ahem—we can't talk of such things without toddy. Mother, will you send us some hot water and sugar," shouted the master through the crack of the door in a voice that forced Kustaa to laugh, though a deep disgust at the hypocritical warmth of the words and tone was near to turning his stomach.

The toddy tasted well to Kustaa Salmelus at that moment. Now that he had gone so far, he might just as well go on sitting here. He was on his guard, however, and only surrendered outwardly. Roimala acted in as fatherly a fashion as he knew how; he spoke in almost the same tone as he had used in ordering the hot water. He tried to offer different prices on different conditions, now for the farm alone, now for the farm and movable property, now for the farm and part of the movables. It was on the latter basis that the sale was finally settled. Kustaa was not quite sure what kind of a bargain he had made, but as Roimala had agreed to pay him a good deal more than the sum mentioned by the alderman as a lowest limit, he shook hands to seal the bargain. Roimala counted out a deposit, and a day was appointed on which the deed of sale would be drafted.

Kustaa felt no regret, even in the morning. Hilma, on her part, staggered about with a shawl over her head, nursing her sick children. Seeing money she revived somewhat and began getting ready for a trip to the village—there was wheat flour to be bought and the house had run out of coffee. The trip was made.

There was also, however, the future to be planned. Best move to town and start something there, was Hilma's opinion. To this, Kustaa's only answer was the news that Roimala had granted them the right to these two rooms and kitchen up to the autumn, if they wished to stay. In his own mind Kustaa had already decided that he would not stay a day longer than necessary, but would take the first opportunity of securing some smaller place farther south. Strange how he was drawn southward. He had so much money over that he knew he would be able to pick up some cabin and a patch of land.

Roimala had his own proposal ready in that matter too. On his backwoods lands there was a cabin that he was prepared to sell. Or he might perhaps

lease it with a bit of land. "You would be a kind of watchman for my timber," said Roimala. Kustaa said nothing, but went out of the room at Salmelus where Roimala was sitting; he had "dropped in to look at this third farm of mine." As he went away through the yard he said to Kustaa:

"I had a good look at those rooms and made up my mind that you won't need the back one, as the one next to the kitchen is so roomy. And anybody can see that you'll soon be less one bed-full, they're that bad, the girl and the boy. . . . Aye, and let's see . . . keep an eye on that corner of the forest next to Plihtari, those 'in-laws of yours have been using it as their own, but seeing that I made a bargain with you for the farm as it stood, what I mean is that it will be your loss like, if anything's taken away there."

Kustaa let the man talk and cough in a self-important manner. And then Roimala was off again. Kustaa went off too, into the house, where "one bed-full" was indeed sobbing out its last breaths. The boy died that same day, the girl kept them waiting for her end the whole of the next day.

In some way life was again high and solemn, as it had not been for long. There was no lack of anything; the cattle got their fodder, the humans their food. Even a faint touch of luxury was not lacking. Hilma had retained a juvenile fondness for pancakes, and now she fried them, thin and greasy, so that they almost crumbled in the hand. Even the maids got their share; the whole population of the farm lived in a state of joint expectancy. One period of waiting, to be sure, was over; the little boy and girl who had always been together, now lay side by side on boards in the store-room, their pinched bodies blue with frost. Little Silja was as well as before. Enwrapping all life was again, now perhaps stronger then ever, that quite special atmosphere of happiness that had made itself felt for the first time at Salmelus when Hilma Plihtari finally settled down there, when the old aunt departed—from that day to the marriage. At other times, too, the same feeling had occasionally embraced everyone on the farm.

For Kustaa luck was favorable in that quite of itself, a new and in his opinion suitable home appeared for them. The sheriff told Kustaa about it when the deed of sale was signed, having heard of it by chance. It was two parishes away to the south and was in the market for a curious reason that the sheriff related over the coffee at Roimala. "You go and look it over," he advised Kustaa. And Kustaa, who had learned to trust the sheriff, followed his advice on this occasion too, making his inspection and closing the bargain on the same trip.

Everything went on excellently now, matters once having begun to do so. Kustaa arranged his movables carefully, setting apart those articles which had to be left to Roimala and those he intended selling by auction. He then arranged for the sale to be held a fortnight later, on a Monday, following the burial of the children on the Sunday.

The time of waiting for the funeral and auction was a time of peaceful and deep rest for the whole family and the farmhands. On the pretext of fetching a piece of timber Kustaa drove through his backwoods, as on a farewell visit, for it was there after all that his dearest memories centered. Some related to little adventures of his boyhood on occasions when he had been allowed to accompany the laborers to those distant sites and had been able to eat from a dinner-pail like a full-grown man. On these farewell rounds he passed Vuorenmaa, that too the scene of an adventure on a misty December day at the time that first still-born child came. The memory of that birth brought a curious pang, and this time he refrained from going into the house, though he watered his horse at the well.

Hilma made a few visits, the nearest on swaying feet, those farther off in the trap—as they still had the horses and hardly any work for them. She paid one visit to her parents at Plihtari, and the visit troubled Kustaa not at all.

Then came a day when the joiner brought the children's coffins ordered from him and the bodies were laid in them and dressed out. The baptismal robe had been preserved and was now used for the dead girl; thin as she had become, it was not too small for her. "Let her take the baptismal dress with her, no more children of mine will be baptized, and other people's children are nothing to me," said Hilma with a dim smile when one of the servants made a timid reference to that side of the matter.

During those days little Silja was a kind of outside being whom no one knew how to treat in a natural manner. Kustaa carried her in his arms, oftener than ever before. Even outside the house the master was seen carrying the thickly-clad girl. He was heard to talk to the child in a lively manner, which the farmhands found solemn in some strange way, but at the same time touching too. The master had never been heard to chatter like that before, either to children or others.

The appointed days drew nearer. After the lapse of centuries a turn was occurring in the history of Salmelus.

When he sold his farm, Kustaa dispensed with his regular hired hands, who were taken over by Roimala and had latterly been working on his farm. It happened therefore that when the dead children were taken to the grave it was Vuorenmaa, with the usual expression of slightly ill-tempered gravity on his face, who drove the hearse. Kustaa drove his own sleigh with the family in it. Hilma was very tired and it was not particularly wise to expose Silja to the sharp late-winter wind, but someone had to escort the poor dead.

This was in fact the last time that the couple drove from the Salmelus estate as master and mistress; already the next day the auction was to take place. There they now drove, and that was about all they had accomplished by their marriage. They drove almost as once before, many years ago, to Plihtari, on that Christmas holiday, a little before the birth of the first child.

Now both were much older; in Hilma hardly a trace was left of the features with which the young master of Salmelus had fallen in love. She now looked like any cottar's wife, some of her teeth gone, the others dimmed, like her hair. During her mistress-ship she had not even put on the usual flesh of her status, but the delicious softness too of her girlhood had vanished and given way to angularity.

In Kustaa's face and figure, older as he had become, the inherited marks of race were indelibly visible. On this journey they seemed clearer than ever. A woman who, in her youth, had looked with favor on Kustaa Salmelus, and perhaps hoped that he would return her glance, was among those in the churchyard, standing apart from the rest. She was able to see Kustaa in profile, and her heart was moved and warmed when Kustaa stood bareheaded during the service.

She saw Kustaa again as he walked up the aisle in the church, erect and with his head in a familiar pose, and sat down in the Salmelus pew. A slight mist rose before the eyes of many acquaintances as they looked at the couple: the calm man, on whose face was always the finest shadow of a smile, and the weary woman, of whom no one could really say a bad word, only that that body too has probably done what she could, but from whom could a Plihtari girl have learned the skill demanded of a mistress of Salmelus.

Nor did the little girl escape notice, as she toddled, the only survivor, between her parents, tending to ask a little too loudly what everything was, for it was her first time in church. A brown-eyed girl with a well-shaped head, in which one could note resemblances to her father and mother. A pity the child was not able to grow a little older in the family house.

The child was suddenly heard to ask in a high-pitched voice where Laura and Taave had been left: why hadn't they come into church, were they still in their coffins? The whole congregation was as one family at the moment when the child's words vibrated in the air. Then the organ began humming and gave little Silja an impression she remembered all her life. Surely in her fading consciousness the same music accompanied the twittering of the swallows on that early morning when she died in the bath-house at Kierikka. Now, however, she was alive and could not quite understand why Laura and Taave were not alive too. On the way home she still demanded, as they passed the churchyard, that now, at any rate, they ought to be fetched from there. Her mother said that they had gone to Heaven and would never come back any more. Silja pondered over this in silence all the way home. She could not understand what good all that grandeur was if they were never to have the chance of telling anyone about it.

No funeral feast was held, except for the people on the farm. Roimala chanced to join in unbidden—he might have come, of course, on the strength of his ownership. As it happened, he had an errand. He said that he had expected to find a good many people there. He was collecting signatures to a paper that was to be presented to the Czar and was a petition asking that the rights of Finland should not be violated. Kustaa understood what it was about and had indeed heard of it before somewhere, though the matter now seemed rather irrelevant. He routed out, however, an ink-bottle and pen and began writing his name. Hilma too came into the room and said: "Haven't you had enough of Roimala's papers?" The visitor told her, slightly ruffled: "This is no paper of Roimala's—and for that matter Kustaa had not had any worse experiences of Roimala's papers than of Plihtari's papers." Whereafter he trumpeted his nose on a familiar note.

Sunday afternoon passed quite ordinarily; a sunbeam traveled along the floor of the living-room as it had done during the centuries the pine building had stood. The smoky-red rocking chair for two, with its back-rest of two skillfully carved lyres, stood exactly where it had stood before, over the hollows in the floor worn by the rockers and the feet of sitters. The clock ticked on the back wall, the almanac hung from its nail beside the window, a special faint smell was in the air. Yet everything was different in that the prevailing peace had in it the expectation of a coming unrest, like waiting for the execution of a death sentence. Even Roimala asked Kustaa as a round-off to his farewell:

"Well, you'll be beginning tomorrow at nine, I suppose?"

"Nine's the hour announced," answered Kustaa, his eyes smiling. Hilma went staggering away from them with a grumbling remark that remained inaudible.

The auction was unusually well attended and the auctioneers had thus an adequate sounding-board for their quips. Here and there an old fellow had had a glass too much and made rude remarks when some homely object, a garment or article, was put up for sale. Iivari Plihtari, for whom the day was of course a kind of festival, behaved in similar fashion. Joking remarks were addressed to him now and again, and he was quick to retort. The crowd knew perfectly well that Iivari would not take offense.

This was the last time the brothers-in-law were face to face. On this occasion the meeting led to a brief encounter. Kustaa went away for a moment and in his absence the auctioneer took his joiner's bench and tools and offered them for sale. Kustaa had meant to keep them; now his own resource was to bid for them—against Iivari Plihtari, who was bidding for them in earnest.

"What do you want a joiner's bench for—I'm told you're looking for a job as farmhand," said Iivari, and was rewarded with a delighted crowing by his like.

Iivari raised his bid until it was nearly more than a fair price. Kustaa at once raised his, being determined not to part with his bench.

"Are you sure you can answer for your bid?" shouted Iivari.

This was going very far, but among the crowd were still enough spectators with mouths cruelly agape, ready to bite at any quip thrown to them by Iivari Plihtari. They continued to crow.

Kustaa blushed slightly; his faint smile thinned almost to extinction. The joint feeling among the honorable element in the crowd had now gained in weight and was on Kustaa's side, on the side of the man who had escorted two children to the grave the day before and now had to leave the family estate. The roar awakened by Iivari's words quickly died down when Kustaa answered:

"Well, I have a small claim on you, I believe."

Everyone recalled that event many years ago, which had after all impressed itself deeply on the local mind, to the shame of Iivari; a minor shame perhaps, but still a shame and not a merit. The joint mood of even such a crowd as was then assembled fluctuates easily; the moment it was spoken, Kustaa's remark further revealed the manliness shown by him in sticking to Plihtari's daughter, and not trying to buy her off, though it might have been better for him if he had done so. The whole of this sympathy for Kustaa now compressed itself into the frame of his half-compulsory exile from his lands when he hinted at the considerable sums he had paid on behalf of that rascal Iivari, paid twice over. Up to that moment no one had ever heard Kustaa refer to them by a single word.

"Well, keep your muck then," said Iivari and turned away with a boastful gesture, trying to find some support for his words in the glances of those nearest to him. But now the crowd's sympathies were all on Kustaa's side, and Iivari stood alone. One aged throat emitted a bellowing laugh, but it was aimed at Iivari.

It was almost as though the bench had become dearer to its owner after that encounter. During the first few months in his new home he used it very often. Partly because the household, in its new shape, needed all kinds of articles that had not been worth carting from the old home, partly because he had begun to turn out farm implements for his new neighbors, who soon learned to know him as a skillful and reliable man. At Salmelus there had been a large stock of seasoned timber which lay unutilized under the rafters during those years of trouble, part of it placed there by Kustaa's father. Kustaa did not sell this wood, but took it with him.

Hilma wept on their departure. A feeble thin crying, the submission of a weak person to the unavoidable. She wept over the cows and other animals given over to strangers, over the cat left on the farm, the cat that the children had let in and out of the door in winter—yes, and she now wept over her dead children, left behind in another parish; almost she wept over the sole remaining child in her lap, big-eyed, long-lashed Silja. Weakly crying she left the house to which she had come on a certain autumn day with her young heart full of a bliss that somehow seemed unnatural. At a time when the strong spirit of the old master and his unspoken thoughts had still filled the air of the farm. Into that air, in a manner unnatural, had come the young, insignificant cottar's girl with her own knowledge and preferences.

She now departed, thin, angular, with tearful eyes. At a corner of the road her mother, Tilta Plihtari, and her younger sister, had come to witness her departure. Both of them had of course grown older as the years passed, but age had not altered the general tone of their appearance much. Now, as before, a mocking word seemed to hang, ready to fall, at one corner of Tilta's mouth; the head of the youngest had the same sage tilt as before; almost one expected to see it trembling a little already. Neither had the courage to come boldly forward. Old Vuorenmaa was still the driver; he drove the loads, while Kustaa himself drove the sleigh with the family. On Vuorenmaa's face was an expression of stern gravity. Instinctively he too felt that at this moment he represented the last vestige of the old Salmelus times.

The farm was left behind, and soon the backwoods road leading to Plihtari was passed. Up to this, Hilma's weeping had been silent, now she broke into a fit of sobbing, for in her heart she knew that she would never walk that road again, that the journey begun along a strange road would carry her to ever more unfamiliar scenes and ultimately to the wholly unknown.

Kustaa neither did nor said anything to her, merely adjusting little Silja's cap, for the spring wind still blew. Not that there was really anything to adjust in the cap. The day was in no wise hard to bear for Kustaa. He had fought out his inward battles long ago and knew whither he was bound; he felt himself freer today than for a long time past.

Hilma went on sobbing until the forest became less familiar. Vuorenmaa, coming on behind, swore unnecesarily at a horse. The fellow was getting so old that his jaw felt inclined to shake and his eyes to fill with tears at the cross-roads when he saw Hilma begin to sob and remembered all that linked these two fates with the road, remembered too his own connection with the two here and those at the end of the road.

The forest through which the road now ran was part of the Salmelus lands. Kustaa would scarcely have thought of it if he had not seen men at one spot felling a tree. They were Roimala's men, some of them formerly in Kustaa's service. They had cut down a mighty drooping spruce and were lopping off the boughs. Seeing the procession on the road they stopped working and stared stupidly at the sleighs, remaining standing there long afterwards, as though the episode had ended too soon.

At that part of the journey Kustaa's peace of mind was slightly shaken; it was as though he was again staring absently through the barn doorway at Salmelus, at the place where his father died. He thought for a moment or two of his own death and of how and where it would happen. Hilma had calmed down again, and old Vuorenmaa had given the horse its own head. The day of removal was passing, the destination drawing near.

5

Matters turned out so well that little Silja received no conscious impression of her arrival at the new home. She slept soundly all through the last part of the journey, and did not awaken even when she was carried into the house. The departing inhabitants had heated the stoves to a festive glow in honor of their departure, and the heat was now welcome owing to the length of time the doors had to be open while the furniture was being carried in. Silja slept on the living-room table in her traveling clothes until the bed had been warmed after its exposure to the air.

The next morning the first thing to greet her awakening eyes was the sun, which now let its golden ray play on the floor of this new and wonderful room. Father and mother were there, looking just the same as before. But father was now busy planing beside the side window and mother was peeling potatoes near the range, which had been fitted into the side of the heating stove. No Taave or Laura, they had been left there in the graveyard, or they might have been left in the store-room, which wasn't anywhere here, that she could see. Beautiful curly shavings were starting up under father's plane—was this the living-room then? Never before had Silja awakened to see her father working at his bench. It was one of the marvels of this day. Mother's knife moved skillfully round the potatoes—could this be the kitchen, and had mother begun to do Loviisa's work? Most wonderful of all, however, was the sun and this light that came from three windows; in the old home the two windows had been in the same wall, and there were only doors in the other walls. And still more wonderful that father and mother were busy in the same room when she awoke.

So happy all this was. To be sure, mother was coughing as she peeled the potatoes and looked anxious as usual. But Silja knew quite well that when she should climb down from the bed and go to her mother, her mother would stop working and hug and pat her, and father would stop planing and turn his smile to where she was with mother. Later, father would be sure to lift her on to his arm and carry her outside, where the marvelous light on the floor came from.

This situation was Silja's first fully clear impression, one that remained in her memory throughout her life. She remembered, too, that her father did carry her on his arm all over the grounds of the new house and talk to her, the whole time, sometimes putting her down to make something funny of snow, which he would throw at her, trying to make her laugh. All this Silja clearly remembered; what she did not remember was how she came from the bed to her father's arm outside.

The child did not remember it for the reason that when she climbed out of bed, her mother had not petted and hugged her as sometimes before, but with the same worried look that Silja had observed from the bed still on her face, had begun to dress her.

An anxious-looking woman peeling potatoes—that was the last impression gained by the surviving child of its mother. Hilma lived, indeed, for some time afterwards, but her life was such that the subconscious part of the child's mind retained no impression of it. When the ice on the lake near by began to be in such condition that careful farmers no longer drove across it and the foolhardy were giving their horses a ducking, Hilma Salmelus, as she was called in the new locality, took to her bed, from which she was never more to rise. This fatal illness of Hilma's was another significant period in Kustaa's life, his last trial, in its own way the deepest depression in the curve of his life, as that evening in Roimala's room had been, when the sale of his farm was finally settled. Only in the present case there was nothing humbling, rather was it in the nature of a decisive turn in Kustaa Salmelus's path of purification.

The man had once laid his reins on the porch of his old home over the shoulder of a young and fair servant-girl and by that act was drawn very close to her. Now the local woman called in as help saw the newcomer Salmelus press his cheek against the forehead of his dying wife. The wife was still fully conscious, and smiled as well as she could at her husband. The strange woman who witnessed this scene could not divine everything that went to that smile.

Silja was toddling outside at that moment. She too was living through a new experience. From the lake came a strange uninterrupted tinkling, rattling, roaring, and occasionally a real frightening sound. The noise seemed to come from quite near. It affected the girl so that she was hardly aware of anything else. Even the removal of her mother's body was unnoticed by her. Not until late evening was she told that mother had gone the way of Taave and Laura at their former home. Just then, however, it was more important for Silja to be told quite clearly what the tinkling and rattling was that had sounded the whole afternoon from the lake. Father explained it to her as he put her to sleep—this time in his own bed. "You see, when summer has gone, it gets cold, ever colder and colder, until all the flowers and butterflies die and the lakes freeze up. That lake of ours froze up too last autumn. Then the sun begins to climb higher again and everything becomes brighter and warmer. That makes the ice melt in the lake, and as it melts and disappears it makes that tinkling and rattling."

The father saw that his only child, his only one in every sense now, was asleep. The child had fallen asleep while he was talking of flowers and butterflies. It was as though she had wished to follow those dear friends of hers along their easy road of death.

6

The spring wore on. Kustaa Salmelus lived in his cabin, lived and grew older; but he was now free from much that had weighed down his spirit. This weight had been borne by him so long that he could not have said when it originated, only that behind it all glowed the memory of something happy and strong: the golden solitary days of his youth. Solitary they had been indeed, they too, and in that respect his days had never changed; it was only that the gold had worn off the days of his later adult life until now, when he was nearing old age.

The spring advanced, and life rose and grew in Nature. Silja, too, seemed to be growing at a quicker rate than before under the eyes of her father. She had to be found new clothes, her worn winter clothes were beginning to resemble the mottled earth reappearing from under the snow. The child had to be found something new and more colorful—as flowers arose in the gray aftermath of winter in the home brushwood. A visit had to be paid to the village seamstress, and the best time for that was Sunday morning. There was laughter and mild joking at their destination, and the faces of all wore a kind expression while the little girl was being measured. In some small degree it was due to the special circumstance that so staid a father gave the orders. "Yes, think, the poor child lost her mother as soon as they moved here," the talk ran on the seamstress's porch when Kustaa and Silja had gone, "but the father is greatly attached to the girl." And then everyone recounted the little they knew of the newcomers. Someone said that they had lost their farm three parishes away, but another speaker argued that he didn't look like a ruined man, wasn't he living on his means—moreover he had heard that the man had only grown tired of farming after his wife became ill and his children died and all sorts of little worries came, and had wanted to take some little place like this.

Meanwhile Silja and Kustaa stepped out along the road, making their observations of nature and telling them to each other.

"What makes the lake there so alive, like lots of little bright animals on it?" asked the girl.

"Those are little waves running on it, like this"—Kustaa described the motion of a wave with his hand—"and for one moment the wall of every wave is like a looking-glass that catches the sun. Wait till we get in and I'll show you."

They went into the cabin, Silja humming and tripping ahead and the father behind like an instructive big brother. The mirror was taken from its peg beside the window and father had to show how the lake's surface glittered. He was forced to smile, however, and laugh at his pupil, and soon to take care that the mirror did not fall or was not dashed against the wall. The play of the sunbeam was so hugely exciting to Silja that it was vain to speak to her of waves in connection with it. Unwearyingly the child flashed the beam along the walls, the floor, the stove, and her mirth overflowed when the idea struck her of flashing it on her father's coat, then on his chin and lastly in his eyes, so that he had to shut them and turn his head away. . . . And then on to the leg of the bed and the joiner's bench, and again on to father.

Kustaa could not help wondering at the child's joy. Without thinking that it was so, he sensed something touching in the matter, in that the child had never before played with a sunbeam. There had never happened to be a looking-glass and the sun together in the same place. By now her play was going so far that he had to forbid it. The girl had begun to wave the mirror behind her back, and it would soon be broken.

So they lived without serious troubles. The father spent most of his time at his joiner's bench, except when he was cooking their meals. Kustaa would have no stranger in the house if he could by any means be without. When he was in need of help he would fetch Miina from the other end of the village, Miina, who lived entirely on odd jobs. In the village were an old farmer and farmwife who had known the Salmelus family a long time back; there may even have been a blood-tie, very remote, between the families. The mistress of that farm often sent Kustaa and Silja part of her baking, especially after Kustaa had made her a neat low rocking-chair, in which it was unusually pleasant for her to rock her old body.

The first summer passed of Silja's and Kustaa's life together. The child became acquainted with many kinds of birds and still more kinds of flowers. She saw boys fishing. They wore big hats and had the legs of their trousers rolled up. They walked along the edge of the lake and looked with a stranger's eye at the neatly dressed little girl standing on the top of the bank. Each of the boys had heard talk in his own cabin of the new tenants of that house, the old man and the little girl who bothered so little about other people.

Harvest-time came. The friendly farmer asked Kustaa to help in the fields, and Kustaa went. He had to take Silja with him and leave her at the farmhouse.

There were the children of some of the other reapers, including the two of Miina's, the woman-of-all-work. They had no father, Silja was told.

"Did he die and was he taken to the grave at church like mother and Taave and Laura?" asked Silja of her father at dinner-time in the farmyard.

"I suppose that's what happened," said Kustaa with a smile, but refrained from turning his smile on the other men lying in the grass. Instinctively he observed the same shades of behavior as he had done in the days of his masterhood.

"He's not in any grave, but hopping about over yonder in Kokkinen's fields this very day," remarked the loose-mouthed tailor, who had climbed down from his table while the harvest hurry was on and taken to the sickle.

In the old days Kustaa Salmelus would have risen and without a word gone into the house, by which the men would have known that "the old man didn't seem to like that." But he was no longer anybody's "old man," only one of a group of reapers in another farmer's yard. Where could he have gone until the bell rang for him to go to the fields? He had to stay where he was, and the child with him, waiting for the moment when the girl would be left until supper-time with those "fatherless" children. A moment of distasteful annoyance—when Silja, hearing the tailor's words, persisted that they had a father after all. Kustaa remarked, in a suitable tone: "Well, that tailor seems to know something about it," and added to Silja in a voice that made her obey him, "and you'll ask no more questions."

Silja walked silently away, but did not join Miina's children at once. Nor did the men say anything. Their impression of Kustaa Salmelus had been enriched by a little, but effective feature. Rather soon after dinner, the reapers drawing nearer to the house, the children went out into the fields and for the rest of that day Silja remained near her father.

The summer passed; soon the smell of smoke spread from the threshing-barns, and on the window-sill, right before Silja's face, appeared a lively little bird, peering into the room with its head on one side. "It's a tomtit," said father, and brought meat and bread crumbs, which he spread on the sill. Pickysoo—pickysoo—pickysoo—tee—tee—tee—heard Silja, and hardly was father in the room again before the tomtit was at its former place and pecking eagerly at a bit of meat which it held between its claws. The bird became a new all-winter companion for Silja. Silja looked on it as the same bird, as there was very seldom more than one on the window-sill. If two did happen to fly on to the sill, Silja was sure the first was the "right" one.

7

Little Silja sailed the sea of her life, leaving ever farther behind the shore whence she set out. Her senses developed, their circle of observation widened. Every impression sent through them by the life around her to the storehouse of her consciousness remained there, though some of them sank at once into such distant recesses that the keeper of the storehouse, the human being that was Silja would never when grown up believe they were there; though they failed not to exert their influence even from their secret hiding-place.

During this first conscious winter there was one such hiatus. For over a week Silja's tomtits could cry their "pickysoo" as eagerly as they liked around the house and strut however livelily and peer in at the windows, without those delicious crumbs appearing on the sill. The living-room was silent; no child's face appeared at the window; and even the man moved cautiously. In the circumstances even a tomtit could be excused for remaining sitting disconsolately on the sill for a long time. Not until the moon rose did it move to its customary roost in the attic. During those silent days and nights too, Silja was in the house. On this night she is just awakening. She does not know when she fell asleep. It feels almost as though she had never existed before, familiar as the objects looming through the darkness seem.

Silja is dreadfully hot and her mouth very dry, but she is unable to ask for anything. It is dark, but near the window it is light, a special kind of white light, as though something very big, invisible to her eye, were looking into the room from the top of the house. So much of the light flowed through the window that the apparition sitting beside the table before the window showed up clearly against it. At the same moment a loud crack sounded, as though all this white silence had only been there to give one a chance to wait for some such sudden noise. Silja gave a start, as did that human apparition by the window. It turned towards her, Silja, lying in bed. It was father; the child recognized it now that it moved. Father came and touched her forehead and breast, then took a mug from the table and, holding up Silja with one hand, let her drink from it.

The child sank into unconsciousness again and the man sat down in his former place. He cannot sleep, now that the child is so bad. He wonders whether he will lose this one too. The man tries to envisage his solitude; such thoughts run easily, as though speeding along the moonlit snowdrifts outside. He would be left quite alone, as he always has been. For him too it would be death, as he had earlier died to so much. The child over there is his only tie with life.

Ever more agitated grows the mind of the solitary night watcher. The child's breathing is hardly audible; now and then she gives a slight moan, her body trying in its exceeding weakness to give voice to its pain. Hidden deep in the body is the tiny soul, deep in the shadow of the fevered body, and yet it feels an immense cold. It believes itself to be lying in the big living-room at Salmelus, as whose heiress it was joyfully conceived and happily born. But it is there quite alone; the door has been left open, snow flies through the crack, and with the snow glides in a big cat, not the house cat, but a stranger. It is big, almost the size of a dog, and of terrifying colors, yellow and green in its eyes and the gap of its mouth. It mews spitefully, as though it too was cold, then seeing the child, balances for a moment on its paws as though preparing to spring on a mouse or a straw and jumps straight on to the moveless child, sits on her chest, licks its own chest and purrs. It is heavy, so heavy; it settles down to sleep, a dread weight. Then it rises and begins to stretch itself, straightening its paws, and at each movement the claws sink into the child's breast; then it begins to whet its claws, as though awakening on a fence.

By this time the father had lit the lamp, sat down beside the bed and crossed his arms. A wave of love, long and low, flowed into his male heart at that moment. He did not touch the child, as he could see that the crisis was on her, yet with a sweeping strong movement he drew her into the depths of his embrace, closer than by any arms of flesh. Prayer filled his mind, though he sought not words. He saw the child living, ripening, growing to full maturity, beautiful, fair, but retaining the same soul that now burned in fire. The vision was a hope, a passionate prayer, in the realization of which the father now unconditionally believed. He remembered some of his own bad deeds and had the feeling that the child's fever was burning the dross from him, the father, too.

Morning drew near. The father felt the child's forehead and chest and found them perspiring freely; his hand came away quite wet. Unused to sickbeds, all the father could do was to leave the child in peace and cover her still more closely, lest in her perspiration she should feel cold. He tucked eagerly at the bedclothes with a faint impression that the mother, a woman, was somewhere beside him. He lit a fire in the range and hunted out clean clothes for Silja, in order to be able to change her linen when she awoke. He put the coffee-pot on the range and brewed strong coffee to keep himself awake. Everything was well, the child's breathing was more regular; warming a nightdress over the range he considered the best way of substituting it for Silja's damp nightdress. He might give the child a drop of coffee.

All this he did The fever had left the child, so quickly that the father was anxious. But after Silja had drunk her drop of coffee, she was so far revived as to talk already clearly, almost merrily. Her tiny sentences were as full of hope as the rising day. Soon it would be summer again—even if she were to die then, she would not have to stay in the cold store-room, would she? Silja remembered her tomtits too, and asked about their crumbs. The father laughed, realizing that he had altogether forgotten to feed those pets. Almost at a run he made haste to do so, and was soon able to tell the girl that their table was spread, all she had to do was to wait. "The birds went away so as not to disturb you with their chirping while you were ill. They're sure to some back soon when they hear that you are better. Try to keep very quiet now, for fear the fever might rise again."

The birds came very soon, and the child wanted so much to see them, that Kustaa was forced to take her carefully up in his arms and carry her to the window. Silja looked and laughed, her constricted chest giving her laughter a strange hoarse note. The child's breathing became rapid again. Kustaa heard a faint panting beside his ear and hastened to carry the child back to bed.

That same day the mistress of the friendly farm, knowing how matters stood in the house, came to see the father and child and bring the sick child some suitable food. She found the two inhabitants of the house asleep in the same big bed, in which they slept at night. Silja lay, half on one side, beside Kustaa, whose arm was wound so skillfully round her neck that few mothers could have slept so well beside their child: so thought the good-natured farmwife to herself before proceeding to arouse them.

Kustaa had the feeling, after that illness, of having been given the child a second time. Silja's convalescence was a blissful time; looking at the child without her knowledge, Kustaa would often pause to think what would have happened if he had really lost her. However, as she did recover, she was surely intended for something in this world. And Kustaa keyed his mind again and again to that particular state of hope that was like a long, perfect prayer, though the pure-minded man would never have thought of calling it that. To this state of hope was invariably attached an invincible belief in the realization of the hope, while deeds and thoughts of his own that conscience had sometimes condemned would recur to him.

When she was fully recovered, Silja again began to grow and mature, quicker it seemed than before. Now and again she would wander beyond the confines of the house, a matter that kept Kustaa on the alert, as he did not want her to stray about the village in the same way as Miina's children. It was difficult, however, for Kustaa to explain to the child in words everything she was not supposed to do, and consequently Silja sometimes erred in her outings. She would go off on a Sunday afternoon with Miina's children to a reaping-bee near the cabins on the edge of the village, where life was very pleasant and full of fun and new to Silja, until Kustaa's voice would be heard calling from the bend of the road. At that everybody would stop working, and all eyes would watch Silja's passage from the merry harvesters to her waiting father. That was a severer punishment than any hiding, not that a hiding ever followed. The father took his daughter by the hand, and so they would walk through the evening shadows on the leafy road, soft and muddy in places. The mud scrunched between her toes as she walked on regardless of where she stepped. So, without a word, they came home. Silja went straight into the house with her muddy feet, but her father fetched a bucket of water, brought it into the house, and his first word was to tell Silja to wash the mud off her feet.

As the girl grew up, such more or less serious incidents occurred, owing perhaps in part to Kustaa's inability directly to teach the girl.

Then came the time when Silja had to learn to read. Kustaa brought home a new a—b—c book from the village shop as gravely as any other purchase and began teaching her the alphabet and spelling. In this the father was near to lagging behind. One of the village girls with whom Silja had been much together sometimes visited her just then, and the girls whispered together over the a—b—c book. After such visits Kustaa noted that Silja knew things in the a—b—c book that he had not taught her, even things that he himself did not rightly understand. Kustaa felt almost as though she had again been on some forbidden excursion.

Silja went to a couple of ambulatory classes and then to the elementary school in a village about a mile away. She was in the last class when an event occurred one spring Sunday that was unlike anything else that had happened between father and daughter. The day was a warm, thawy Sunday. Kustaa lay as was his wont on the bed and Silja idly thumbed her lessons. As she had plenty of time she looked at and read things that were not in her home lessons and occasionally spoke a word or two to her father. If it was only a remark Kustaa made no answer and did not open his eyes, but if the child asked him something, he moved his eyelids and in time gave some kind of answer. Silja turned the pages of her Bible history, which had a map of Palestine as frontispiece. It gave rise to many questions:

"Is there really a Jerusalem—and Bethlehem, even today?"

"Of course, if they are on the map."

"Why is it called the Holy Land?"

And there began a long discussion, during the course of which Kustaa found his own knowledge very deficient. He remembered, however, as they talked of Jerusalem, that there was a long account of its destruction at the end of the hymnbook; his mother had sometimes made him read it out on some such languid Sunday at Salmelus as today. Kustaa got up from the bed, went with eager steps to the corner shelf and took down the big hymnbook. Silja watched him with curious eyes as he searched for the page. Having found it he placed the book before her, pointed with his middle finger at a passage, and told her to read it aloud. He himself returned to the bed and resumed his recent position.

Silja read, and wondered to herself that all this was in the hymnbook—"Then at the Emperor's command Vespasian went to Galilee, where dwelt many people, and plundered and ravaged the land so sorely, that of murder, robbery and fire there was no end. Then were many Jews killed, at one time fifty thousand strong picked fighting-men, besides women, children and other men. The enemy pitied neither young nor old, neither women with child nor babes in their cradle. Vespasian sent six thousand young men to Achaia to dig across a cape. Thirty thousand Jew warriors were sold into slavery, and fifty thousand broke their necks, in their despair dashing themselves down from high places in the mountains. . . . Then he took their town Gadara, and with his lieutenant Placidus killed nearly thirty thousand of the fleeing inhabitants and took two thousand of the fleeing inhabitants and took two thousand prisoners; those who escaped threw themselves in to the River Jordan, and the river bore their dead bodies down to the Lake of Pitch, known as the Dead Sea."

The girl's voice ran on in the Sunday peace of the room. The father lay on the bed and listened as the girl went on reading, now and then stopping for breath in the wrong places, until she had reached the end: "Wherefore let none believe that the punishment of sin lies not in wait in the doorway; for verily it shall go with the godless as with Jerusalem. This we must consider in all truth and impress on our hearts, repent us of our sins and turn to knowledge of the true Christ. Amen."

Having come so far, Silja rapidly turned over the remaining pages and from the end of the book, as though to free herself of something, read the last hymn in a singsong note as she would some child's jingle. Then the wooden covers of the book closed with a bang.

The father lay without moving on the bed, as though wishing to deepen the impression left by the reading. But Silja's cheeks were a hot red; she pranced up and down the floor, helplessly, as one trying to remember what she had to do. In the yard the silence of a Sunday thaw continued. Noon was long since past, but there was still abundant light and glamour in the air, on the ground and in the treetops. Silja took a shawl for her head, watching whether father would have anything to say. But father was still lying in the same attitude on his back with his eyes closed, his head bent slightly back, so that Silja could see the under side of his chin, his curving nostrils and the hollows of his eyes. The sight was curiously unfamiliar to her just then. As though to flee from it, Silja rushed into the yard and with no thought of where she was going, slid on her skis down to the bank and on to the ice.

On the melting snow the light girl sped quickly as on a forbidden path. The loose snow had already melted from the surface of the lake, and on the ice her skis skimmed still easier. In one place water showed, only a narrow bridge joining the ice sheet of the middle of the lake to the shore ice. Across this bridge Silja skillfully guided her skis, the fever born of the reading still in her veins. Soon she found herself confronted by a hole in the ice. She stopped and listened for a moment to the measured beat of the blood in her ears, to which was joined another sound, the one she had listened to on the day her sick mother vanished from the house. The sound was now fainter, but came from somewhere quite close. It seemed to whisper an accusation in her ear. . . . The bridge over which she had recently skimmed had collapsed. Fear entered the child's mind; she hurried landward, but there too was water, brownish after-winter water. The ice beneath her was moving. In the rattle of the ice and the beat of her heart she now seemed to distinguish her father's warning voice. What would happen to her now? She was unable to cry out; her body only crouched a little and her face contorted into a fit of weeping. Along the road came a couple of Sunday idlers, who stopped to watch. Silja shouted and tried to fix her glance on the house windows through the trees on the bank.

The ice-floe moved slowly, but relentlessly. The men left the road and made for the shore, at a slightly quicker pace than they had been walking They had almost reached the water's edge when Kustaa Salmelus dashed past them, bareheaded and coatless, in his eyes a queer flickering flame. Before the walkers could guess his intention, he had jumped on to the ice-floe, the edge of which broke under his first step, but held under his second, so that he was able to stride on to it and seize the girl. He took her up in his arms and jumped back. But the intervening space had meanwhile widened so much that he came down in open water. He succeeded, however, in throwing the girl clear, so that only one of her boots was wetted.

Kustaa sank to his armpits in the water before he could get a firm enough hold of the ice-crust on the shore to enable him to draw himself on to dry land. The two villagers hardly got beyond a thunderstruck stare. In the eyes of the man fighting to regain dry land was still the same alarming glow that had been in them when he ran to the shore; the men drew back a little, vaguely afraid he would strike them. But Kustaa rushed up to Silja, and his first act was to seize her by the hair and shake her severely. The girl uttered no sound, only stared at her father with terrified eyes.

"So that's what you found to do," he muttered. His jaw trembled violently. Gradually, however, he seemed to wake up and look around him. He began pushing the child towards the house.

The old mistress of the neighboring farm had been rocking gently in her little chair and had witnessed the whole incident. It was over before she had time to lever herself out of the chair. She knew, however, what she had to do. Waddling over to the cupboard, she took out a bottle containing spirits and pieces of camphor, called the maid and gave brief orders. "If Salmelus doesn't happen to have any medicine in the house, he's a dead man. Run across with this and tell him to take a big dose."

The girl snatched her shawl and went. The old mistress too put on her outdoor things and set out for Kustaa's cabin. The maid met her halfway and said that Salmelus had carried out her instruction at once.

Kustaa was in his underwear when the old farmwife came into the room. His cheeks were flushed and the glow in his eyes had turned into a dull shine. He talked incessantly about how he woke up in that bed and without knowing anything rushed to the shore, quite as though he had been told in his sleep that the girl was in danger. In the cup on the table was still a little of the camphor and spirits mixed with coffee. Kustaa emptied it into his mouth and went on with increasing warmth: "I was so muddled that I laid hold of the child's hair, and I still feel a bit dizzy, though it was a fine thing that you sent me this, or I don't know what would have happened to me."

The old farmwife was not quite sure what was going to happen to him even now. Was his present extravagant condition due to the spirits or the accident? To make doubly sure, the woman mixed another dose and advised Kustaa to swallow it and then go to bed. She examined Silja too, and being convinced that no harm was likely to come to her, went off with slow dignity along the road she had come. As she drew homeward she smiled at the couple: how cosily she had found them lying together when it was the girl who was recovering. The old woman's heart was very warm.

The day faded into evening. Kustaa lay on the bed and Silja sat beside the window. Her father's wet clothes hung near the range, and Silja's boots lay upturned near the stove. No words were spoken. To Silja life felt very strange now, and not only because of the incident in the daytime. The morning when she had read aloud from the hymnbook seemed immensely distant. The man, too, breathing in the bed was quite a different being from the one who had shown her the piece about the destruction of Jerusalem. This man had seized her by the hair and had then told the old farmwife about it as though telling her something wonderful. Against her will she laid note once more to the under part of her father's jaw and the hollows of his eyes.

Kustaa did not contract any direct illness as a result of his wetting; the following day he went about his work as usual and sent Silja to take the camphor bottle back to the old farmwife. But the strange softness of mood that had come over him after the rescue of Silja seemed to continue. During the next few days he told everybody who chanced to be within hearing, in an ever merrier tone, how he had been so agitated that he "even laid hold of that girl's hair." When, by this chatter, he finally made Silja too smile, he looked curiously happy.

8

The spring came when Silja would have to pass her Confirmation class. From Kustaa's dwelling to the church the distance was about six miles, so that he had to find lodgings where she could sleep on weekday nights. There were many girls in the same situation; they lodged in groups in the village houses and assembled in the evenings on the bridge and the quay, conscious of the clumsy remarks and coarse bursts of laughter from boys of like age and a little older. Some of the girls already felt a strong inclination for such company. They gave back as good as they received. And even the minds of the shyest were moved by certain hitherto dimly perceived matters. They were on the threshold of maidenhood. The summer that now unfolded from day to evening in the open spaces around the church, was to be their first summer of liberty, during the course of which many were already to experience why they had been born women.

When Saturday evening came they could be seen happily trudging away along all the roads leading from the village. At cross-roads they stopped and chattered a while before parting, in that, too, resembling older women in a faintly ludicrous manner. For the boys of Confirmation age, partings at cross-roads were of a very different character: bold impertinences were shouted at boys from other hamlets; stones flew, and sometimes, on suitable occasions, a group would be chased, when blood flowed freely from noses that had tended to tilt too far skyward in the churchyard and on the village paths in the evenings. There no one had dared to fight for fear of the constable and the curates.

The girls walked as became young women; a few of the farmers from the most distant hamlets had left their trip to the village to Saturday afternoon, and now the daughter would be perched up on the trap beside her stout father on her way home for Sunday. Cries were exchanged between the girls too, between those on foot and those driving, but these cries were merry and decently worded.

The evening rays seemed to rejoice in the flashing of eyes and the gleam of teeth.

On one road Silja Salmelus walked homeward, first with two companions, then with one, and after the departure of this last friend alone. Her father could see her coming nearer. He stood beside the wood-pile and chopped fuel for the bath-house. Silja came, cast an open glance at her father, but said no word of greeting as she passed him on her way inside. The strokes of Kustaa's ax echoed and the billets crackled; it was a delightful Saturday evening in early summer. Then Silja came out of the house in familiar working dress. She came straight to her father and asked him for something to do, though she knew quite well what there was to be done.

"Take the wood in and make a fire, and we'll get it over all the earlier," said Kustaa.

Their voices had exchanged greetings. The Saturday evening work passed smoothly for the couple, father and daughter, joined together by a warm mutual feeling. A feeling of deep human happiness, from which, as the years passed, everything inessential or disturbing had fallen away.

Not until they had returned from the bath-house, and Kustaa sat in his shirt-sleeves beside the back window, combing his still thick hair before a mirror, and Silja flitted about the range like a pale ghost of evening, did they begin to discuss anything. The father asked over his shoulder how she liked her lodgings, the family being unknown to him. If anything she said was not quite to his liking, he did not stop to explain it to the girl, but went on asking and commenting in such a way that the conversation between father and daughter revealed that both were of one mind. There he sat, her father; the girl caught a glimpse now and again of his strong and fine profile against the window as she had once done in her childhood, while in bed with fever. Then the man got into the bed and said no more to his daughter, and did not even seem to be following her movements. Silence had settled down on the room; one could almost feel the dignified evening thoughts of the man in the air.

Softly, as though gliding, and taking care not to rattle the door, the daughter went out into the yard, still wrapped in the spring-like twilight of early summer The flowering bird-cherry bushes on the distant bank and along the roads beyond the lake seemed to be floating in that dimness. The birds gradually grew silent near the house, but in the crowns of the farther backwoods one could guess that some of the bigger songsters were giving voice in long, long melodies to the deepest meaning of the northern summer night, for which they had so cheerily come so far. There were nests already, and in them eggs—the depicter of the northern summer night soon finds himself under the spell of well-worn phrases. Under the pallid sky in the dimness flowers, the fading music of Nature, somewhere a solitary maiden—Silja Salmelus stood and moved, listening to and sensing the summer night.

She moved gradually to the end of the point of land on their own part of the shore, to the leafy verge of the bank, and sat down there on the trunk of a birch, bent near the roots. Her young mind seemed to expand and grow bolder. No one and nothing could disturb her there. Yonder in the house, within hearing, her father slept lightly, and no path led past here.

The water with its shores and islands rested as in a picture she had once seen. In the water the reflections repeated towards the depths all that rose to the heights on the banks. Everything the senses could grasp seemed to be gravely and eagerly assuring the consciousness of its goodness, to be whispering to the girl that if you still sigh for anything all we can do is to soothe your longing with what you now see. This direct message from Nature made the girl's eyes expand, as though they too, like the lake, had wanted to reflect in their depths everything in view. There was much the sixteen-year-old girl might have sighed for, something she might have owned and knew from hearsay had been hers, though she had never consciously missed it. That was perhaps why her eyes, having expanded, grew slightly moist and her breast heaved in a gentle sigh on this night on which she had come home from her Confirmation class to see her lonely father. Yes, he was lonely, the old man sleeping in the cabin. The thought lent support to her own melancholy; she felt herself his safeguard. Silja looked into her own being and saw that she was a woman.

The night grew deeper. Silja rose and took a few steps towards the shore, intending to climb back a little later to the house. She would have liked to stay too: in some way the landscape became imbued with a stronger life as a boat came forward from behind an island, traveling apparently from south to north. The rhythm of the oars revealed the rower's mood: how the summer night had taken possession of it, deciding the direction in which thought should run and thereby the interval between the strokes. The approaching sound did not disturb, only interpreted. Silja gathered a flower from the ground, without intending to do so, and looked sidelong at the oncoming boat. The rower let his oars rest, as though in answer to the girl's movement, although it was almost impossible that he could have seen her. He seemed after all to be no real traveler but only a lonely spectator of the night, a youth, apparently unknown, in clothes that were neither working-clothes nor holiday attire, that she could distinguish. A summer visitor from one of the distant villas, boating. Silja was quite certain she had seen him, some weekday in the village, on a bicycle. That was why she could make out his clothes at this distance. His nose was slightly hooked and his front teeth showed easily when he spoke to the baker's wife. Yes, it was he, right opposite her now, so that they might be looking each other in the eye. Silja made a few plucking motions at her flower, the brown eyes looked forth once or twice under the long lashes, then the girl began moving towards the house in such fashion that each step was like a separate little event, a confirmation of something. As she went the girl did not fail to note that the youth still rested on his oars, there behind her back. Not until the girl had been in the shadow of the foliage for some time, wholly invisible from the lake, did she hear the youth make a few strokes and then wait again for a moment or two, and when at last he started to row away the rhythm of his oars was unlike what it was when he came.

The night would by now be at its deepest. How long had she lingered near the water? As Silja came into the cabin she herself was aware that she brought with her in the folds of her dress a faint breath of the perfume of the night air. The flower was still in her hand. She felt like saving everything that had accompanied her from outside.

Sleep seemed unwilling to come even now, so she sat down at the side window, from which she had a view over the fields towards the village. So wonderful the night was, the first of its kind for Silja in her life so far. In the rear corner of the bed she could distinguish the white-clad figure of a man: father usually slept uncovered. Silja gazed in his direction and somehow the way in which she now looked at him surprised her. Father was an old man, who had been through much in his life, so she had been told. I am together with that old man cast here, he is my father. What does it mean?

Her father slept on his back, moveless. Even his breathing was inaudible: there was something mildly terrifying in him. Silja remembered that her grandfather had been found dead in the threshing-barn; no one had seen the manner of his end. Was father awake, although he said nothing? Silja could not ask him, nor could she go nearer to make sure. She looked in turn out of all of the three windows. Everywhere the night met her, seeming now much emptier than a while ago. On the lake the reflections had grown dim.

At last came a movement from the bed and a faint sound as of choked coughing. Her father rose to a sitting position and then went over to the window giving on the point. Leaning against the window-frame he remained there moveless for a few moments. Then, sighing, he turned, and saw Silja at the other side of the room.

"Ah—have you come in," the old man said in a sleep-befuddled voice and went to bed again. Silja grasped that he had not seen her when he got up from the bed.

In the corner of the room the slender figure of the girl could be seen noiselessly moving, turning gradually white and disappearing into the bed. Sleep had fallen over the house. Outside there was no further sound of oars for long. Only a brief moment was left to the dawn of the approaching Sunday morning.

9

It was one of those Sundays before Midsummer, characteristic of which are their brightness and length. Man and his beasts of burden taste the delights of rest and warmth. Even an old man can move freely in his shirt-sleeves, for the sun finds its way nearly everywhere. The live things about the house too, ignorant as they are of what a Sunday denotes—the dog, cat, cock and hens and the swallows—respond somehow by their manner of existing to the prevailing mood of the humans. A person sitting on the steps has time to observe the ways of these creatures, whom he scarcely notices during the weekday round.

No cause for surprise, even if an old person should feel the urge to walk, merely to pass the Sunday hours. The young foliage of hedges and trees is so irresistible, so alive with the might of Nature, that admiration of it throughout a Sunday is no shame even to a manly man. The most barren-souled farmer may set out to view and calculate his hopes of a harvest. To a poor cabin-dweller, with only an acre or two of land, who labors hard on weekdays in fields owned by others, this quiet bliss of a day of rest, costing him nothing, is still better suited.

The same expanse of water that had so tenderly mirrored its shores and islands during the night, now flashed and glittered in the light of the all-embracing sun. Kustaa walks on the point of land, in the direction he had perceived his daughter to move the night before. There was the curving stem of a birch, but it is not fitting that he should sit down on it, or stand around too long. He has no intention of doing so; indeed, he is hardly conscious that he is being led by his observations of the night. No day is quite like another even in a very long life, but old Kustaa Salmelus has a feeling that this Sunday is a quite special day. Perhaps for the reason that the girl to whom he is so deeply attached, his only child, had been out of his eyesight a whole week for the first time and was now at home again, soon to depart once more. By the evening boat.

Even at this moment she was not actually at home. Most likely she was in the village attending to some question of clothes, in the seamstress's little room, where girls tried on their new dresses on Sunday mornings, or confidentially discussed with the dressmaker the cut and pattern of a coming new dress. In another week, maybe, it would be Silja's great day—what was it called: the confirmation of her baptism. Aye, when was it Silja was baptized, in the big room at Salmelus . . . and now the girl was ordering her Confirmation dress. The gray faces of the dead children crept into his mind.

Into the mind of a lonely old man all kinds of matters steal when he walks without any particular errand to the uttermost edge of his land and stands on the shore. He was in his waistcoat; the blue sleeves of his shirt ended in strong wrists and male fingers pliable in spite of their age. If the man's mother had chanced to soar down with only such knowledge as she possessed at her death, she might have taken him for her husband Vihtori, of Salmelus. The color of the son's hair and eyes, originally inherited from her, had faded in the storms and calms of life so much as to resemble the coloring of his departed father.

There he climbs back again to his cabin, Kustaa Salmelus, Vihtori's son. About ripe, he too. But now he looks whether the girl is not coming home by now. He is well able to lay the table for his meal, and has done so innumerable times during the past few years. Yet it would be very pleasant if the girl's hands were to do it today, seeing that she is at home.

She is coming. He can see her walking with another girl of her own age. They stop at the lane leading from the main road to the cabin. They sway and hop as they talk in a lively manner, take leave of each other and draw apart, but continue even then to stretch out their conversation, until they finally allow it to end in a few shouted remarks. Then Silja walks swiftly towards the cabin, but to the spectator it looks as though her thoughts were not speeding ahead of her, but lagging behind. Kustaa asks her:

"Who was that girl you came with and were speaking to?"

Apparently there was something strange in the question, for Silja looks at her father with an air of mild surprise before uttering the girl's name.

"Oh, is that who she was. I can't tell them apart any more," muttered Kustaa, to get rid of the subject.

Silja laid the table, moving quicker at this task too than she was wont. She looked absently at the table and then in her usual manner at her father as though to say: you can begin now. The father came towards the table, and glanced over it, he too, before sitting down. He then looked at Silja, a slightly broader smile than usual on his face, and said:

"Well, aren't you going to give me any bread?"

This was a queer Sunday, for all its beauty and brightness. Silja and Kustaa exchanging such remarks. The girl nearly looked irritated as she brought the bread.

Kustaa had the need to talk a little while he was eating, if there was a single hearer present. He had become used to it in the days when he was master on his own farm, and had inherited the habit from his father. At the table of a big household the talk easily ran riot if the master failed to rule it by his example. Thus Silja was used to hearing her father talk to her at meal-times of matters in general, of things not directly connected with the household. At meal-times he also uttered his little criticisms of people and happenings in the neighborhood. And Silja, if she had ever given thought to the matter, could not have remembered a single sentence of her father's table-talk that could have harmed her. On the contrary, it often charmed her, and sometimes aroused in her a silent admiration for her father that made her gaze at his head unobserved by him.

Now her father went on eating, and not a sentence came from him. He did not look vexed, but seemed to be lost in thought, as though far away. Silja refrained from attracting his notice and tried to sharpen her attention, to avoid making any further absent-minded mistake in her waiting. Kustaa failed to get out what he ought to say—"I hear she has begun to run about at night"—for he was not absolutely sure it was true. He was already finishing his meal when he finally said:

"Eat, dear child, you too."

Even that sentence was not altogether according to their habit. In spite of its gentle tone, it somehow made Silja sad. It sounded as though it had been uttered by a very weak invalid. Silja was unable to begin her meal until her father had got up and gone over to the bed for his usual rest after a meal.

The day was already at noon. Ever brighter, calm and happy, it worked irresistibly on all Nature, living or lifeless. It tempted, led and satisfied people of different ages in different ways. The sun—symbol and exciter of all the instincts and passions attaching to human life.

When Silja had eaten, Kustaa, still lying on the bed, heard the girl say:

"I think I'll go to Mikkola for a bit."

Mikkola was the farm where the girl she had come home with lived. Kustaa did not know what to say, and the silence lasted a little longer than was natural.

"I suppose you'll take care not to be late for the boat, so that you won't have to walk," Kustaa said.

"Yes," came the girl's answer in a rather uncertain tone.

The girl went and the father was again alone in his sunny cabin. He lingered in bed, his wordless thoughts coalescing into an unexpectedly overwhelming mood.

The blissful summer Sunday still lasted. Several hours after noon it was still potent and full of happiness. Good-natured people who met on the road interpreted it to each other.

Silja stayed at Mikkola all through the middle part of the day. Kustaa made the coffee himself as he waited for her. Then he saw the girl coming along the road, slowly this time, and swinging a branch of flowering bird-cherry. Only a couple of hours remained to the arrival of the boat. Then the father would be left alone again for a week, the girl would go back to her class to prepare for her Confirmation on Midsummer Day. A happy time, though Silja Salmelus would not be able to stand on this occasion before the altar where her ancestors for so many generations back had waited, with minds solemnly attuned to purity, for those marvelous symbols. This was a different parish, in an unfamiliar district.

One would have thought that old Kustaa's mind would have been uplifted and solemn these days. But for the most it was curiously confused, especially on this Sunday when Silja was at home. The reason was unfathomable even to the man himself. For was not the girl as fair and pure-looking as before, well-behaved and balanced? Even if she did pay a visit, what was there surprising in that? Surely she could not be expected to sit indoors the whole day, on her holiday. And the only girl of her age in the neighborhood was Mikkola's. To tell the truth, Kustaa did not know anything for certain against the girl. A few unwittingly overheard remarks, that was all. That Silja should stay out a little on a fine Saturday night near her own yard, that was only devotion. The child wanted of course to think over in solitude the thoughts awakened during the week by the parson's strong exhortations.

In some way, however, the band between father and daughter, firm as it had grown, was shaken.

It was by no means the first time that the father brewed coffee and set it on the table. Silja had often seen it happen, even after she had grown into a big girl, when she chanced to be unwell. On such occasions Kustaa would not seek female help from the village, but would leave his own work and do the kitchen tasks with fair skill. But today, when Silja entered the room on her return from her visit and saw her father setting out the cups, and the smell of freshly-made coffee reached her nostrils, the embarrassment of that morning, though now in a softer, more touching form, once more assailed her. Father looked so strangely old, a state Silja had hitherto not thought of connecting with her father. Something akin to pity flooded the girl's mind. She hastened to take over the task from him.

In Silja's departure that day to the big village there was much more solemnity than on her first departure a week ago. Then it had been an active Monday morning, and Kustaa had driven her there, as the steamer did not run that way in the mornings. On that occasion Silja had been homesick for the cabin, she felt defenseless among so many strangers. Now she could not help waiting for the moment of departure; it was so exciting to travel on the boat; there would be two or three girls on board from the villages beyond theirs, from the direction whence the boy had come rowing last night. It would be nice too in the yard of the house where she lodged; there was a big level lawn, where young people were said to assemble for games on Sunday nights.

Kustaa sat without making any remark, only looking on as she made her preparations. His ear, too, was able to follow her movements, for she was humming. The tune resembled some sacred song, or was it a hymn, something anyhow, picked up during the week. The girl bustled and hummed, but did not look at her father a single time. Until while looking for something she asked him a very humdrum question in the middle of her humming, as one might open ajar the festival chamber of one's soul to shout some order to the menials' room. At the same time she looked unconsciously and without any shyness at her father, on her face a matter-of-fact, hurrying expression. She saw in her father's eyes that which made her stop to look, straight into the old man's pupils, without being able to look away soon. . . . Her father did not appear to have heard her question, that she saw by the strange gleam in his eyes; in them was, as though in answer, another and more solemn question.

Her father got up and went towards the bed.

"I feel a bit sick," he said. "Is there any water here?"

Silja left her own tasks and hurried to the water-pail. It was empty. The girl hastened out. Kustaa was left alone.

And now the air in the room assumed almost the proportions of a character in the scene; to Kustaa it was as though the air was watching him, as though it alone had divined everything, as though in the air had been something with which he would hereafter be called on to associate, abjuring everything else. Sick in body he stared at the middle of the floor, and again there came into his mind the memory of a similar stare long ago. He fancied himself looking in through the doorway of the barn at Salmelus, the old farm which he had nearly forgotten. He rose from the bed, turning first towards the window beside which hung the mirror. Some whim made him look into it; he could not have said when he had last looked into a mirror as now, studying his reflection. He saw a man, but who? It was the man who had once come to him looking like that and asked his opinion about something connected with the farm, during that last phase of his life . . . by that question and the pitifully moved glance that accompanied it, by those alone Vihtori Salmelus, long dead, had made over his estate to his young son Kustaa. From the mirror the same man now looked out, the same nose and mouth, the same questioning agony in the eyes. What would happen now? What said the air in the room, and the floor?

Silja!—she would come—and soon go. No, no,—he must know how to behave —as sometimes before—on certain occasions in his life.

The child bore the pail in silence to its place and then looked at her father; he came towards her, a hectic flush on his cheeks, took the dipper and drank.

"Mustn't you be going now, dear child?" he asked as he put back the dipper.

There it was again, that "dear child," out of use long ago, a phrase her father uttered for the second time that day. The long midday sojourn in the village, the many contacts with sky, land, and the glances and words of human beings, had caused the girl to forget the weight that had lain over the house that morning; unconsciously she had fled mostly from that, but the weight had only grown heavier. Did not her father say a moment ago that he felt bad, that he was ill? Like old age, that was something Silja had been unable to connect easily with her father. She now looked at him as at some approaching disaster that could no longer be averted. Her father was aware before she was that tears were rolling down her cheeks.

"Don't be anxious, Silja darling," said Kustaa. "It'll soon be over. You see you don't miss the boat."

Silja's distress moved Kustaa so much that he wholly forgot his own condition; his body had to live through the last stage of its life unobserved by his mind. Silja had to go; the bows of the steamer might emerge at any moment from behind the farthest headland. Silja went, and Kustaa went to see her off, walking beside her to the main road. There he stopped, watching the departure of his only child, which he could no longer recall. The girl went, stepping daintily on the path of that early summer Sunday, her aged father watching her elastic step from the end of the lane. The father had time to see another girl come at the right moment from another lane farther on to join Silja with expressions of joy. After the two girls had proceeded some distance, they met two youths, as Kustaa could clearly distinguish. The youths stopped and the girls stopped. Then the boys turned and began walking, they too, towards the quay. All this Kustaa saw before he went back to his cabin. For he still had time to get back to the cabin—there was even a witness to that—where he was subsequently found dead. Quite as his father had been found dead in the barn on the family estate.

Silja had time to settle down in her lodgings, and even to take part in the games on the lawn, before the news reached her. The boy from the village shop brought word to her, speaking as glibly as he had learned to do over the counter. To Silja, at that moment, it was as though in reality she had left her father for dead at the end of the home lane, though she had not known it. She looked at the people around her with wondering glance, as though they had known it and had notwithstanding enticed her to play with them. Even the shop-boy seemed in no hurry to depart. Almost they seemed to be waiting for her to go, so that they could go on practicing their dance. Silja too had tried to learn it; she knew the tune and even the words.

There was no one to advise Silja what to do in her plight. The mistress of the house seemed to be more concerned with some other matter than the death of that Confirmation class girl's father. She was not quite sure how well off he had been, and now the money for the girl's lodging. . . . Probably she spoke about it to her own husband.

The road from the big village to the cabin was not very familiar to Silja, and it was late; but she set off at once, going without another word to anybody. The mistress was left to wonder, and to comfort herself with the reflection that in no case could the girl have disappeared forever, as her Confirmation class was still unfinished.

Silja fared along her road. It was Sunday night, and along the village road lounged groups of youths, who stared with cheerful impudence at the girl as she passed them. No one made any special attempt to molest her, her queer expression keeping off these starers, greatly as such loungers enjoy teasing the helpless.

It was nearly ten o'clock when Silja again stood at the end of the lane where she had left her father a few hours earlier. Without being aware of it, she paused here, as though she had only just understood what it all meant. She had walked the whole of the way home in a kind of protest against what the shop-boy had said to her in the yard. Now, faced with the short walk down the home lane, the act seemed to imply some measure of acknowledgment of the news.

Silja came into the yard and saw that the cabin doors had been locked on the outside. She went to a window; the curtains had been drawn inside. A small opening had been left in the middle, but nothing could be seen through it. Complete silence; not a walker on the road. The tender moods of the night before and the sunny joys of the day on roads and lawns were immensely far.

The master of Mikkola came slowly along the road. He saw Silja while some distance away, but did not quicken his pace. He drew steadily nearer, while Silja, a girl in her Confirmation year, stood pallid in the summer night on the threshold of her deserted home, in a yard that seemed to have grown cold. "Well, well, that's what happened here, poor child—you had only just gone when . . ." On ordinary occasions Mikkola was rather rough in his behavior, but now he too spoke to the girl in a gentle voice, telling her at length how the matter had been discovered, and how it had then fallen to his lot to act, and that what he had done was to lay out the corpse on boards and send word to Silja.

Ever farther at an ever swifter speed receded her life of a few hours ago, her whole life in fact up to now, her childhood. In the mild and, to others, delightful summer night the cold winds of life blew on the orphan. Mikkola was now speaking to her as to a full-grown person, the first time Silja had been addressed as such. The man observed to her that he had not been in the house alone, but had first fetched a witness—so that no one would have anything to say. As he spoke he opened the locks on the door and went on ahead into the dim room.

Silja too entered the cabin. The dead spread around him a limitless potent silence. The curtains were drawn, so that at first Silja could not see.

Mikkola went to the big table. "We

lifted him on to this table, as he had fallen just there, right against it—we thought . . ." The man moved away again and drew aside the curtains, remaining a little apart from her.

Silja saw again the under side of her father's jaw, the curving nostrils and hollows of the eyes, as once before, at a certain decisive moment. The eyes were slightly open, as they had often been while her father was lying on the bed and Silja moved about the room quietly working, or said something that did not call for an answer. There lay the silent man, on his face the last faint shadow of the smile that he had needed so often at the turns in his life's road. He lay there undisturbed, as though smiling at the fact that Silja and Mikkola were watching him, perhaps waiting for him to change his position. He did not move, merely lay, on that table on . . . Apparently it was only now that the matter penetrated to the bottom of Silja's consciousness, for she now burst into a fit of crying, the note of which was light and musical as that of a child. Her father had once told her in a very funny way how she had slept her first sleep in the cabin on that same table.

The hard-natured farmer could find nothing more to say. He moved gradually towards the door, came back again, and began drawing the curtains. "I'll put these—so they won't come peeping—not that he would know whether they did or not, but it's better . . ." Mikkola muttered amid Silja's slowly receding fit of crying. "Mm—I suppose you'll come to our place for the night. You can sleep with Tyyne—you won't be going back to the big village tonight—and we ought to make up our minds about when he's to be buried, seeing it's so warm— I'll do everything, unless you want someone else to manage for you—he's left enough money, there won't be any need to go to the parish, I know that— I haven't looked yet to see whether he's got that much at home, but there'll be some in the bank, and I can lend some of my own for the time being. . . ."

The grass wetted Silja's new boots, for the dew had already fallen. A midnight sound or two was heard, a stray scent breathed. Silja and the master of Mikkola, a queer couple to be together at that time of the night, moved past the sleeping houses towards Mikkola. Here and there in a yard a curious woman still waited, who, having seen Mikkola pass on his way to Salmelus's cabin, and guessing his errand, wanted to hear and see whether "the girl was taking it very badly that her father should go off so sudden."—"Solemn-looking she was, but she wasn't crying when she went past here," the woman would then report to her husband, already in bed.

The couple came to Mikkola, where the family was still awake. The mistress, and even Tyyne, with whom Silja had spent part of her day, were so embarrassed that they shook hands with Silja, and Tyyne spoke in a strange voice, as though reading the words from a book. Then Silja was given something tasty for supper, but she was unable to eat it, for tears poured from her eyes and her mouth grew dry when she tried to chew. So they all went to bed, Silja together with Tyyne.

The orphan's first night was an unlucky one so far as sleep was concerned. Tyyne fell asleep almost at once and disturbed her bedfellow, who merely dozed occasionally, by her abrupt movements in her sleep. In its own way this helped to keep Silja's mind off the subject on which it tended to dwell. The sturdy farmer's daughter cast her leg over the much more delicately-built Silja, and pressed so hard that Silja had to struggle to escape from the weight, whereupon Tyyne turned altogether towards her and embraced her passionately, murmuring meanwhile to herself. Her breath was faintly night-tainted. Silja had never slept in the same bed with anyone else than her father, nor did she afterwards for many years. Now, as she lay awake, she thought of how near she had been to Tyyne yesterday, walking together and smiling in the sunshine. Of how they had met those boys on their way to the boat, and what Tyyne had said. And what father had asked her and what he had said.

After that night Silja never felt any tie of affection for Tyyne Mikkola, who had been on the way to becoming her girl-friend. It was as though, at this first cross-roads of her life at least, old Kustaa Salmelus had stood guiding her in the right direction.

Weary, Silja went off in the morning to continue her Confirmation class, and Mikkola began to arrange all the practical matters connected with the death, which Silja would not of course have known how to arrange. Kustaa was buried on the same Sunday as Silja was confirmed, but neither event made any very deep impression on Silja or remained long in her memory.

THE LIFE AND WORKS OF FRANS EEMIL SILLANPÄÄ

By OLOF ENCKELL

FINNISH literary prose made a relatively late appearance. It was created just over a hundred years ago by Aleksis Kivi, a tailor's son of genius, who about 1860 wrote his powerful rural epic *Seitsemän veljestä* (The Seven Brothers), with its vivid descriptions of primitive men living in a remote corner of the Finnish countryside. With this novel Kivi opened the way for many works of the same type which stand out as landmarks in the subsequent development of Finnish epic prose. It is no exaggeration to say that, until quite recently, both the Finnish novel and the short story have found their finest expression in the delineation of peasant life—a way of life which, though thoroughly Finnish and intensely local, is in its essential qualities universal and classical. Even today, many of the best Finnish prose writers may justly claim to be rightful descendants of the Seven Brothers of Jukola whose destinies are recounted by Aleksis Kivi in a strain all his own, effectively blending pathos and high spirits, human sympathy and artistic daring.

The works of Frans Eemil Sillanpää also belong to this school of descriptive writing about peasant life, about ways and manners characteristically Finnish and essentially human.

Sillanpää was born September 16, 1888, at Kierikkala in southwestern Finland. His birthplace was an outlying town far from the main roads, and the home into which he was born was poor and humble. His father owned a small cabin near the mill head of Kierikkala, and earned his living mostly as a day laborer. To eke out his meager wages and better provide for his wife and children, he set up in a corner of his house a village store in miniature where he sold a few staples—coffee, sugar, tobacco, and flour—to the people of the neighborhood. From this childhood home near the local mill race the boy Frans Eemil took his surname. In reality his father's name was Frans Koskinen, but in keeping with the time-honored custom of Finnish villages he assumed the name of the land on which he lived: Sillanpää (literally, bridgehead).

Although Frans Eemil Sillanpää was familiar with poverty from his boyhood and country bred in a remote town of southwestern Finland, it must not be supposed that he was a child of the wilderness with no family background or traditions to feed and stir a young imagination. On the contrary, the province of Satakunta is one of Finland's oldest agricultural districts, where peasant life and lore are rich and varied. His father and mother were both descended from peasant landowners who had run into debt and lost their holdings. The pride of the peasant proprietor is a universal phenomenon, and its imprint has been especially strong on the freeholders of rural Finland.

To show in brief how far these origins and family background went to shape the personality and writings of Sillanpää, we need only draw attention to three points. First, he grew up in a home where material difficulties were a matter of daily concern, and most of his best work deals with poverty and poor children. Secondly, he belonged to a family which had come down in the world, whose social status had been reduced from that of peasant landowners with their own farmstead to that of cottagers in narrow circumstances, dependent on others; and here we touch on one of the main themes of his stories, treated most memorably in *Hurskas kurjuus* (Meek Heritage, 1919) and *Nuorena nukkunut* (The Maid Silja, 1931). But on that very account—and this is the third point—he preserved in the outward conduct of life a hereditary peasant pride that ennobled his rugged countryman's features and which, in his work, comes through most strongly in his novel *Miehen tie* (A Man's Way, 1932) and his long short story "Vanha valtias" (The Old Lord, 1936).

Three children had been born in the Sillanpää cabin. Two of them died in infancy. The parents' loving care was then lavished on their only surviving son. Of his father and mother Sillanpää later wrote: "At the age of ten I was able to exert a decisive influence that changed their life and destiny."

In the 1890s, when Sillanpää was a boy, compulsory education had not yet been introduced in Finland; there was no state system of public schools, and most children in rural areas received only casual instruction dispensed by itinerant schoolmasters in makeshift schoolrooms. Sillanpää was fortunate: after a grounding in the rudiments at a good village primary school, he was sent on to the town of Hankijärvi, some distance away but still in his native parish, where his quick intelligence and aptitude for learning gained him admittance to a newly founded grammar school. His parents then decided to follow him and moved to Hankijärvi, lodging in a small room near the school. Several years later the family took an even bolder step, one that called for heavy sacrifices. At the grammar school he had taken so eagerly to books and reading that in the autumn of 1896 his father resolved to give him the benefit of the better educational facilities available in the industrial city of Tampere.

There a new life began for the eight-year-old schoolboy, a complete departure from his previous experience. Starting from a rude cabin in an outlying province, he had arrived in the largest industrial city of Finland where living conditions and the tempo of life were totally different. For several years he lived with a motley group of other tenants in the house of an impecunious carpenter. In this milieu he learned to sympathize with the aspirations of the working class toward social betterment. But he also had opportunities to see what life was like in wider circles of the society in which he now found himself. His father's resources were insufficient to meet all his expenses and the boy had to earn what he could on the side. Through the good offices of the principal of his school, he was engaged as a private tutor for the son of a rich industrialist; he then left the carpenter's house for a room in the comfortable home of a Tampere patrician.

Thus it was given to Sillanpää in early youth to see and experience at first hand widely different walks of life. At the age of nineteen, when he obtained his school-leaving certificate and went to the capital of Finland in the spring of 1908, he already possessed a considerable fund of experience. On May 21, 1908, he matriculated in the physico-mathematical section of the faculty of philosophy in the Imperial Alexander University in Helsinki.

His studies in Helsinki produced no apparent result. Sillanpää never sat for any examinations and took no degree. But the five years he spent at the university were a period of cardinal importance for the future writer. When he decided to study the natural sciences, he was undoubtedly acting in obedience to some inner prompting. In his country childhood, often alone and thrown on his own resources, he had found a companion and confidant in nature. His work as a writer continually testifies to the fascination he always felt for life in its more mysterious manifestations.

Also, it was during his university years that Sillanpää laid the conscious intellectual foundations of his world view, just as we find them, given poetic shape, in his writings. His view of the world was colored and mellowed by his profound reverence for life in all its forms as well as by a resigned wonder, carried to the point of fatalism, over the laws governing our life processes. But Sillanpää did not retreat into the closed world of biological doctrines. He described his philosophy or faith, founded on his studies and his experience of life, one day in December 1924 when he wrote: "I am a materialist, I believe in matter, but I am not so naive as to imagine that I know all there is to know about matter. I do not believe in supernatural phenomena, but I find it strange indeed that anyone should think man capable of elucidating everything in the natural world."

While his intellectual orientation lay in the direction of biology, this was by no means the sole concern of his student years. In Helsinki he became close friends with a fellow student who belonged to one of the most prominent aristocratic families in Finland. His new friend was the son of the painter Eero Järnefelt, an outstanding figure in the history of Finnish art. Through young Järnefelt, Sillanpää was introduced at twenty-two to the famous circle of artists who had settled at Tuusula, outside Helsinki; this was a creative center to which early twentieth-century Finland owed the enrichment of its cultural life. At Tuusula, in addition to the Järnefelt family, lived the painter Pekka Halonen, the composer Jan Sibelius, and many representatives of the highest social and intellectual spheres. Sillanpää was welcomed into this circle with a generous and disinterested kindness which uplifted and stimulated him, although at first it almost overwhelmed the poor provincial student. Once his shyness wore off, the group took an interest in the unknown youth from Hämeenkyro and he was made to feel at home. From here, a vast and varied prospect of possibilities opened before him, more stimulating for his imagination than those offered by the working program of a student of botany and zoology.

Very soon, Sillanpää rebelled against the constraints of the academic routine. And no wonder, now that he had experienced at Tuusula the determining stimulus of free creative expression on a free artistic basis.

In the course of his freshman year in Helsinki, Sillanpää began to show symptoms of psychic instability. He suffered from a morbid dread of open spaces (agoraphobia). It is thought that these fears may have had their origin in the strains and sense of insecurity that resulted from the sudden changes in his social status, first as a schoolboy, then as a young man.

His parents had moved from Hämeenkyrö to the town of Heinijärvi, where his father had bought a small cabin. To this extremely humble home, now well known to Finnish readers under the name of Töllinmäki (Shanty Hill), their son returned on Christmas eve in 1913, at the age of twenty-five. He had come home to stay. The gifted and promising young man had broken off his studies and, it seemed, burned his bridges. The townsfolk were only too eager to assume the worst; he was over his head in debt, had failed his examinations, dashed the hopes of his parents, and made a mockery of their sacrifices.

Proof that he returned home with no regrets to re-immerse himself purposely in his childhood environment may be seen in a step he now took which fixed the course of his private life for years to come. In the summer of 1914, on one of the estates at Hämeenkyrö, he chanced to meet a seventeen-year-old servant girl named Sigrid Maria Salomäki, the daughter of a poor tenant farmer in the parish. Two years later he married her, thus implicitly asserting his affinity with the peasant class to which he belonged by birth.

During the first winter of World War I, the influential Helsinki newspaper *Uusi Suometar* published a series of sketches and stories which at once commanded attention. They were remarkable for their rich and varied insights into nature, the supple melody of the language, and a personal accent which seemed to recognize no limits in its frankness. The author, who called himself E. Syväri, was quite unknown.

Among those who read and admired these stories were the directors of the publishing house of Werner Söderström at Porvoo. Through the editor of the paper they found out who the author was and obtained his address. One day in the spring of 1915 a letter arrived at Hämeenkyrö inviting Sillanpää to get in touch with the Porvoo publishers. It was this outside encouragement that at last decided his career. From boyhood he had been a voracious reader, and during his student years in Helsinki he had become an enthusiastic admirer of Maeterlinck's *Treasure of the Humble,* the great Norwegian novelist Knut Hamsun, and the art of the Russian storytellers. The praise bestowed now on his own stories gave him the courage to devote himself to literature.

Sillanpää was a newly married man of twenty-eight when in the autumn of 1916 he published his first novel *Elämä ja aurinko* (Life and Sun). The book at once aroused considerable interest. Some defenders of propriety expressed indignation at the erotic intensity of certain scenes. But most readers were delighted with this love story set in the open air and sunshine of the Finnish countryside; few could have guessed that this genial romance was written during a trying period of transition in the author's life.

What struck readers most of all was the poetic range of the young writer's style. There is a wide cast of characters in the story, but it is not always men and women who occupy the foreground; plants and animals, sun and moon, sky and earth all give form and meaning to the author's vision. Over man and nature hovers a promise of concord which makes the action, though broken into subplots, move forward like a single wave, steadily unfolding with ever increasing power. All life seems attuned to the breathing of mighty lungs. Out of the smooth-surfaced depths of this world rises love, the transfiguring love of twenty-year-olds. One might say that the subject of the book is the rapt bewilderment of young life following its instincts in the open air, on the warm, steaming earth. The poetry springs from a hesitation between the desire for something the will is powerless to grasp and the consciousness of something for which the mind refuses to accept responsibility. Moral principles simply lapse in this lover's world; only impulse and the elemental force of natural ties hold sway and act on each other.

This first novel was published in the autumn of 1916. In the autumn of the following year the Russian Revolution broke out; it was to cast its shadow over Finnish life for a long time to come. Social unrest quickly spread throughout Finland, which at that time was part of the Russian empire. Lawlessness and violence led to bloodshed, and in January 1918, a brutal conflict began between the "Whites" and the "Reds," which in the history of Finland has been variously called the War of Independence, the Civil War, and the Red Rebellion. After three months of bitter fighting and often wanton slaughter, the White forces led by General Mannerheim gained a decisive victory over the Reds. In the eyes of the bourgeoisie, the Finnish proletariat appeared as a rebellious, blood-stained rabble inspiring fear and disgust.

Sillanpää lived through the national tragedy at Hämeenkyrö. He held aloof, refusing to fight for one side or the other. The course of his life had brought him into close contact with all classes of society, and he knew well enough that the distinction between good and evil did not necessarily correspond to the distinction between Whites and Reds. His own origins naturally made him sympathetic toward those who knew poverty and hardship. When the fighting ended, when the sufferings of the innocent were already fading from memory in the jubilation of the victorious Whites, he felt impelled to analyze the social and psychological equilibrium which had worked itself out at the expense of a backward and despised proletariat. The result of his reflections was that memorable epic of Finland's poor, the novel *Hurskas kurjuus* (Meek Heritage), published in February 1919.

This book, remarkable both as literature and as social history, is pervaded by a mood of resigned acceptance which undoubtedly reflects the philosophy of fatalism confirmed in Sillanpää by his study of the natural sciences. But the descriptions of people and lives could only have been written by one who had made a thorough study of the social history of Finland since the famine years of the 1860s.

The orphan boy on whom the story turns, an outcast for whom there seems to be no place in society, is representative of the down-trodden men of the working class: the odds are against any change in his lowly status. His life is at the mercy of the fitful moods of a fate which has failed to endow him with spiritual resources; it has given him no means of steeling his character or forging a personality. Even a name of his own has been denied him, according to the places where he chances to work, as lumberman or farmhand, and the people he is thrown in with, he is called Jussi Nikkilä or Jussi Tuorila, then Juha Toivola or Janne Toivola. As a child he was an unlikable, bow-legged little fellow with a scrawny neck, his mouth agape in a head too large for his size. After a life of drudgery he was a bald, repulsive-looking old man with a sharp nose, his face covered with a mongrel growth of tangled hair. Most decent folk preferred to have no dealings with him.

Sillanpää tells his story with an art so sober and dispassionate, with a human vision so lucid and searching, that he keeps forcing the reader to ask himself the disturbing question: Was this man, this broken vessel, only made to be used and discarded, or was he not meant to be loved? Is it not the full measure of degradation when in their relations with a man his fellowmen no longer feel themselves bound by the commandment, "Love thy neighbor as thyself"? Let this hapless Jussi Nikkilä or Juha Toivola be what he may, there is no changing that. But it remains in our power to try to judge him humanly and fairly. Have we not all a debt to pay to men such as Jussi who in the game of life find themselves on the losing side?

Sillanpää's first book, *Life and Sun* was the most radiant he ever wrote; his second was the gloomiest. Both, for different reasons, grated on the feelings of the old-fashioned conservative reader. But the critical reader of taste and judgment realized at once that in Sillanpää the Finnish people had found a spokesman who, in poetic power and human understanding, had no peer and few rivals in contemporary Finnish literature. Some of his most discriminating admirers still feel that he never surpassed these first two novels, one describing the rapture of young love on a sunny earth, the other the joyless life of a poor toiler borne down by an unrelenting fate.

As the 1920s began, all the future hopes of Finnish literature seemed to center on Sillanpää. Expectations rose to almost absurd heights, and were followed by impatience as time passed and they were not fulfilled. Then he published two books: the short novel *Hiltu ja Ragnar* (Hiltu and Ragnar, 1923) and a volume of stories, *Enkelten suojatit* (Wards of the Angels, 1923). But these short pieces failed to satisfy the rather excessive ambitions conceived for him by his publisher, the critics, and the public. What all of them were calling for was the "great Finnish novel," something sizable and weighty, in both the literal and the figurative sense of those words. Sillanpää, now in his late thirties and still living in countrified aloofness, went his own way. Further volumes with his name on the cover appeared at intervals in the bookshops, but there were no novels among them; they contained short stories, essays, and autobiographical sketches. The 1920s came to an end, he had passed his fortieth year, and still the great, long-awaited work had not appeared.

For Sillanpää this whole period had been a time of trials. Near his father's cabin at Töllinmäki he had had a house of his own built—somewhat rashly, for the cost of building and furnishing a house proved to be beyond his means. There was a growing family to provide for; by 1926 he had six children. His debts mounted. Because he could not pay his electricity bills, the power cables leading to his house were cut off. His affairs were in a muddle. To help him straighten them out, his publisher offered him the editorship of a new literary journal, *Panu;* he accepted, though it meant moving with his family to Porvoo. For three years he endured the office routine of a busy editor, but he was not much better off than before. As Sillanpää grew older, he grew more incapable of handling money or managing his affairs. The resulting involvements threatened to unbalance a mind none too stable at the best of times. This period ended in an unsettled year of bewilderment and frustration, during which he drifted between Hämeenkyrö and Tampere, the city where he had gone to school.

Today when we read Sillanpää's writings of the twenties, stories and tales of apparently slender build, sketches and random thoughts, we find it hard to understand that his publisher and the public should have wished for anything more than what he gave them. The books of those years illustrate admirably his most characteristic qualities, even more so perhaps than the more ambitious novels of the thirties, with which he finally satisfied the expectations of his contemporaries. In the four volumes just mentioned, containing a long sequence of autobiographical and descriptive fragments, each in itself of seemingly small account but together telling vividly of real lives and real things, the heart of Finland is laid bare and its beat felt. Even in his slightest sketches there is a sure, spontaneous grasp of human realities. Small wonder then if the parish of Hämeenkyrö has become perhaps the best known of all on the literary map of Finland. It is easy enough to assume a priori that such writings, so directly concerned with the author himself and the daily life of a remote northern province, can have little interest for the non-Finnish reader. But in fact, these short pieces, these stories and marginal notes, convey a love of truth and a view of life that are profoundly universal. Their subject matter is local, but their human implications carry far. In the best tales of Hämeenkyrö parish, as in Maupassant's tales of Normandy, one hears the heartbeat of all humanity.

By the early spring of 1929, Sillanpää seemed to be at the end of his resources. He appealed to his publisher for an advance, but his immediate needs were only partially met. In the stress of despair he wrote a letter to the rival publishing firm of Otava; briefly and forcibly he described his plight and practically offered the rights for all his future work. The response was immediate. The owner and director of Otava, Professor Alvar Renqvist, a highly cultured man, came to his assistance with ungrudging generosity. Thereafter Sillanpää's books appeared under the Otava imprint. Indulgent and liberal, his new publisher took over the management of his affairs for him, thus protecting him against his own improvidence. One result of these arrangements was that, at the beginning of 1930, Sillanpää moved to Helsinki.

Thanks to the generous backing of Otava, he was able to make a fresh start. His self-confidence restored, he entered on the most productive period of his career. During the years 1930–1936 he published six books, including three major novels, *Nuorena nukkunut* (The Maid Silja, 1931), *Miehen tie* (A Man's Way, 1932), and *Ihmiset suviyössä* (People in the Summer Night, 1934). In this great spurt of creative activity he more than fulfilled the hopes he had raised years before, and by the middle thirties he was acknowledged as Finland's greatest living writer. Each year his name was high on the list of favored candidates for the Nobel Prize.

None of Sillanpää's books enjoyed so immediate and triumphant a success as *The Maid Silja.* This long novel was probably overestimated—or to some extent misjudged—in the initial enthusiasm with which the Finnish public of 1931 received what it had so long demanded from him: a methodically written novel. A later generation seems better qualified to give a considered judgment, and perhaps a more discerning one; certainly the present-day reader of the book cannot help chafing at flaws in its construction and at irrelevant digressions. But in this later epic of Hämeenkyrö are the same admirable qualities of style and the memorable insights that had distinguished his first two novels and his masterly stories of the 1920s. Here, as always, he excelled in casting over his descriptions of nature and human relations the transfiguring light of a poetry closely akin to what may fairly be called wisdom.

The story turns on the peasant Kustaa Salmelus and his daughter Silja, "the last offshoots of an old family tree." Neither is a match for the harsh realities that beset them. The peasant himself is shiftless and inept: his big horny hands are ill-fitted to work the farm bequeathed to him, nor were they created for the caresses that might express the affection he dumbly feels for his daughter. So Silja grows up alone and unaided, enjoys a brief moment of happiness, and then dies, passing unnoticed from a world where only the strong and hardened survive. Sillanpää's art is seen at its finest in his description of a lonely and innocent life, that of a peasant girl untouched, in her purity, by all that is degrading and primitive in her surroundings. For the Finnish reader Silja is the incarnation of girlhood, for she leads the prosaic life of thousands of girls in the provinces of rural Finland. She attends the village dance on Saturday night; she lies dreaming in her bed, while the farmhand on the other side of the wall tries to entice her into his; she feels the stirrings of first love. Nothing has any hold over her; an artless village girl, left to herself, in meek but steady self-reliance she goes her way as traced out by nature, from barefooted child to full-grown woman. For a brief hour she experiences the fullness of life and love; then it only remains for her to die and be gone.

Miehen tie is a tribute to the wholesome power of well-directed energies. It is written with a single-minded purposefulness whose rigor exceeds anything to be found in his earlier books; its very starkness excluded that rich vein of philosophical meditation on life which had been so essential a part of other books.

Conversely, *Ihmiset suviyössä* is a vibrant expression of Sillanpää's poetic powers in their most characteristic strain. In this novel, whose plot unfolds in the twenty-four hours of a Finnish summer's night, the orchestration is extraordinarily rich. It can hardly be said that the book contributes anything really new to the corpus of Sillanpää's work. However, this expansive, many-sided novel offers a suggestive synthesis of the author's life experience up to that time. Youthful arrogance is shattered by the disappointments of the grown man; love-smitten melancholy is succeeded by the unthinking brutishness of hard drinking; the mystery of childbirth is counterbalanced by a violent death. For sheer artistry, this book is almost unrivaled among Sillanpää's major novels.

With the publication in 1936 of *Viidestoista* (*The Fifteenth*), an extensive collection of short stories, Sillanpää's writing career came to a standstill. The accumulated strains of many years of overwork had told on him; the emotional balance he had so precariously maintained began to waver. The sums advanced by Otava to discharge his debts mounted up alarmingly. Again Sillanpää strove to meet his obligations and worked doggedly at two more novels—which, however, his exacting critical standards would not allow him to release. They were issued later, in the 1940s, by another publisher, under the title of *Elokuu* (*August*) and *Ihmiselon ihanuus ja kurjuus* (*The Loveliness and Wretchedness of Human Life*). For the student of Sillanpää they have a special interest, for they show him making an attempt to widen the scope of his subject matter. But neither can compare with his best work; indeed they make it clear why he now forsook the social and spiritual spheres which he knew best, and which in almost all his previous work he had described with such loving fidelity. The important part played by alcohol in these two novels is symptomatic.

While he was struggling in the toils of personal and material difficulties, Sillanpää suffered a further blow. His wife Sigrid, who had borne him eight children and had been the mainstay of his existence, died in the autumn of 1939. With this, his self-control began to fail him and threatened to give way altogether. It was a sick man and a confirmed alcoholic who now faced the last eventful months of the year 1939.

Soon after the outbreak of the Second World War, the attention of the world was drawn to Finland. Stalin's Russia demanded the right to install military bases on Finnish territory and threatened to go to war if its demands were not met. This tense situation was watched with growing concern in the neighboring Scandinavian countries. In Sweden, in particular, there was a nationwide expression of sympathy for the Finnish people in its hour of danger. This spontaneous movement of solidarity undoubtedly influenced the deliberations of the Swedish Academy that autumn, when it came time for the Nobel Prize awards, and led it to fix its choice on Finland's greatest living writer.

Thus in November 1939, when Sillanpää was notified that he had been awarded the Nobel Prize for Literature, he was already prepared for the news. The state of mind in which he received this distinction is reflected in a note he penned two and a half years later, in the spring of 1942. He wrote: "Darkness closes in. On the table in front of me is an old magazine, a whole page is covered with illustrations relating to me, and the text on the opposite page tells about me. From all this I gather I was awarded the Nobel Prize. I even learn that I was present and received it." In March 1940, he returned to Finland. His new marriage broke up soon afterward, and Sillanpää had to be admitted to a psychiatric hospital. When he was released, though only in his middle fifties, he was already a broken old man. During the last twenty years of his life he lived quietly with his family not far from Helsinki.

During the 1950s an occasional volume appeared bearing his name; the last was published in 1957. These books consist almost entirely of short narratives and autobiographical fragments touching on his early life. The only novelty of his old age was a series of Christmas talks broadcast by the Finnish radio. Utterly unpretentious, these modest sermons were imbued with the same cordial endorsement of life, the same ready humor and uncomplaining resignation that had marked all his writings. In his last years, up to his death in 1964 at the age of seventy-five, his patriarchal figure, with a black skullcap on his bald head and a gray, wavy prophet's beard, could still be seen on rare occasions in the streets of Helsinki.

Olof Enckell is head of the history department at the University of Helsinki.
Translated by James Emmons.

THE 1939 PRIZE

By KJELL STRÖMBERG

WHEN Frans Eemil Sillanpää won the Nobel Prize for Literature for 1939, the award marked Finland's first. Conditions that autumn were such that the chances of the Prize falling to that little corner of the world were exceptionally favorable. A new European war had broken out. Hitler's Germany, without firing a shot, had occupied Austria and Czechoslovakia and had just completed the military annihilation of Poland. Soviet Russia, allied for the moment with Nazi Germany, had wiped out the independence of the three Baltic nations and was preparing to do the same to Finland, the last free nation of those created in the North by World War I. And now Finland—which for the six centuries preceding 1809 had been an integral part of the Kingdom of Sweden—was resisting the aggressor from the east and was putting up a valiant defense. In Sweden, the sector of public opinion which backed the Finnish cause had grown so powerful that a coalition government comprising all political parties was created in an effort to maintain, at least on paper, absolute neutrality on all sides. Volunteers came forth for beleaguered Finland, which was shortly not only threatened but fiercely attacked by her powerful neighbor.

There is no doubt that sooner or later Sillanpää would have won his Nobel Prize, even without a war to place him in the limelight, and he was certainly as deserving as any other who had won the award before him. The author of *Hurskas kurjuus* (*Meek Heritage*) Sillanpää had been proposed for the high honor by various supporters every year since 1930. True, he had shared this distinction with several fellow Finns, both those writing in Swedish and those writing in Finnish. On several occasions partisans had proposed the names of Bertel Gripenberg and Jarl Hemmer, distinguished Swedish-language poets who were highly esteemed on both sides of the Baltic, as well as those of the novelists Sally Salminen and Malva Talvio, both of whom, like Sillanpää, wrote in Finnish. A fifth writer was the distinguished poet and literary historian Veikko Antero Koskenniemi, who also wrote in Swedish.

The fact that the Nobel Committee waited until 1939 to make its choice from among this group is explained by the equivocal position occupied by the Swedish language in Finland. It had remained as a second official language although it is spoken by an extremely small minority (then about ten percent). Finnish is a language totally unrelated to any Scandinavian language. Very few Swedes speak or read it; thus, as is the case everywhere else in the world, readers in Sweden can know Finnish literature only in translation. Since the liberation of Finland in 1918 there had been a strong current of public opinion arguing that Finnish should be the national language, and there was a time when Parliament seemed to be ready to ban the use of Swedish in the university and the high schools of the capital, where it was still dominant. This struggle between the two languages was settled by a compromise. But meanwhile it had obviously made the selection of a Finnish candidate difficult. If a candidate spoke and wrote in the Swedish language, his election would look like an ill-advised favoritism, while if a candidate spoke and wrote Finnish it might look like tactless intervention in an effort to influence the faction hostile to the other language.

Apparently, committee members had considered surmounting the problem by dividing the Prize between two Finnish writers representing the two national languages. Particular attention was given to Gripenberg, the poet of the great patriotic deeds of the First War of Liberation, and Sillanpää, whose sympathies were more on the side of the defeated "Red" forces. (At the beginning of the war with Communist Russia this latter faction gave its loyal service to the common fatherland which had been attacked by their former friends and protectors in Russia.) Thus the Nobel Prize would have served as a symbolic seal to Finnish national unity, not only from a linguistic point of view but from an ideological and social point of view as well.

Such was the hope of the poet Verner von Heidenstam (Nobel Prize, 1916) and, for a long time, of his colleagues in the Swedish Academy. Finally it was decided, since an unmistakable homage was to be paid to Finland, to award the whole Prize to the writer who had attracted the endorsement of an impressive number of his countrymen. Sillanpää had always been received with enthusiasm in Sweden, where most of his works had appeared at the same time that they were published in Finland, and where, surprisingly, they had been hailed by an even more appreciative critical public than in his homeland.

The theory that a more or less decisive political reason lay behind the choice of Sillanpää is supported by the five or six confidential reports prepared on his works, which are uniformly highly favorable, especially in regard to *Meek Heritage* and *The Maid*. The author of these reports, Per Hallström, then Permanent Secretary of the Academy, stressed the artistic mastery displayed by Sillanpää in his descriptions of peasant life—powerful, realistic, not to say naturalistic, descriptions in the tradition of Zola, of human misery as observed in the poor villages and isolated farms of Tavastland on the Russian border, where Sillanpää had been born. The primitive people and the virgin landscape, Hallström explained, had inspired Sillanpää with a poetic lyricism close to the poetry of the best popular works in the *Kalevala*. His imagery was indeed of the soil, Hallström remarked, but because of his rather superficial psychological insights his characters were simple folk whose sentimental vicissitudes were without great complication.

Moved by the desire to do honor to their hard-pressed brothers, the Swedish Academicians paid little attention to these purely literary reservations expressed by their colleague. Very probably the vote was unanimous when the choice was finally made, chiefly "for his deep comprehension and exquisite art in painting the nature of his country and the life of its peasants in their mutual relations."

Sillanpää received the news in Helsinki, where he had gone as soon as the national crisis commenced. "This Prize is due my country as much as to me." Such was his first remark at a press conference.

Because of the war no ceremony was held. Two German scientists to whom awards had been voted were forced by Hitler's government to refuse the honor. The other winners of Nobel Prizes in the sciences (a Belgian and an American) received their awards via diplomatic pouch, while as in 1938, the Peace Prize was not given. Sillanpää made the long trip to Stockholm from Helsinki by railway, rounding the Gulf of Bothnia by way of the Lapp tundra through Tornea-Haparanda, for the ice of a particularly severe winter and the threat of Russian soldiers made the direct route over the Baltic Sea too dangerous for regular civilian transport, either boat or airline.

At a regular meeting of the Swedish Academy, followed by a small dinner upstairs in the old palace which the Academy shares with the Stockholm Stock Exchange, the medal and the check were presented to the laureate by the Permanent Secretary.

Sillanpää's award was the last Nobel Prize given for a period. By royal command, the activities of all Nobel institutions were suspended. They were not resumed until 1944, near the end of World War II.

Translated by Dale McAdoo.

René Sully-Prudhomme

1901

"In special recognition of his poetic composition, which gives evidence of lofty idealism, artistic perfection, and a rare combination of the qualities of both heart and intellect"

Illustrated by ANDRÉ HAMBOURG

PRESENTATION ADDRESS

By C. D. AF WIRSÉN

PERMANENT SECRETARY
OF THE SWEDISH ACADEMY

WHEN ALFRED NOBEL decided to make the great donation which has justly received much attention, his entire life's work led him to favor the study of nature and to reward discoveries in some of the sciences concerned with it. Likewise, his cosmopolitan aspirations made him an advocate of peace and of the brotherhood of nations. In his will he also included literature, although he placed it after the sciences, to which he felt most drawn.

Literature is grateful to him that its practitioners have also been the object of his solicitude; one could argue that it comes last in the group of Swedish Prizes for the very sound reason that the supreme flower of civilization, perhaps most beautiful yet also most delicate, will now bloom on the firm ground of reality.

In any event, the laureates receive in these floral tributes of modern times a recompense surpassing in material value the golden violets of a past era.

The award of the Nobel Prize for Literature poses its own problems. "Literature" is a very inclusive term and the statutes of the Nobel Foundation rightly specify that the competition must include not only belles-lettres but also works which, by their form as well as by their exposition, have literary value. But thereby the field is expanded and the difficulties are compounded. If it is difficult to decide—supposing that the merits of the proposed authors otherwise are approximately equal—whether the Prize should be granted to a lyric, an epic, or a dramatic poet, the task is complicated even more if it becomes a matter of choosing among an eminent historian, a great philosopher, and a poet of genius. The dimensions become, as the mathematicians say, incommensurable. But one may be consoled with the thought that, since the Prize is an annual one, more than one writer of merit who has to yield his place to another equally great, may be able to receive some other year the award he deserves.

Numerous and excellent recommendations for the literature Prize have reached the Swedish Academy. It has submitted them to the most scrupulous examination and in its choice among different names of universal reputation and almost equal literary importance, it has decided on one which it believed should have priority this time from several points of view. It has awarded the first Nobel Prize for Literature to the poet and philosopher Sully-Prudhomme of the French Academy.

Sully-Prudhomme was born March 16, 1839, and in 1865 emerged as an accomplished poet in his *Stances et Poèmes* (Stanzas and Poems). This volume was followed by several others of verse, philosophy, and esthetics. If the imagination of other poets is primarily turned outward and reflects the life and the world surrounding us, Sully-Prudhomme has an introverted nature as sensitive as it is delicate. His poetry is rarely concerned with images and exterior situations as such, but principally with the extent to which they can serve as a mirror of poetic contemplation. The love of the spiritual, his doubts, his sorrows, which nothing earthly can dissipate, are the usual subjects of his work which, in its finished form and sculptural beauty, suffers no useless word. His poetry appears in exuberant colors and only rarely takes on the character of melodious music; but it is all the more plastic in the creation of forms suited to expressing feelings and ideas. Noble, profoundly pensive, and turned toward sadness, his soul reveals itself in this poetry, tender yet not sentimental—a sorrowful analysis which inspires a melancholy sympathy in the reader.

Through the charm of his exquisite diction and through his consummate art, Sully-Prudhomme is one of the major poets of our time, and some of his poems are pearls of imperishable value. The Swedish Academy has been less attracted by his didactic or abstract poems than by his smaller lyric compositions, which are full of feeling and contemplation, and which charm by their nobility and dignity and by the extremely rare union of delicate reflection and rich sentiment.

In conclusion, it is necessary to emphasize one characteristic. Sully-

Prudhomme's work reveals an inquiring and observing mind which finds no rest in what passes and which, as it seems impossible to him to know more, finds evidence of man's supernatural destiny in the moral realm, in the voice of conscience, and in the lofty and undeniable prescriptions of duty. From this point of view, Sully-Prudhomme represents better than most writers what the testator called "an idealistic tendency" in literature. Thus the Academy believed it was acting in the spirit of Nobel's will when, for the first time it awarded the Prize, it gave its approval, among so many illustrious men of letters, to Sully-Prudhomme.

As the laureate has agreed to accept this distinction but is unfortunately prevented by illness from being in our midst today, I have the honor to ask the Minister of France to receive the Prize and to present it to him in the name of the Swedish Academy.

There was no formal Acceptance Speech by Sully-Prudhomme.

POEMS

By *RENÉ SULLY-PRUDHOMME*

Translated by William Frederic Giese

THE LOST CRY

From the abysm of immemorial time
A spirit rose and haunted me unbid,
Witness of Cheops' glory and his crime,
And toiler at his granite pyramid.
His knees shook, and his fragile body bent
With weight of stone and stress of torrid heat;
His muscles swelled, his fevered pulses beat,
And, like a tree the thunderbolt has rent,
He uttered a great cry. It shook the air;
It scaled the heavens; it shot beyond the stars,
Seeking that partial power that molds and mars,
Gives bliss to some and unto some despair.
Three thousand years that cry has pealed unheard,
And Cheops in his glory sleeps unstirred.

THE DANAÏDES

Their amphores by their ivory arms upheld,
Callidia, Theano, Danaë,
Forever to their cruel task compelled,
Run with their leaking urns unceasingly.

The porous clay reddens their shoulders white;
Their slender arms grow weary of the load:
"Ah! why this futile labor day and night,
And wherefore pace this never-ending road?"
Their lagging feet give way, their spirits droop—
But younger, gayer, sweet Theano sings,
Till faith returning spreads her shining wings:
Thus our illusions fail but not our hope.
More young and gay, she sings her glad refrain
And cries: "Come, sisters, and begin again."

WE SHALL FORGET

I love you while I wait the immortal spouse
Who watches for me at the opening gate
Of blissful Eden, home of changeless vows,
Of fadeless flowers and bridals coronate.
There I shall see, in God's resplendent house,
Where lovers dead choose an eternal mate,
Your sisters gathered under olive boughs
Where I my earthly love will abdicate.
And you, not jealous, at some angel's call
Will leave me when you hear his blessèd voice
Name you of all the blest his heavenly choice.
We shall forget our old love's human thrall
As fellow-travelers at the parting way
Forget the frail bonds of a passing day.

BLUE EYES AND BLACK

Blue eyes and black, belovèd eyes,
Eyes numberless have seen the dawn,

Eyes closed by us in days bygone,
Yet each day brought a new sunrise,

And night more gentle than the day
Brought its sweet balm to eyes untold.
The stars still glisten as of old,
Though all these eyes are sealed with clay.

Are they then all amerced of sight?
Alas! we will not think them so!
They have but closed on mortal woe
To open in celestial light.

As firmamental stars grow dim
And disappear, yet haunt the sky
And shine below the ocean's rim,
So they, too, set but do not die.

Blue eyes and black, belovèd eyes,
The eyes we closed in days agone,
Reopening on a wider dawn
Behold a brighter day arise.

THE BROKEN VASE

The vase that holds this dying rose,
Tapped lightly by a lady's fan,
Cracked at this slightest of all blows,
Though not an eye the flaw could scan.

And yet the line, so light, so slight,
Etched ever deeper on the bowl,
Spread to the left, spread to the right,
Until it circled round the whole.

The water sinks, the petals fall,
Yet none divines, no word is spoken;
The surface seems intact to all;
Ah! touch it not—the vase is broken.

Thus oft the heart is lightly bruised
By some slight word of those we cherished;
Yet through the wound our blood has oozed,
And lo! the flower of love has perished.

Though to the world our life seems whole,
The hidden wound is unforgot;
It grows and weeps within the soul:
The heart is broken—touch it not.

AN INTIMATE JOURNAL

By RENÉ SULLY-PRUDHOMME

Translated by Camilla Sykes

[Selections]

1862

1st October. A good day.—Roman law: enjoyed the work . . . I am better at it than I thought. At five o'clock, deep psychological thoughts about conscience (it is, and it knows that it is). . . . Reflections on happiness: it must not be dreamed of outside the essential nature of humanity: and our essential nature includes satiety and boredom; happiness therefore is not the *satisfaction* of our essence, but the exercise of our faculties; it is earthly. Poem: *You resemble my youth.*

2nd October. Moments of disgust: is life worth living? I worked at a clay figure. Reflections on art: one must get one's hand in, everything requires craftsmanship, craftsmanship is skill acquired through habit, it is the relationship between the artist and his material. There remains feeling: many artists of feeling exist: but the true artist tries to enjoy it by suppressing it. . . . Art would have wearied me because of the resistance of material and the futility of detailed work. . . .

Friday 3rd. During the day, nothing outstanding. Study of the nature of time. —Certainly nobody leads such an enclosed life as I do.—Dinner with my sister. Her happiness, which I can feel, tells me how much I love her.—I must not forget this morning's lecture on poetry by Ruffin: he has unerring taste and the creative spirit. I only started composing verse this year; unity, sobriety, the fittingness of comparisons, they are all there.

Saturday 4th. What is one to think of a young man who keeps watch on an innocent girl in order to ruin her? The nicest boy I know is doing this. It is not that he wants to ruin her: he wants to love her, he does love her. There is no malice in him: it is just that his blood is possessed by ancient and all-powerful Nature, and she cries out to him, "Go on! Run! Propagate!" Our customs mean that when a girl gives herself she is ruined: but what do they matter to him?

Shall I ever have done with the question of time? When somewhere the infinite shows a scrap of its dress, it casts its immense shadow over the problem; one starts to grope, one wastes one's time.

Sunday 5th. Pascal, I admire you, you belong to me, I penetrate your thought as though I were thinking inside you; magnanimous sorrow, deep, deep as the night; how full it is of distant gleams of light! Be my master, adopt me: my suffering is infinite, I gravitate round the truth, I never reach it. Did you really believe in revelation? When a genius such as this gives up reason, do I dare to doubt from where his strength and his glory come? Yet I do doubt, and sincerely, painfully. One feels that your tenderness of heart was purely human, but that you were conquered and disillusioned: yes, at a certain moment you surrendered to the strength of an angel, who seized you violently by the hand and put your finger in Christ's wound. Then you believed, but with a sense of irritation. You are without doubt the irritated, forced, untamed believer.

. . . Music floats up to me from the drawing room and the vague sounds speak to my soul; they are like a delicate and shy caress. Alas! my soul is very sick, it likes to be flattered in this way.

Big dinner party (on the return from a honeymoon) . . . Evening party, dancing . . . Oh, the past! silent collapse of things one loves which disappear into the darkness, drifting I know not where and alas! Irretrievable! It is over, the charm will never return, it has been driven away by time . . .

Music: it has an astonishing hold over me. I believe in an unknown world revealed by the anguish, the sobs, the cries of a heart drunk with harmony. It seems to say: Open! Oh, for pity's sake, open the door! You see I am heartbroken, torn, bleeding, and I feel that you are there, my God, and you are letting me die!

Young girls: I have felt the charm of modesty, it is worth all sensual pleasure. Blushing, and ignorance, are the charms of virtue; he who knows how to appreciate them enjoys the virtue which is in beauty. Supreme delights.

I have noticed that when a man is a success, those who are jealous are the most eager to congratulate him; in this way, the baseness of jealousy always betrays itself, either by offended reserve or by servile attentiveness. Pride is afraid of nothing so much as of seeming jealous.

Tuesday 7th. Chapus' studio: the bust of Monsieur Sédille, the likeness lies especially in the details. The artist's life, made up of drunkenness and distress. Obscurity, futile work: glory, colloquy with the ideal. The unhappiest man must be the one who knows himself to be mediocre; but there is the state of grace, and that man does not exist. Passion in mediocrity, what misery it would be if one were not blinded! I did some psychology, mostly this evening: at last the memoir is finished, or as good as.

Not much law: some psychology, with success. My indifference toward my poetry, I even hate it at certain times: I am like a father among his children, supposing them all to be lame, one-eyed, deformed. My bits of verse are above all badly composed.

Wednesday 8th. An auction sale, a mass of rapacious and disgusting fat people; they are ugly, their life, their taste, their thoughts, everything about them is ugly. To be able to reason is not enough to distinguish us from animals; intelligence is an instrument without any dignity in itself. These men are gross bodies animated by calculated cupidity which, being part of free will, is a thousand times more odious than animal instinct. Dignity and grandeur are in the idea of beauty applied to daily actions. Of what use under the sun are all these people?

Sensuality does not always seek for beauty, strangeness of form will do. . . .

A prodigious amount of knowledge and genius is spent on work that is without glory. In order to shine among men one must boldly attack that which is considered inaccessible: a piece of verse can give you more luster than a magnificent speech for the defense. The ambitious man will either be miserable or famous, because he takes on a task which is superhuman, which either he cannot accomplish, or which raises him above everyone else.

A big dinner party at my sister's.—Monsieur Ratouis, a good man, nice, profound without realizing it, and sprightly too. To be profound without realizing it, that is true genius, when it is not strained after, and when a person can see without a knitting of the brows. This unconscious intuition is quite simply the natural play of a good mind; the effort of paying attention is not noticeable. Sadness is not so much the sign of a true genius as the effect of fatigue on a mediocre mind.—I am sad. The only thing in me of value is my curiosity. I search, I search, and in the end I encounter.

Thursday 9th. The man who can talk about sensual pleasure without sadness is neither poet nor artist. I feel very weary when writing about my day. . . .

Women are delighted with the poems one writes for them, or rather they are delighted that one does write poems for them, for it is not essential that they should understand them.

I went to the *Revue des Deux-Mondes*, certain of a defeat—which did not fail to materialize. Monsieur de Mars unbent a little: his letter had been severe, he should not have written to me so frankly, he said to me. It seemed that he was encouraging me to send him something more, if indeed Monsieur de Mars can, or can deign, to encourage. I believe I shall manage it; but I am short of time, and it will be slow work. Monsieur Billoteau, who I have to see tomorrow, will perhaps get me out of my predicament. My future becomes precarious at least twice a year, but my natural inclination makes light of it, and it carries me away. I dined with B. and his friend, a serious young man, sincere, but just a shade lugubrious. This evening I saw M. again, a healthy young man, cheerful, happy, and intelligent, but one who has no gnawing internal worries . . . Oh for the nakedness and the cold of the cloister! That is the kind of bath which I need . . .

Saturday 11th. I daydreamed for an hour after waking up . . . Jules was waiting for me: I cannot bear breaking promises. I realize that I myself am of a mechanical exactness, the result of school life; it has also left me with profound respect for the rules in everything: in this way the world is to me a matter of indifference and yet I follow its laws and its customs with passive docility. During the lecture on law, I drew women's faces. . . .

Cafes are an invention which favors displays of affection: *giving someone a drink* has become synonymous with *giving proof of friendly feelings*. Hence the necessity of accepting in order not to offend. I got out of it by producing I know not what excuse!

The study of time, activity, motion, speed; these questions confound reason with imagination and imagination with reason; impossible to emerge honorably in support of either one or the other.

Lovers are just as happy with the sensual pleasure they give as with that which they receive.—Love consists of an unending wish to make the loved one happy; in this lies all—perhaps its only—dignity.

Sunday 12th. I wake up, without experiencing the fatigue which I had feared. . . . I am always looking for the thing which I dread. Today, all my daydreams were of the waltz of kisses. The waltz produces a superhuman sensual pleasure, which saddens me profoundly: it is a flight heavenwards but alas! one whirls, one remains, and bodies do not follow hearts in their upward flight . . .

A walk in the Bois. Monsieur Ratouis. My first opinion of him is confirmed: he is no stranger to everything connected with the soul; his ugly face is transfigured by spiritual grace. His views on beauty, on the professions: he says that man must preserve the integrity of all his powers and not atrophy one in order to benefit some special talent . . . Artistic criticism lacks principles. A conversation is delightful under these conditions; one talks in order to be appreciated and one listens in order to flatter: self-esteem is mutually caressed; a good, sincere talk is, moreover, consoling and strengthening through sympathy. To sympathize is to feel the same, it is to join forces against the same sorrows, to double the cup from which one drinks of the same joys: basically, it means not being alone, which is to say all. Monsieur Ratouis' formula: where one sees, with whom one sees, what one sees. When these three conditions are favorable, pleasure is supreme.

The reading aloud of my verse, torture to me; reading verse aloud in a drawing room has always seemed pretentious to me. A book is something confidential which one murmurs in a low voice in the reader's ear: public reading is impertinent and immodest. Pouring out one's heart in a whisper to twenty people is not the same thing as surrendering it to them out loud: one prefers that they should be unable to communicate their impressions to each other. All poets have felt this, at any rate to start with; later on apparently one loses all shame, and nudity no longer costs anything . . . Monsieur Ratouis was not delighted with my poems, except perhaps for one or two. I am decidedly mediocre, but I am not going to give it up as a bad job.

There is a limit to what one can say to a respectable woman; one can hint at everything, but one cannot say everything; words have their own virtue, a sign board which is independent from their meaning.

Monday 13th. It is morning, sadness. My mother.—At Saint-Eustache, a gleam of sunshine enters my soul: Oh all you men, I love you: happiness is possible, it exists! These attacks of joy last for a minute at most with me, just long enough to plunge my face in the refreshing stream and to withdraw it, the time it takes for hope to wing its way through the night of thought and vanish . . . A poem to be written on human suffering, based on the following point of view: man is organized to act and enjoy without going into the principle of action and enjoyment, without reflecting on the play of his faculties, or the law of the universe . . . But man has tried to discover the reason for his happiness in order to grasp the secret and make happiness increase . . .

Silly hypocrites who sigh tenderly and eat that which has lived; an animal is just food to them; they have a moral code which is particularly suited to themselves, one which is good between men . . . Nature must seem most immoral to them, if their thought is rational.

I buy *Faust*. What a poem! Goethe wrote it at the age of twenty-three, my age. Well, this poem teaches me nothing: I cannot find it in any pain which is new to me, or any thought which has not occurred to me. But what deep reflection, and what ingenious details with such powerful effect! What sobriety; what strength, and also what grace! Tears welled up into my eyes and could not run away because of the heaviness in my heart. This reading has moved me more than anything I have read before; I was predisposed to suffer through it . . . Here, I am at my ease, I can express my emotion through cries and exclamations; these are hardly permissible in books, except for the "alas!"-es, which are never uttered anywhere else. Nevertheless, in the soul all is cries and exclamations: feeling is an intimate prolonged cry, and this is what differentiates it from sensation, which is all passion. . . .

Reflections on death: the height of man's misery is the fear of that which could deliver him from his misery, the fear of death. One cannot think of real suffering without a shudder; such as having no friends in the middle of an animated great city, being hungry, cold, ill, and alone . . . And God not there, silent. . . . We always appeal to someone, we complain, we grieve like spoiled children; but to be alone and at grips with inexorable, brutal poverty—I cannot imagine it. The mild melancholy of the poet! Everything about me is mediocre, even my unhappiness.

It sometimes seems to me that love is unworthy to be the subject of a great work, because it implies that woman is ignorant, vain, and frivolous: but I often find that love seizes Nature by the entrails, guesses its secret, foreshadows it and becomes initiatory and prophetic, and then I can no longer conceive of a great work without love. Thus, Marguerite in *Faust* opens up infinite horizons of hope: it is no longer a question of the little girl, the spinning wheel, and the kiss. It is a question of kindness, of God's immense pity for the world; a candid smile, and the Creator is justified! . . . In this last case, love resembles the grace of the Catholics.

Friday 17th. Roman law from midday till five o'clock. I feel that I am wasting my time, and I feel that I am getting stuck in the mud. . . . A blank day. This evening, the *Courier de Lyon.* Why was I not moved by it? I knew the plot too well, from having heard it discussed before the performance: the comedy in this play is clumsy. I like to fathom all the degrees of horror, pitilessly: I dread that which is going to distress me, and I enjoy it. People say, "What is the good of trying to experience artificial emotions in a play? Everyday life is quite full enough of them." What banality! A play provides us with the voluptuousness of sympathy; to think about suffering instead of feeling it has a special charm . . . thus the tyrants of the ancient world were cruel in order to experience the emotion of sympathy; a hard heart is never cruel.

Saturday 18th. A dreary day: I hope it was the weather which was having a bad effect on my thoughts . . . The evenings weigh me down; I drag myself round, half-asleep. Roman law: how little interested I am in the distinction between things corporal and incorporal, as I know nothing about their nature! One should be sparing with one's life and only use it to study that which benefits the mind. . . . My melancholy was real; I felt the burden of my years. Cursed be my weakness which makes me tolerate such existence! A messenger boy from the bank is happier than I am: he is quite unconcerned at being a liveried servant, he does not think he is being humiliated: a commonplace mind is a blessing from heaven.—Some more psychology; a difficult task; nothing in our understanding is infallible.

Friendship with a woman is impossible for me: a woman is only good for love. She never tells us anything worthwhile about God or Nature: a friend who does not talk to me about these things is of no use to me.

A woman's past is the root of the flower: the root goes deep down into the mud, and yet you raise the flower to your lips. Who ever takes it into his head to discover what happens under the ground? I do, I try and find out . . .

Music is the highest form of all the arts; it does not shape thought, it is rather its pure substance. It is through music that we draw near to God; it makes us truly understand that a superior world exists, a happiness, that which is called Heaven . . . What disgust it gives us for work and life!

Monday 20th. A strange dream last night: I was drawing up a declaration made by some Jews to a sovereign . . . I only had a very little time in which to finish it . . . hideous anxiety . . . This dream is odd because it bears no relation to any impression received during the previous day, and because it has nothing in common with my usual preoccupations. This is how some god takes possession of my faculties and plays about with them to suit his whim during my sleep; my brain harbors a guest who amuses himself like a child in a workshop, turning all the knobs haphazard . . . What does man do between sleeps, and what becomes of him when he is asleep? In any case he takes good care of his liberty. Midnight is striking.

Tuesday 21st. Nothing, nothing, nothing: I have worked without interruption; time has seemed to pass slowly . . .

Neither joy nor suffering, just a state of death; that is what mediocrity really is: let it try and make me love it! The rainy weather has prevented me from going to dinner with my sister (added to my disappointment the day before yesterday at not finding her at Châtenay: she is good, gay, kind, and has all the grace and bloom of real happiness) . . . Why does not Léon write to me? He would have to get the paper ready, choose his pen, think of nice things to say . . . I am just the same: laziness is stronger than friendship; it is only conquered by love. At five o'clock, history; I need to do it; the death of Lucan, I feel there is some tragedy behind it.

The heart is incorruptible: it is diamond-hard and sensitive at the same time. There are two ways of deriving pleasure from love: to incite the most delicate caresses of sensuality and passion through subtle and ingenious tenderness, or else to turn away the person one adores, listening to the crying, the sobbing, the supplications, and remaining silent and pitiless . . . pitiless, oh no! but delighted to be loved, burning with the love which one conceals in order to pour it forth the more freely later on.

Wednesday 22nd. A good day: my dignity is returning in waves.

Adjudication: the common people: what is called manners: when they are natural they are gestures of the soul, giving it outward expression . . . A visit to Gaston Paris; a first-rate mind, astonishing memory, the love of study; is not all this sufficient to raise oneself to the heights? I fear that he lacks the creative spirit; one realizes that one possesses it when one cannot read beautiful things without feeling jealous, without hearing the god who cries out from the bottom of one's heart: And I too!—That is why the profession of critic, which stems from sterility, is odious to me. Such thoughts as these reinvigorate and console me; I emerge from them feeling more worthy, less unhappy, full of dreams and fiery enthusiasm; I shall correct my piece on Musset, it is definitely good.

My dear mother; I kiss her with unbelievable joy; goodness is the whole virtue of the soul. A mother is dear to the heart like a pillow is to the head; one does not feel the pillow, it supports while giving way, it is all kisses . . .

Poetry must flow from a woman's lips like the dew must run from the calyx of a flower; certain poetry must be heard; the pure and gentle voice of a woman is its real music: books are the smiles of the dead. Past midnight . . . I reread my work on Might and Right with pleasure.

Sunday 26th. We get up late . . . Church: strange feeling I have when I listen to the priest preaching about pious practices. Seriousness in such matters astonishes me: I am far, very far, from the spirit of Catholicism. The person on my right: a well-made body is discernible under monstrous clothes; the strength that goes with good proportions, the grace of slender and rather sloping shoulders which support a small, proud, delicate head. Rain all day: boredom all round.

In the evening, Henri Monnier. There are very few writers to be found who agree to surrender their own individuality with quite such determination. He certainly has a feeling for stupidity, that stupidity of every second, which is in every suggestion, and which nobody notices.

Monday 27th. Today, nothing—except my visit to Monsieur Billotcau, where it is decided that I give up the law. A little dinner at Barate's with Louis. For friendship, it is not necessary to have the same views: kindness, on both sides, is sufficient. Kindness! the supreme virtue.

Tuesday 28th. Come on! Let's be brave, it is half-past midnight . . . must write: I felt tired all day; the responsibility was not entirely mine. I was trying to recapture and harmonize my thoughts: impossible. Nevertheless, psychology lost nothing; the flash of truth; the part played by instinct. I felt strongly that one must not seek for absolute liberty in man; will power and instinct combine, there is no word to describe this mixture; will power can only adhere to the essential nature of things; one wants, but one only wants, but one only wants according to one's essential nature (Spinoza, Descartes). When one digs deep into a subject, one does not at once see the extent of the conquest which has been made; it seems that nothing new has been discovered; but later, on thinking it over, one realizes how far one has gone. A rehearsal of Law with Lacourtie. Deplorable memory; I have none; logic is the only memory I have; if I am incapable of reasoning, then I know nothing.—Dinner with Louis and Adolphe at Barate's: the waiter in this restaurant is a very strange person; contact with the world has given him a certain polish, but his ignorance and his baseness make him vile—the result is a complex character, pretty odious . . .

The days go by and I create nothing . . . I only hope that my ideas are maturing; that is my one consolation.

Wednesday 29th. Eviradnus by Victor Hugo. Must study the richness and the facileness of the versification; a little more accuracy and reserve in the analogies, fewer speeches, and it would be impossible to fault it. That man's poetry has the ring of bronze; it can never perish.—Léon Renard and Decrais, who returned to Paris this very day, came to fetch me from my work; these young men have attached themselves to me, they have faith in the success of my poetry, and they communicate their hopes to me; so I am surrounded by friends, I cannot be unhappy.

November

Wednesday 5th. I have neglected my diary for several days. I have no energy, or rather I do not feel that the result is worth the expenditure of energy.

Friday 7th. Lafenestre: his poem *Pasquette;* infinite grace, the feel of the countryside; an interesting philosophical foundation; a few rather forced comparisons; a youthful and facile style. I feel like a poet each time that the goddess smiles at me as she passes by, and then I fall flat again; I cry out from the bottom of an abyss, I see a chink of blue, I make a great effort . . . but I cannot manage it.

Saturday 8th. . . . I have what is needed to hold my own in any *salon,* I ought to talk as much as the next man; the mediocrity of my position disgusts me and paralyzes me.

Sunday 9th. I am reading Plato; I discover that he is much more analytical than I had realized. *Philebus* in particular is prodigious; the question of happiness is put forward in masterly fashion. His morality must be compared with Christ's; I have not found the true formula of their relationship. Note: Does the word *beauty* appear once in the Gospels? I do not think so; and beauty is the basis of Greek morality. The equivalent of the word charity is not met with in the dialectic of Socrates.

Dinner at my cousin's: Monsieur Robillard, a great mind; how rarely does one find a man like him! Ideas on education.

The truly liberal principle which governs education is, in my view, as follows: to develop and strengthen the faculties independently of their content; to impose knowledge only when it is acquired scientifically; in addition, to listen to the pupil's heart searchings, provide for the natural needs of moral sensitivity and satisfy them by giving the only nourishment indicated by the instincts; in a word, it is to teach that which is certain and suitably to convey knowledge of the uncertain. One must respect doubt, because it is not error. It is like the haven of intelligence in the ocean of doctrines.

Monday 10th. Nothing outstanding: dinner at my brother-in-law's. My sister is becoming a possible *confidente.* The trees in the Tuileries at dusk; I recite aloud my dream of a poem on Socrates and Jesus Christ. . . . About lying; it sometimes happens that I do not tell the truth, when it is only a question of my private affairs and when the truth would merely be satisfying someone's curiosity; I maintain that my conscience is the only judge of my actions; I am only bound to be truthful to my conscience insofar as it concerns those acts of my life which do not reflect on anyone else. In this way I explain to myself why I am either so frank or so untruthful, according to the subject.

Yesterday, great disgust. The depths to which I have sunk, my master treats me like a small boy who cannot see that he is being exploited.

Sadness. What is life for? I aspire to the heights, I cannot remain in the same place. He who sets his heart on great things becomes more ambitious, and he is lost . . . A twopenny-halfpenny dinner.

1863

February

Thursday 19th. One must be able to say to oneself: you cannot, you must not . . .

It is as though I were dazed. Men pass by, come and go around me, like colored, echoing shadows: I do not even manage to pull myself together through my conscience any more; I am like a free being floating paralyzed in a fatal sea, every influence makes game of my will power, I say: What is the use? The word God no longer means anything to my mind. Joys which are far beyond all my ambitions exist only a few yards away from me for vulgar men: such as that of possessing a loving woman who is good, oh so good! That is to say, filled with compassion for those inexpressible sorrows which fill the heart and for which the lips have found no name. And this woman would suffer too, and I would know how to console her in my turn with delicate adoration.

Do not believe, my friend, that man is capable of feeling as much happiness as he can conceive of; there is less strength in desire and imagination than in feeling. Supposing that you were suddenly allowed to live in some delicious country like the one we pictured to ourselves this winter in such brilliant colors, when we were tramping along the wooden pavements; you would want to rush there and live there always, you would believe that you could enjoy it, but your helpless heart would not be able to keep the promise made by your brain. You would feel the surprise and embarrassment of an entirely new existence, wide open and vast, to which your narrow and tortuous life has made you forever unsuited. We experience a similar feeling when we contemplate the night sky in summer; the poets may well praise it, but they cannot feel all the pleasure they describe; the spectacle merely invites them to partake of a joy which they understand, but which passes them by. I feel this incomplete emotion today. This beautiful, proud young girl, breathing in air which is, so to speak, made up of praise and homage, whose every whim and fancy is watched over like so many precious opportunities of winning a smile from her, this young girl comes up to me, gives her hand to me, to me alone, lets me press it and (may I say so without hesitation?) returns this caress with a pressure which is a thousand times sweeter. Ah well! I do not know why, but this extraordinary good fortune astonishes me and oppresses me, and instead of savoring its infinite sweetness I tremble, I cannot rise to the occasion, I long to be an angel in order to experience divine joy; and if I was not greeted by her the next day, I would only suffer the disillusionment following a beautiful dream which is interrupted by waking, or the foreseen return of some object found and reclaimed by its owner. . . .

February. Yesterday, on the boulevard des Italiens, at that time of the evening when the cafes turn into seraglios, I met one of my old school friends. When I first knew him he was short and fat, now he was tall and thin; he seemed to me like a little elastic man who had been stretched out to a prodigious length. In fact, this was the only thing about him which interested me, and I must have been hardly recognizable to him. So we shook hands with real pleasure.—"Well," I said to him, "how are you? Have you ever seen Bolet again?" Bolet was a boy who had been a friend of us both; when two old friends meet again, their first thought is for a third one. "No, I have never seen him again. Have you?" "No, I haven't either." As the talk about Bolet was beginning to flag I added hurriedly: "What are you doing now?" "I am working with a very good firm of drapers. Here, if you'd like to have it, here is the address of the shop," and he took from his pocket a card with a picture on it which I read without taking it in and stuffed carelessly into my own pocket. "And how about you, my dear friend, what are you doing?" This question, which always embarrasses me, I answered with calm, and fixing him with a look in order truly to enjoy the stupefaction I was going to cause him: "My dear fellow, I am looking for a definition of man." He stood stock still, cigar in hand, with half-opened mouth: then, smiling, "You have plenty of leisure, I congratulate you," he said. "Me, plenty of leisure! This kind of research leaves me none at all." "Then you are rich." "As rich as Job." "You do surprise me. Supposing you find this definition, what will you do with it?" "I shall put it into verse!" This was the finishing touch. He could only shake off his stupefaction by taking some exercise. He therefore walked away as quickly as possible, with a slightly dazed look, though I have to admit that it was also compassionate.

1864
January

Thursday 28th. Today I felt that I had mastered a major aesthetic principle, that of unity of composition, and also that of the true means of expression, the *absolute* propriety of terms. An artist is incomplete so long as he has not realized the full meaning of things like these. Composition is one of them, or rather composition only exists when everything in the work combines to produce a unique effect by the perfect aptness and sobriety of the comparisons. Certain comparisons are richer than one wants them to be and introduce new aspects which bring distractions to the mind by destroying the unity of effect; thus, there should be extreme simplicity in the comparisons, and this does not mean poverty, but strength and truth. Let us add to this quality of comparisons something which is still more important in composition, namely the relationship of accessory ideas to the principal one; the accessory ones must flow into the principal one, like brooks flow into streams and streams into rivers. All this rhetoric which is so disparaged because it is merely taught, becomes astonishingly right and precious when it is discovered; as for writing and philosophy, practically nothing benefits from that which comes directly from the master. I mean to say that expression can define itself: it is the exact reflection of thought in the external world by means of whatever mirror it may be, whether language, marble, or canvas. Regarding this subject, here is a very striking illustration: a sculptor's work is threefold; first, he decides on the right pose for his model, which is the work of composition; then he studies the natural presentation, the anatomy of the limbs, the work of capturing some special expression (the overall expression must result in part from this, but especially from the composition); finally he polishes and finishes the preliminary sketch until the clay is definite, pure, as smooth as bronze, which is rather mechanical work but which will always be a need for the artist with style. I apply this distinction to literary work. The human body is an excellent model of unity; there is no pose that is not felt in every part of the body and as far as the extremities: consequently it is an incomparable means of expression. All work must be a man, as harmonious as a face. I do not want this image to leave me, it is to be my rule and my model.

We must not look for elegance elsewhere than in accuracy because we have the choice of two things, either we faithfully express what we feel, and we cannot conceive of anything else but what is superfluous, or we make no progress beyond our own limited sphere, and there are no extraneous embellishments which can save us from this basic vice. Style can never be worth more than thought, and only exists by it and for it. What can any ornamentation which is not delicacy of idea or feeling really be? An excrescence, an agreeable parasite, but an indiscretion. It is true that through long usage, a kind of habit acquired by the ear, words have a virtue of their own through their grouping, like the musical scale, and they can give pleasure to a sense which has been formed in us and which one can confuse with what is known as the genius of language. This new sense is very strange; it concerns the music of languages to such an extent that some good poets are detestable musicians. A prose writer can do without it better than a poet; Montaigne, who was often confronted by this, remains none the less the greatest stylist through his singular forcefulness of expression; Ronsard possesses this sense to a supreme degree; Lamartine sacrificed ideas to it. The superiority of a poet such as Musset consists of the perfect union in him between the genius of language and the truthfulness of expression. The greatest poet is the one who strikes the right note for each impression, plays it alone, and gives it in its entirety.

The writer must be on his guard against the special circumstances of his position: he is at the same time the one who thinks and the one who explains, but the public reads before appropriating his thought. Hence the danger to a writer who criticizes himself and believes himself to be in the place of the reader, because what he has just written is sufficient indication to himself as he already knows the subject; or at any rate this indication always seems to him in some way relative to his subject, because he holds one end of the thread which leads from one to the other. In spite of himself, the writer progresses from the idea to the word: the reader, on the contrary, progresses from the word to the idea and he has to open that same door with the key with which he has been provided; the writer who rereads his work is already at home, and he is more encumbered than helped by the key. What quantities of bunches of keys there are, for which the locks have never been found! I understand why Horace insists that a writer should let his work lie dormant for such a long time, so that he should become an expert at self-criticism; he would like one to stand outside one's front door on returning home after a long absence to find that everything is locked up: he insists that one should be able to retrace the forgotten idea by means of the word which remains.

The writer gives birth to strange scruples: something which he has just written is in his eyes either sublime or unintelligible, according to the slant of his criticism; his vision darkens, he loses his literary subtlety, he must go before a judge and submit to the cruellest disappointment, or listen to revelations on the merit of his own work which will astonish him.

Friday 29th. Midnight. Weakness of character. I gave in to the insistence of a friend through fear of displeasing him; I do not know how to say no, I search for an expedient, for some so-called duty, or the excuse of tiredness, I slip away. This pusillanimity is the result of a wrong idea of the impression made by a refusal. I have noticed that rough, frank men wound less than they intimidate; they do what they want without damaging themselves in the eyes of importuners; people like a refusal to be sincere, they prefer straightforward resistance to oblique pretenses; defeats have something false and vile about them which is badly received. A vice to be corrected.

Chapus has finished my medallion. I criticized his Virgin, the queen of Heaven. I felt that she had an antique, not very Christian look. I could feel the charm of the antique there; I felt that although she was quite simple, she was nevertheless not without some affectation, not entirely unself-conscious. She is not *humble,* like Christian simplicity; she is sober rather than simple. The attitude of the *Venus de Milo* is neither voluptuous nor deliberate nor too imposing; it is simple, but one realizes that an attitude such as this, produced by a firm, hard, powerful movement of Nature, would not be suitable to a Christian. The antique Virgin is not ignorant of herself, she is proud of her pure and intact state: the Christian Virgin is, if I may say so, incorporeal. They are both equally naive, in the sense that there is no art in their bearing; but one is the daughter of Nature, the other the daughter of Heaven.

I have rewritten several of my old sonnets. I versify much more easily, I soften and amplify the verse. I no longer measure it with a carpenter's rule, all stiff and articulated, I throw it forward like a liberated, slender snake, which always falls in a curve. I am pleased with my present breeziness: what compositions I could produce, if it were not for Law!

I drew a portrait of F. at Chapus'. Quite remarkable for me, but I draw like a cockchafer that's fallen into the inkpot.

I think about L. The irresistible attraction of scorned happiness! The past has veiled looks which kill. A letter has been in my pocket for a week. Will it ever be sent? What imprudence! but also what promised emotion! To lie with my head on her knees and rest from living. To say to her: it is to you that I will always return, what delicious returning which is always foreseen and longed for in the midst of the violent divergences of my life. To love tenderly and violently.

Saturday 30th. When one has got to the bottom of a philosophical question one must, as it were, stand back like a painter and look at what one has produced. The president of the intelligence then announces if intelligence has done its work well: this secret president is the center of gravity of the system of the intellectual faculties, I do not know it, but I feel it and consult it; it is called common sense.

Common sense is the minimal but sufficient dose of veracity which Nature has put into intelligence, for the needs of life and the subsistence of the subject. It was necessary that the mind should at least possess certainty up to a point in order to be a useful instrument, just as legs must be able to stretch a certain distance in order to be able to walk; otherwise, why have a mind at all? So, common sense is the measure of the amount of veracity bestowed on the human spirit by Nature for the solution of the main problems of life. Philosophers have forced common sense to take on work in which it deteriorates and becomes blunted; there is certainly the same relationship between a man of common sense and a metaphysician as there is between a good walker and an acrobat. Our minds are moral acrobats which make the infinite smile, like the sun smiling at the diving board.

Sunday 31st. The respect which men inspire in us can be measured by the quality of our confidences. We are not always outspoken with the best of them, because one can be reserved for two reasons: either because one is afraid of harming oneself by stumbling against vulgarity of feeling, or on the contrary, because by admitting certain faults one fears that the freshness of a friendship founded on high-minded ideas will be tarnished.

A discussion on form in literature: the reverence for success.

A really delicate question: the arts explain the artist's thought, but for whom? Ought he to modify the form according to the public, like one modifies one's language when one wants to make a peasant understand? In a word, does the form not matter, as long as everyone understands the idea? I do not think so, when it concerns works of art. I would answer in the affirmative if it were only a question of spreading an idea and making it penetrate to the crowd: but in literature proper, for instance, language has an aesthetical quality of its own called style, which is not determined by the pure expression of ideas. Everyone conceives an expression of his ideas, not so that they should be understood by the peasant, but to represent to oneself exactly what one thinks or imagines. In literature one does not set out to adapt one's style to suit such and such a category of reader, one seeks for the truly artistic satisfaction of setting out one's conception in the form which best reproduces it in the eyes of the author himself. *One expresses oneself for one's own satisfaction.* Something which has been well expressed to oneself will not lack appreciative readers, because one is a man, but it could be that the general public would hardly appreciate it because, even though it may represent feelings in general and man's outstanding characteristics, it does not give the special characteristics which go to make individuals. Doubtless the outward expression of ideas for one's own satisfaction will be considered puerile, because it is certain that signals are made for the communication of ideas and feelings. The person who raises this objection may perhaps be a publicist, but he will never be a literary man nor an artist.

February

Monday 1st. I woke up at six o'clock and lay thinking until nine o'clock. It is one of my favorite sensual delights to spend several hours dreaming in my bed in the morning. But it is a bad habit because one's thoughts have no shape under such conditions; everything is exaggerated and darkened; passions take on a special character of violence and desolation; suicide seems easy and one seriously argues about its possibility. I choose a remembered woman and for the hundredth time I renew an old, broken romance; I re-establish the situation and I watch myself taking action. The hours go by with astonishing speed in these daydreams: I am distressed by the clock striking, because it seems that my heart could feast for all eternity on the work of my imagination. Is it not the time of day when I am most alive? Facts have less impact on my feelings when they make a direct impression than when they are seen at a reflected angle in the prism of my imagination. I observe once again that I feel what I want to feel.

A ghastly fire at a church in Santiago. I cannot think of it without terror, and I do not know what to think of God when such useless horrors as this happen. Subject for a poem: all the disasters, all the scourges, all the miseries of humanity as opposed to the living fountain of joy and sensual pleasure which never ceases to flow untainted from life. The smile of a little girl and the glare of a tiger are both the work of the same Being, in the theory of the Creation—is it not strange? All our ideas about good, kindness, and cruelty are turned upside down as soon as we try to apply them to the divine spirit. Creation, as seen from a human point of view, is a monstrous work which is neither revolting nor edifying, but inconceivable, contradictory, and absurd. We have no basis on which to judge it; the moral law which rules us watches over the preservation and the uplift of our kind, but it is not universal jurisdiction; there is a good and a justification in everything according to some principle, that is certain, but the principle escapes us, it is not made for us, it does not concern us and it does not deign to make itself clear to our minds.

Poetry: the hesitation of Hercules.—Discussion on sensuality: it reveals its baseness, the scorn which it inspires, and its fits of remorse, but it is delicious and one abandons oneself to it in spite of everything. It has something of the infinite, as seen in the small valley of the eyes. It is so approachable, so obliging; it throws the soul into forgetfulness and moral indifference in a fall which is so soft that it produces, as it were, pleasure in letting oneself go, in discouragement, in the complete abandonment of all one's strength and it encourages the soul to plunge so low that it can no longer raise itself from such depths. It has something which is more actual and more tangible than the joys of glory, it is within reach of every soul. It is a kind of ruination which makes one love the abyss and look on the heights with admiration and pity.

Discussion on Virtue: it should never promise anything, it rejoices in its own actions; it proposes every kind of suffering as a reward to courage and crowns life with the pure sensation of worthiness.

One could say that sensuality reduces human life to a kind of passive attraction and frees it from the worries of deliberation and the martyrdom of effort.

I brought home a proof of my medallion. It did not satisfy my family. The bourgeoisie's opinion in matters of art is naive and brutal; the subtleties and skill of the work matter little to them. Are they wrong only to judge of the result and not to go beyond the outward impression in the scholarly search for beauty?

What did I go to the rue M. for? Some people are swept away by their passions, mine drag me; I go sadly toward wickedness like a bullock to the slaughter house; I do not resist the impulses of my heart any more than I do a friend, or temptation any more than an importunity.

Tuesday 2nd. I have clearly realized the absurdity of applying human morals to the works of Nature and I recited a few wordless lines to myself on this subject, which were rather well thought out and rather advanced. Nature is as implacable as an industrial machine. The picture of unhappiness suffered by humanity is intolerable to the heart; and humanity is so determined to live and its life is still so full of sweetness that it does its best to justify the executioner and would like to compensate all the cruelty which he inflicts on it by the vague and fugitive smile which it gives him through *irony and pity*. I crossed out these last two words, firstly through vanity seeing that they weaken the sentence, and also for a better reason, which is that they express an overemphatic and false idea. There is no irony in Nature's actions. Let us leave this chimera to the speech makers; there is also no pity; everything happens solemnly and seriously in the Universe, with the characteristics of ripe inevitability. Try and find a chemical formula exactly to describe the combination which is human flesh, that is to say hydrogen, the carbon which it contains with oxygen, and you will have Nature's version of the ghastly accident of Santiago. A chemical phenomenon was produced; to introduce God into it is dangerous and foolish. The world of laws and the world of liberty are contiguous; they constantly encroach on each other, they have no right to complain of each other; they act in good faith according to essence and should not judge from the point of view of one or the other, each having its own contrary principles.

Adolphe dined with us: conversation about trade. People may try as hard as they can to ennoble trade, it is essentially hostile to the disinterestedness without which moral uplift cannot be conceived. A man who is interested in truth and beauty will never be able to compel himself to handle material objects, buying them in order to sell them, all his life. This continual association with merchandise and cash can only debase his mind, however high its tone may be. The enjoyment of art and science is of such a proud and sensitive nature that it can never endure an occupation of this kind: at first it is repelled by it, and soon it rejects it completely.

Thursday 4th. Visit to the Louvre with Adolphe. The *Venus de Milo.* The way a masterpiece reacts on the spirit. The head is delicate, rather small. The neck . . . The shoulders? . . . Is this the ideal? One cannot think without a shudder that here, perhaps, is the perfection of the female form and that the model of what is in Nature's conscience is before one's eyes.

I spend my day in setting out my theory of memory. Clarity of exposition is the sure sign of maturity of conception; at least that is what Boileau says. I believe I have elucidated my ideas on this subject and I am not far from reaching a conclusion. This is how I spend the evening before an examination on a subject of which I know not one word—doing five hours of psychology! What a passion! What a lure Science is—or how weak my resolution is! At any rate it was a complete day. Am I defeated? Can I stand up and say No? Virtue is always more tempting than sensuality, but so difficult! Is there still time to return to it?

An evening with Hendlé: a serious and scholarly mind. I expound my ideas on philosophy to him, and I clarify them to myself in explaining them. Equation: the Whole which we conceive of as being perfect, complete, and satisfying to the intelligence, forms the second member of the equation; the first includes what we know of the world which is the function of an unknown variant x. The contingency, which has so humiliated the philosophers, rights itself in my eyes by expressing and implying liberty. Hence my definition of God: *that which exists of necessity and acts freely.*

Good talk: Hendlé certainly rectified my opinion of the orator's art which I defined as the art of persuasion. The orator has his speciality like every man of letters and he can be great without possessing the gift of inculcating no matter whom with no matter what opinion.

There is perhaps nothing in the world as delightful as a sympathetic exchange of ideas, because in it all the powers of the mind and the heart are exerted, with enough respect toward the interlocutor only to express noble thoughts. These exchanges of warmth and light are beautiful, strengthening and instructive.

Friday 5th. Bewilderment which is deserved. There is a tragedy to to be written on bankruptcy: the poet is business. I ruminated on my poem *The Happy City;* I have not yet properly mastered my subject.

A. dines with us. A household scene. A virtue exists which I gladly call the virtue of domesticity; it consists in greasing the wheels of everyday life by kindness and sacrifice. Why does one reserve harshness and neglect for one's own people when one is so polite, so base, so cunning with strangers? Alas! one has to admit that as soon as we are natural we are bad. No, virtue is not just a word, its effects are too deeply felt for its existence to be denied; if we could love one another, the face of the world would be changed.

I am going to be twenty-five; is it not time for me to think about a life worthy of my aspirations? I certainly feel that the strong and vigilant exercise of good will together with the cult of beauty is the only conduct suited to man. Self-possession, to be true to oneself, to dispose at will of one's instincts and one's faculties, this is what is to be admired, and I shall never be able to do it. I am bothered by Catholicism which seems to flout the generous effort of the Stoics. If I had been born at the time of Zeno, perhaps I would have been better. I would prefer the dark night of antiquity, where every man had to feel his way and face risks bravely, to this uncertain half-light in which conscience floats about still dragging with it the trammels of its first Catholic education. One does not dare to take upon oneself a reform which might only be in vain and very painful, when one lives side-by-side with people who read *The Imitation of Christ* and become better.

I cannot find the logical sequence for my thoughts which is needed to make my book on psychology a whole and complete work; I do not know whether this art calls for methodical exposition; everything in it is according to rule, so that one sees no reason for beginning with one analysis rather than another.

An evening at J. E.'s house—Ferry's book *The Electoral Contest;* politics, the object of which is the greatest aim that can occupy man, is in its procedure, its applied principles, its prejudices, its iniquities, the narrowest and most monstrous thing imaginable. It is because interest and power are still the only things which people have brought into it. When will it be the turn of love? Humanity will be worn out down to the marrow before achieving this.

The world is disgusting; it is all very well arguing, and trying to evaluate life in order to make oneself useful and honorable, but it seems that one would gain more honor by refusing to get mixed up in the mess. Cheerful men who think over seriously things which are done under their noses, who talk about them passionately and make common cause with other beings, excite my astonishment and, according to their dignity and their conviction, my admiration or my pity or my aversion. It is I who am sick: good health can be recognized by the fact that life agrees to plunge its roots deep into its terrestrial element and delights in it; all revolt against Nature, against essential conditions, is sterile and morbid. Oh you Greeks, valiant race of joyful and magnanimous children who sanctified the earth, loved your city, and defended your rights, you can be characterized in a word: you were a *healthy* generation. Your health did not last, and your corruption inoculated the world and putrefied it.

A line of verse:

I feel my will power to be stronger than my life.

Saturday 6th. Accarias, before giving his lesson, is quite willing to talk politics. It is remarkable that the less knowledge one has of politics the greater is one's interest: I am not alluding to the devotees, I am talking of serious, moderate men. The ease of circumstances and the facility of a life which is reduced to mechanical occupations atrophies the bud of just revolt. One always finds that the most intelligent people are the most liberal and that the less educated are the most radical. Nobody is more attached to a principle, either true or untrue, than the ignorant man; he is incapable of grasping the subtleties which link principle to practice by modifications which are necessary at the present time, and he straight away implants a system into the heart of life: now, life is all habit and transaction, it is made up of compromises between our needs and our maxims. Nothing is easier to disorganize than the happiness of a man; it is the result of

an infinity of very fragile and yet very deep causes and conditions. Who dares to touch this house of cards without the complete knowlege of our nature and of what is right?

I have finished my sonnet on the *siesta*. That one will have cost me more time and trouble than it is worth.

Monsieur V. dines with us. The smile is capable of a multitude of meanings. One can express everything with a smile, except perhaps anger; but from indignation to love, passing by way of disdain, the smile can give all the affections of the mind. A face is really a marvelous keyboard. The subtlest thought modifies the line of the lips with an incredible exactness of expression. When observing these pictures of the language of lines, which are so varied, it is with difficulty that one believes in a system of artificial signs taught by education and habit. One does not teach anybody to smile and yet it carries a clear meaning for everyone in itself. One must go further; not only is the expression of the face not a thing of instruction, but perhaps it does not result from the intrinsic quality of the lines, which are in themselves either pleasant or hard on the eye, agreeable or disagreeable in their capacity of pure sensation; I do not think that when considering two smiles with a completely different meaning one can explain this difference by the physical effect (which is purely of the senses) of their sinuosities on the retina; there is, certainly, an interpretation of these diverse forms which would be impossible in a preestablished direct relationship between the line and the feeling. I agree that a woman's face owes much of its sweetness to the absence of angles and the subtlety of its curves; it would indeed be inconceivable that lines which were angular and offensive to the eye should be carefully chosen to express a loving spirit; the form of the line suits that which it has to say by its physical quality, I agree; but is this enough to account for the whole relationship between the soul and the face which one so much admires? And for instance, does one notice that in the smile and in the state which indicates affliction, the curves are essentially contrary in their physical aspect? In one case the eyebrows are lifted by the extremities adjacent to the nose, and in the other by the extremities which meet the temples, and it is the same for the other features; they are lowered or lifted without the agreeable or disagreeable element of the sensation of form being really modified. In order to realize the virtue of expression and its independence from the physical quality, one has only to eliminate all form which is graceful in itself, all curves in the diagram of a face in which only the oval shape is favorable to the eye and could be suppressed. The child smiles when he is smiled at.

An evening with Lecomte de Lisle. Not many people. He agrees with me on the question I was discussing on Thursday with Hendlé. The artist must produce according to the *form* he feels to be right, and await people's sympathy . . . He approved my correction of the sonnet on *Shadow*. Nobody dares to admit that they do not like poetry. It is paying homage to the Muse. Lecomte de Lisle is not joking when he calls contempt for Letters a *crime*.—A nice witticism: a gentleman blames poetry for not being something natural. Women do not like poetry: they like the noise of it.

Sunday 7th. An uninteresting day.—I met D.; he thought I looked very tired. Indeed I am, and I feel like weeping. I am sad because of the void in my heart. The effect of masquerades on me: I feel sorry for these people who enjoy dressing-up. Do I not disguise myself completely the whole time? I am Hamlet, Werther, Faust, Pascal and a thousand others, without feeling any surprise; the flood of ideas which is always racing through my imagination changes from one moment to the next and brings me the thoughts of every century, the joys and the sufferings of all men. They wore Pierrot costumes! What a lark! That is something to really laugh about, and what laughter! Stupid, idiotic laughter, worthy of the worn pavement they tread and the skyline of ramshackle buildings they look at. When am I ever myself? Or which man am I, as I undergo so many transformations in the same day? I have only my conscience to tell me that I am not any of the people I admire, and a deep unity in which thoroughly to concentrate my grief. Give love and pride to a shadow, and that is me. If I had laid bare my soul to all the blows I would doubtless be dead, but I have the gift of being able to turn it against wounds and to cauterize it by a kind of indolence; my adventures make me suffer when I think about them, but I know how not to think about them. I seem to realize that I have no right to be happy, and therefore I am less affected by disappointments. But there are moments when I descend into that part of my soul where the ruins lie, and then I voluntarily make myself very unhappy.

By chance I met Georges Guéroult. He told me about our friend C.'s marriage. I did not know that C. had been in love for so long with the woman who is now his wife. In spite of all our high-minded ideas, and the abstraction and rigidity of our works, it is love's dream which wins in the end; we cannot free ourselves from natural impulses by the enforced, artificial pleasures of Science; we only rise above the limits of our essence in short-lived bounds; Nature does not look on us as such high-up beings in the universe; she considers that a sweet face and a kind heart are what best suit both our eyes and our feelings; and this is how it is, in spite of our breathless aspirations toward the unknown and toward the ideal.

Alas, how deeply I feel such things! I thought of you, dear L.; I did love you, you beautiful girl! I had to lose you completely in order to feel it so strongly. What have you done? Oh, if only you had said one word to me of your plan! But I just heard of it by chance one day, I do not know how! So all my affection, all my declarations are as nothing! That treasure which I laid at your feet to see whether you would dare walk on it, you did not kick it away but lightly and discreetly pushed it aside with the tip of your little slipper, to make room for yourself to escape. Well brought-up girl, sensible, hard-hearted girl, that is what you have done. And you think that everything is safe, and that I have kept no passion and no rights? No, I still love you, and you know it.

What would I not give for an hour with her!

I walk between suicide and success, and as I go forward these two boundaries draw nearer together and enclose me more tightly, and I am a little drunk. On which of them shall I sit down and rest?

Go to bed, unhappy creature. Yet another day's sunshine which I have not looked at. Tomorrow there will be another sun which I shall not look at either. To be able to enjoy the daylight without thinking about it!

My poems seem to me good or bad according to the people to whom I am going to read them. In the same way I can feel my ideas becoming false when I want to disclose them to certain people but soaring to the heavens when I meet a friend.

Monday 8th. A ball at Mme. M.'s. I cannot think how an ugly woman can appear at a ball; it does not make sense.

It is a strange illusion on the part of women to imagine that the clothes make one forget about the face and the figure! I hate ugliness, I hate it to the point where I am harsh and unfair toward these poor disgraced creatures. Ugliness is a groping, a stupidity, a farce of Nature's; it revolts me. An ugly woman covered in finery is and can only be a prop, and one regrets that the clothes do not hide her completely.—A dark woman, with fine eyes and superb, thick, black hair; I was made fully aware of the effect of black hair piled above a very white neck; but the words *black* and *white* in literature describe two colors which are too great a contrast, too distinct:

> a delicate, white neck
> Bends, and outshines the brilliance of snow.

These lines of Chénier are charming rather than true; the whiteness of skin, so tender, so mat, has nothing in common with the crude, strident whiteness of snow. Poets have such a limited palette that they get used to inaccuracies and conventional comparisons. Subtleties are missing from the palette; language certainly provides the tones which are indicated, but as their graduations are infinite, it cannot keep up with them.

Tuesday 9th. I ought to write down my impressions of each day on the same evening, because I see that by the next day my disposition has changed and my account is no longer so true.

A young man who displeases me: among men who abandon themselves to their passions, I make a definite distinction between those who put their hearts into their love affairs and those who only involve their senses. The serious, calm rake is the kind I hate most; I only excuse the man who, while doing wrong, is sorry that youth cannot love without wrong-doing.

I do not dare commit all the events of my life to paper, I am afraid of these lines of mine being read someday. The need for other people's esteem is one of the most important phenomena of our moral life. How can this need be reconciled with fatalism? What indeed is esteem? Someone else's opinion that we have some value; but what is this value? Is it an invented quality? Or rather do we not have an instinctive certainty that a sort of ladder exists for men, on which each one can occupy a low or a high grade according to the use which he makes of his free will, and also according to his beauty, his strength, etc. . . . ? We all of us obviously have in our minds our ideal type of the perfect man and it is a point of honor to inspire others with the thought that we are getting near to this type. But let us not confuse esteem as such with admiration for beauty and reverence for strength. A weak and ugly man knows very well that he can win respect for the way he uses his will power, if he is fair and kind. The love of glory is not the same thing as trying to win esteem; it is the passionate desire to inspire admiration mixed with astonishment for the extraordinary power of the faculties, irrespective of the part played by will power in one's work. One prefers a little wit to a great deal of virtue, if one is looking for a reputation, and the opposite when one is anxious to be worthy of esteem.

Where does the joy we experience when we inspire feelings of admiration or respect come from? We may answer naively: from the mere fact that we are the object of these feelings. An answer such as this does not resolve the question of the reason for this joy. For us to experience it inasmuch as we are the object of the admiration, we would have to consider ourselves as truly being the cause of this feeling in others; but how can one manage to put one's pride in a place where one's will power plays no part? . . .

November

28th. A talk with Léon[1] on the spirit of observation (Flaubert). I put this problem to him: of what does this spirit consist? What pleases us in a subtle observation is apparently the act of discovery, the unknown which is surprised and revealed. Nevertheless, to be able to say: "It is well observed" we must *recognize* the action which is described, therefore we too must have witnessed it. But if this is so, then the author has made no discovery, he has only isolated a characteristic which is known to us; it seems therefore that the pleasure he causes us is the slightly vain satisfaction of having seen a thing correctly, and finding the confirmation and verification in the experience of a witty observer.

This analysis does not convince Léon; he resists it without really knowing why; I don't believe in it myself. Molière teaches me something at the same time that I say to myself: "It's obvious!" By seeing something anew through his eyes, I learn.

Does not the spirit of observation consist of noticing what other people have merely seen; detaching the characteristic trait which is mixed up with a crowd of ordinary circumstances in which it has got lost; and lifting the veil with which habit disguises everything alike, just at the salient point? In this way, I had clearly seen the action, but I had not noticed that it bore a trait, that is to say, the marks of a certain kind of action; the subtle moralist shows me a vice, or a failing, where I could only see an indifferent manifestation of the human will. What we both of us knew was the content of his observation, but by his observation he causes the hidden point to emerge from this matter, which is what attracts my attention and educates me.

One might therefore define the spirit of observation as the gift of assessing character through actions. From this it follows that for an observer there are no meaningless actions. In any case, he is not bound to define and explain: the mere choice of the action which he notes, or of the word which he underlines, conveys perfect knowledge of the aspect of human nature from which this action or this word proceed. He does not claim anything more than this; he is not a psychologist and he could well be the loser by becoming one.

The burial of Marcel. Small coffins are not just short, narrow boxes; they have a childish look, they have a certain grace, they seem to say Papa and Mamma for the last time. When the funeral ceremony was over, I realized that one abandons oneself wildly to pleasure, or else one buries oneself deep in fear. To numb one's mind, or to keep vigil: but to think sometimes of the precipice of death, to look over it sometimes, by chance! It means being unable to forget, unable to be on one's guard. Death casts a furtive shadow over life, light but icy-fingered and inevitable.

29th November. Ricard introduces me to Michelet. A little old man with a big head, and an oratorical way of speaking. He has found a basis for his own way of thinking, which dispenses with all metaphysics: it is justice. Two laws suffice to rule universal activity: *right* and *justice.* If the material world is ruled by laws

[1] *Author's note:* Monsieur Léon Bernard-Derosne.

which are destined to create order in it, then the spiritual world would seem to possess its own right, which is justice. He cannot be induced to admit the immortality of the soul, *he does not need to,* but he feels himself obliged to believe in it, through his feeling that there is justice in compensation for wrongs which have been suffered.

To sum up, it is a very thin, very wretched, thoroughly bourgeois philosophy. "I am only a historian," he says. A white waistcoat, a tail coat with velvet lapels; a young wife with a slightly nasal voice, not without charm.

On the subject of the Revolution, he admires the attitude of our forebears during those terrible times: we would have behaved worse in their place. The reports of the official authorities of the time have not been studied thoroughly enough.

He likes to be surrounded by a court of young men whom he eggs on to useless opposition.

General impression: he does not strike me as being a serious and complete man but sincere, nevertheless.

Politics (conversation with Ricard).

The trouble with political theories, to my mind, is that they only take into account the question of right and leave aside the question of natural history which goes with it. Certainly, the political conception is simple if one simplifies the conditions and the qualities of the people concerned; then it is reduced to the conception of justice and the respect for equal rights. Let us imagine a group of male adults established on new soil, with right as their sole aim. They will resolve the political problem; their formula will be simple and easy: to let each man develop his own activity in the way he wishes, as long as it does not come into conflict with any other one. When two activities come up against each other, equal sacrifice from each of them must be demanded, the smallest possible. Without this formula, there can be nothing but injustice, inquisition, despotism.

But the foregoing hypothesis is very much less complex than the reality. In reality, there are two facts which take precedence over speculation: the natural organization of the family, and the agglomeration of families in a limited fatherland in which all the land is occupied. The theory of the family is irreducible to the mere idea of right. Marriage and education are impossible without subordination, the obedience of the weak to the strong, and the obedience of the inexperienced to the one who has been through the ordeal of life. The child must either obey or die, Nature does not listen to reason on this point; woman must obey, unless the man submits to her orders, because in the case of a couple there must be a leader—the vote can only divide, for lack of a decisive majority. So it must be the man who is master of the house, because he has raised the stones with which to build it. He cannot force the woman to live in his house, but when she is there she must obey. Nature is not at all responsible for their union, which is necessarily transitory; she did not make the cruel blunder of delivering a fifteen-year-old girl to a man who may not always love her; laws were needed to consecrate infamies such as these. But Nature has allowed love to survive physical union in order that the children may be sure of the double advantage of kindness and force in education. She has done better than to establish rights for the weak, because rights are violated; for them she has created feelings which disarm force for the benefit of those whom she has to protect. When Nature allows herself to subjugate some activity, she begins by seducing it and making it love its bonds. Love, paternal love, filial respect, are sublime servitudes which one embraces without shame and longs for!

In all this organization of the family, there is no trace of right.

One must not suppose that Nature, which has done so much for the family, has done nothing for society. Humanity is essentially a herd. Men are bound together by a tie which is stronger than love or friendship itself; I am surprised that there is no name for this bond. It is a fact that men would rather fight each other than live separately. Every man must have either a friend or an enemy, either a slave or a master; a living attachment or contradiction is necessary to him; he cannot think for himself. This is not a question of selfishness, or pride, or sympathy (in the ordinary sense) but of something quite different, of an attachment which is so very deep in the heart of politics that politics are not even aware of it. They do not define it any more than geometricians define space, with this difference:—it has never entered the head of a geometrician to suppress space, whereas politics do suppress natural good, the basis of society, in order to substitute a Rousseaulike social or quasisocial contract based on pure right, an abstraction which comes from speculation of the most vain kind.

The word *fatherland,* which they shout so much about, has no meaning apart from this social instinct. In everyone's hearts the symbol of the fatherland is a flag rather than a pair of scales, the emblem of justice and supreme indifference. The Flag is not exactly the sign of unity, it does not prevent civil war; sometimes it gives it a motive and expression. The Flag means: we cannot do without each other, whether we love one another or hate one another; we form a group in which moral affinities develop and combine in the struggle, in the same way that sulphuric acid and lime fuse when boiling.

History is a science because it studies the phenomena of social life and because these phenomena are based on a principle, that of the natural formation of the human masses. I pick up a stone, I analyze it, and I discover that it is a collection of diverse atoms, that is to say, a people; I study the history of a people and find in it a deep fatality, a law of intimate attraction and repulsion, as in the stone. Free will cannot be brought into it: these stresses act on individual wishes like all the other motives, like passion, like desire, and all the instincts which one tries to reconcile with liberty instead of refuting them through it.

The man who refuses to put his powers at the service of society, who stands before it as the champion of absolute right, who thrusts away its tutelage crying: "I am sufficient unto myself!" is the man who makes old Nature smile, like when a child says to its mother: "I am going away!"

You madman, know that you need me, me whom you hate! I shall leave you alone with your right in the most beautiful valley in the world, and when I go to see you, you will embrace me and weep, and you will ask me if your house is still standing, if the Pope is still in Rome, and whether Poland is free. How superficial all their chatter is! They invent recipes and go on diets when they are not hungry: at moments of crisis, when society is threatened with collapse, they throw themselves avidly on dictatorship like dogs on a bone, and the harshest law seems right to them. Then they are quite ready to say that it is no longer a question of justice and right, but of public order, security, etc. In the long run, it is just a question of living.

English aestheticism, *A Study of Ruskin,* by Milsand. Excellent book, one of the rare philosophical works which really instruct. Strange style: the sentences are long without being boring, the expressions provoking, well-chosen, rarely precise; the ideas are developed during the course of the writing; exactness is never achieved straight away, but by pushing forward and delving deep the author reaches it in the end. The discussion then becomes singularly animated; he battles with his theory, pen in hand, instead of studying it first and then transcribing it. To sum up, there is only one idea in this study, and it is a most inadequate one to resolve the complex question of beauty, but it is very valuable and very new. Let us see if I have understood.

The state of a mind which is under an aesthetic impression is at the same time very clear and very obscure, according to whether the mind merely submits to this state or criticizes it. When the mind does not cast serious reflections on this state it rejoices and all pleasure, as such, is clear-cut; except for the rare cases when the will is confined to sorrow, the mind which rejoices reaches out to the cause of its pleasure, perceives it with more or less *intensity*, but with constant clearness. To confine ourselves to reality, it must be supposed that the aesthetic feeling is a simple one and does not depend on a discernment inherent in perception itself; or at least it must be supposed that a true artist reaches, through the rules of his faculties, the unity of aesthetic feeling without going through a process of elimination and consciously thought out selection. In a word, it must be recognized that everything concerned with the formation of this feeling in the true artist is *spontaneous*. When he is in this state, the artist, limiting himself to feeling, makes no analysis of any kind, not even the simplest one of all which is the separation of the *ego* from the *non-ego*. He acts in order to be attentive, without being aware of his action, hence he does not see the world as external, because he cannot see any resistance to his action in it, or to the *non-ego*. He does not see what is objective in his perception; neither can he distinguish what is subjective, that is to say the part which he has contributed to it. Thus, aesthetic ecstasy is an almost incomprehensible state, because it excludes the affirmation of the ego, which would seem to eliminate man, as well as the affirmation of the non-ego, which appears to abolish the world. Nevertheless, man and the world coexist in the way in which it is possible for them to coexist in a state of pure sensitivity, which is in itself impossible to analyze in the smallest degree.

The philosopher professes carefully to separate the subjective from the objective; he is therefore necessarily in a state which is opposed to the aesthetic state. Must one conclude, like Milsand, that this latter state is therefore closed to him? Not at all. A feeling enters the understanding as though it were the essence; my mind knows the feeling of love which my heart has experienced; it also knows the aesthetic feeling, the state in which the subjective and the objective are combined. Milsand is a mediocre psychologist, which does not prevent him from being a subtle and vigorous thinker; but this is a question of psychology, we must take care. In all sensations and in all feelings, whatever they may be, there is a mixture, a confusion of the objective and the subjective, with indistinct perception of both. The distinction only begins at the moment when understanding transforms a sensation into a notion, makes a profit out of the objective, and announces the divorce of the subjective. Let us not wonder any more at finding them united in aesthetic emotion than in the pure sensation of red or blue, or in the feeling of good, right, love, etc. The most brilliant aspect of Milsand's thesis is not the best. I am afraid he has not grasped the point which he discusses. I want to plumb the depths of his idea; it has fecundity in it.

In short, all he does is to establish the existence of a feeling proper to the order of the arts, a declaration which is in fact most important because henceforward philosophers can no longer try to analyze the aesthetic emotion only to relegate it to a few well-known feelings such as, for example, sympathy. But as soon as the aesthetic emotion is noted, it is no good saying that it is both objective and subjective at the same time because, as we have seen, that is the nature of all feeling. Once this feeling has been established, one should analyze it and try to discover in what way it differs from all other feelings; this is what Milsand has done and Ruskin has tried to do, one must give him his due—but how inferior he is to our own Jouffroy! Poor Ruskin fell into the trap which I have just pointed out, and so thoroughly that he breaks down the aesthetic feeling into a host of others. In it, he discovers all man's noblest sentiments in communion with God's perfect creations as exemplified by the beasts; he even brings scientific theory into it.

Milsand is right: his indignation is legitimate when he loudly vindicates the artistic faculty against the baneful usurpations of literature. Bravo! Well done! The heart leaps with pleasure, for the valiant writer provides it with reasons which affect it deeply. Conclusion: there exists a feeling which is proper only to art, and which is absolutely irreducible to other, literary feelings. I love you, Milsand!

I would love you more if you did not deny the ideal. We must have it out between the two of us!

I have said that although the aesthetically moved state of the soul is very obvious when it is felt as pure sensation, this state becomes very obscure when it is criticized by the mind. Where does this obscurity come from? Milsand replies: it comes from the fact that the mind itself has blown out the candle, and by its intervention destroyed precisely that which it seeks to analyze. I repeat that the function of the understanding regarding ideas is to see that the ideas express the most delicate feelings and that, in a word, one gets the *idea of a feeling* and that all feeling is subjective and objective at the same time. But the advantage which the *idea of feeling* has over *feeling* itself is that it delivers up to the work of reflection and analysis a matter which, in its state of pure feeling, resists and evades this analysis. What then is the content of the aesthetic feeling? What subjective and what objective elements go toward its formation? That is the question. It must be admitted that the artist alone can answer it, because the person who has never experienced a feeling can never have any idea of it; I will even agree that one of the conditions of dreaming deeply is to think less. What follows from this? That the faculties of a single man are injurious to each other, and that aestheticism will be created, if ever, by the richest and most powerful moral organization ever to appear on earth. It is no less true that, if an aesthetic feeling exists, a relationship exists between the man who is moved and the world which moves him, consequently two terms. Let us concern ourselves with the second.

At the start of this criticism I raised a difficulty which now appears in all its importance. Milsand assumes that the work of the imagination is spontaneous, so that the aesthetic emotion accompanies it and participates in its spontaneity; I quite agree, I have experienced that this is so. But Milsand does not take into account the anterior work of the mind which, by means of a long series of analyses and syntheses, has since childhood distinguished things and given them names, and noticed established unities in cases where the result of pure sensation only is chaos. The most beautiful countryside, and the one which is the best peopled for pure sensation, is nothing more than a mobile medley like the images produced by a kaleidoscope. Therefore, unless he is to reduce art to pure feeling and the agreeable (which is to deny it), Milsand must recognize that the aesthetic faculty works on a more complicated basis, but one which is more intelligent and is supplied by the conscious or unconscious elaboration of the mind (it matters little to my thesis which of the two it is) . . . "But," Milsand will exclaim, "I have not denied the cooperation of the mind in the work of the imagination and if you allow that this cooperation has been unconscious, then you are in the same boat as me!" Not as much as he thinks: the mind has operated spontaneously but always according to its own laws and through its habitual processes. The mind reacts in the same way, whether the conscience helps in its work or not, that is to say the mind only forms special ideas, crumbs of knowledge, and it only advances slowly by means of vague consultations, without being able to leap with one bound into the right place. The mind finds out, I must confess, because it induces and deduces, but it does not see straight into the heart of things, naive as it is.

There exists nevertheless a means whereby the intelligence can penetrate deeply into the nature of beings whose essence is analogous to the human essence: this consists in seizing hold of the external force which causes the feelings, by means of the feelings themselves and their very quality and movement. Even if the external force itself is not grasped, at least its appearance and its life are. The mind, in fact, distinguishes the *living unities* in the midst of the chaos of feelings thanks to the aptness of expression enjoyed by those feelings which are produced by the unities. To expand on this subject to the extent which it deserves would be to write a whole book. A few notes will indicate my thoughts.

The sensations, lines, shapes, colors, tastes, and smells are agreeable or disagreeable, except for those to which habit has made us indifferent; they have that subjective quality. I say subjective, because although some inevitable external condition may determine the *concatenation* and the *acuteness* of the impressions, it is nothing external which makes them agreeable or disagreeable, and nothing communicates this quality to them, although the quality can be stirred and its rhythm affected by the outside world. The color of a metal only provides the chemist with a fairly useless annotation which teaches him nothing about its nature; it is in itself subjective, and the sound emitted by the metal when vibrating is equally subjective. So also is its shape, unless crystallization reveals some process which it has undergone. Thus, feeling in general is subjective in itself and only becomes objective in its relationship to another feeling; relationships make up the only knowledge we have of objects. But an unusual case arises in which the feeling is in itself objective and provides the knowledge of that very object which produces it, instead of revealing it through relationships: this is the amazing case of *expression*.

Let us consider a face. It is a combination of feelings, it is true, but this combination forms a unity of expression; the face is gay or sad, surprised or pensive, compassionate or cruel, gentle or angry, and so on. It expresses one thing. Which one? the state of the soul, which is the external object in this case. Thus, the soul of a man is so related to the disposition of the muscles of his face that when this face reacts physically on the senses of another man, it reveals this soul to that other man. And so I claim that the feelings, inasmuch as they reveal a soul, are *objective in themselves* in that they are agreeable or disagreeable, which in ordinary language is described by the word *expression.* One example will definitely clarify this statement. When I look at the wallpaper in my room, I see a combination of lines and capricious colors which is purely decorative; but when I daydream, I discover in it a strange face, which is oddly expressive. How is it that the same material picture is so differently interpreted by my mind, according to whether my mind wants to see decoration or a face? It is because my mind can consider this face to be a union of geometrical curves which it conceives through the relationship of the different points to each other, by relating it to a direction, a center, or different areas. Until now, feelings have not provided my mind with anything objective other than relationships; the color of these curves was only subjectively agreeable. But as soon as my mind imagined a face in this design it no longer imagined any relationship, as one would be tempted to believe by the complexity of the feeling; it can only see one simple thing, the soul of which this face is the expression. But, one may say, a moment ago you only imagined one thing, which was a unique curve formed by the relationship between various points, just as you only imagine a face formed by the relationship between various features. This objection bears out my theory marvelously. Undoubtedly, if a moment ago I could only see a curve, I was seeing with the eye of an artist, and to me the curve expressed something if I had seen the curve with the eye of a geometrician I would not have lost sight of the *relationship* between its points, which is the basis of its properties, whilst continuing to recognize the curve from the geometrical point of view. To sum up, feelings are objective in two ways: either through their relationships, which legitimizes science; or in themselves as means of expression, which justifies art. When I say *in themselves,* I mean through their agreeable or disagreeable quality, a quality which obviously can derive from a relationship between several feelings, or from the harmony between them. There is however this difference: that in the first objectivity it is the relationships themselves which form the idea; whereas in the second objectivity it is the unity which is known, and the unity is foreign to the relationships but results from them.

I am immersed in Milsand, because this question of the innate objectivity of expressive feeling does not remove any of its subjectivity, and the remarkable thing is that it is precisely its essentially subjective quality, that of agreeableness, which is also objective in that it is expressive.

But one must go further than Milsand; even if expression is the essence of art, all expression is not its aim. The artist chooses between two faces: one seems preferable to another, not only because it is more expressive but because it expresses a nobler, more *beautiful* nature. This beauty is purely objective because it does not depend on the artist in any way; but as the characteristic of expression is to make the subjective quality of feeling more objective, this beauty is truly present in the feeling. Therefore, one cannot truthfully say that the form is purely agreeable, as the realists would have it: it is agreeable, but with an agreeableness that expresses beauty, an agreeableness which has become significant. What is this beauty, this ideal? It is either specific or absolute. When specific, it is nothing less than the perfection of the species, a beautiful horse, a beautiful man, a beautiful monkey. When absolute, it is the supreme essence, that which is superior to all others in the universal scale, beyond which the Hegelian *becom-*

ing ceases, for lack of a possible better state.

But what is an artist, after all? He is a man gifted with the faculty of deep perception of the agreeable or disagreeable *expressiveness* of feeling, and one who is able to conceive through *expression* an endless series of matter which is more and more noble.

Thus, there can be no artist unless there is a strong feeling for form.

Metaphysical perfection, that is to say the most complete and the richest conceivable essence, only becomes beauty by passing through the agreeable, or form.

Let us add that love introduces new elements into art, a sexual beauty which is quite different to the one which we are discussing here.

30th November. Waiting! A provisional kind of life which does not count! Sterile rage against time, which has to be measured by life, whether we like it or not. Time certainly gets its revenge for the silly speeches about how it flies. Fleeting, time? Oh what a sluggish reptile! How long drawn-out and implacable it is in its slowness!

Waiting might drive me mad. In the end, everything causes me pain; every noise, every face appears to me like a traitor who announces the arrival of the person I am waiting for, and betrays me. Who is that coming? It is she . . . For certain, yes, oh! It must be her! . . . And then the approaching specter disintegrates, and offers me nothing more than the caricature of the beloved. It is impossible to resign myself because after all she could still come . . . Perhaps she is only two minutes away from here. One can become resigned to a loss, but one cannot resign oneself to a missed opportunity. Waiting is the cruelest mixture of hope and despair which can torment the soul; a feeling of impotence and a surge of desire are like a fever.

3rd December. Whist at Colin's.—Playing games. Games have a deep meaning. The essential occupation known as work having been discontinued, and the need for action continuing throughout the whole evening, there had to be an intermediary occupation. But one never does anything without an object therefore this occupation had to have an interest: hence the playing of games. It can be defined as an active interest outside work. Between work and games there is only boredom, which is the feeling produced by idleness and is a feeling as vague as idleness is indeterminate.

Games change their character according to a man's age. To the child, playing a game represents life; to the adolescent it means dreaming about it; to the young man, activating it; while to the mature man, it is distraction from it.

As for the young child and the old man, properly speaking neither the one nor the other is playing a game. These two extremes of age gravitate toward each other and meet. The new-born child experiments ceaselessly, with the seriousness of curiosity: the old man, who has given up business, puts all his working strength into play. Do not believe that whist amuses him, or billiards, or anything else: he transfers all the interest of his working life, though not of his life of affection, to them. Do not expect any indulgence from him, nor mercy for a partner's errors, and do not make the mistake of winning if you are his opponent.

The essence of games does not necessarily involve chance, but chance must have been introduced very early, because it creates interest through doubt: the interest of rivalry came first but doubt, which merely suspends the knowledge of an event, demands less effort, and is as exciting as competition. The throw of a dice is less tiring than a fight and exerts moral activity just as well. One may make a distinction with racing: the jockeys are rivals and the onlookers are the gamblers.

The word gamble has been diverted from its primitive meaning to describe all risky schemes, both commercial and financial.

10th December. Vacherot (*Essay on Critical Philosophy*) Moral.—The infinite comfort this book gave me. What does one not owe to people who give one riches such as these! Yes, the moral principle is now clear to me. From now on I shall no longer grope my way along the path of life. Be a man; that is to say, always subordinate the inferior, animal part of your being to the superior, spiritual part which makes you a *man.* Maine de Biran had noticed this, but he did not add the justification for this rule: this inferior part is only the means, the superior part is the end and it is logical and *reasonable* not to sacrifice the end to the means, for that would be giving up joy in order to confine oneself to pleasure.

1865

13th January. Thoughts of an idler.—I have allowed myself to be persuaded that the straight line is the shortest way from one point to another, but I cannot find anyone who can prove it. Is a line this shape when it is defined as being the shortest? Is it the shortest when it is given this shape? I like to tease it, because I cannot stand it, any more than I can stand the broken line. All instincts rush toward it, all sad things take pleasure in it. The leap of the tiger onto its prey, the blade of the sword, the scepter, rage and insult, Vendôme columns and crutches, the duel of honor which is the shortest road to vengeance, the rope of the guillotine, codes of law which lead straight to prejudice; lastly, and above all else, the boulevard, the highway of the mob: all these things go in straight lines.

I like the curve; hedge-schools,[2] the flight of swallows, waves of the oceans, clouds, valleys, beautiful views, beautiful faces—you are all curves. Justice follows a curve when, instead of cutting the gold bar in two and throwing it to each party, it probes the deepest parts of the soul in order to absorb the needs of each one and to bring to each its nourishment, as the sinuous network of the veins feeds the body, to the extent that justice becomes indistinguishable from charity. Eloquence is a curve because it knows how to envelop certainty with charm, and so is delicacy which either gives or refuses by a mere touch of the hand. Modesty is a delicious turning aside, and a beautiful line of poetry falls and lifts itself up again a dozen times like the coils of a snake. Tolerance allows liberty to circulate everywhere without elbowing anybody. Childhood, youth, maturity, old age—what a curve on life's horizon! Art is not a steep ladder from reality to the ideal nor progress a spiral, but a parabola, that beautiful line which tries to achieve an always fleeting kiss as it reaches its asymptote.

Three beautiful straight lines: the ray of light, the Attic frieze, and loyalty. Three odious curves: diplomacy, the hippodrome, and the vicious circle.

The business man is a straight line, the artist a curve.

The cause of the instability of nations lies entirely in the lack of balance between humanity's culture of the body and its culture of the soul. The barbarian is only strong, the civilized man is only intelligent: neither one nor the other is a *man.* Man's qualities are few and far between, and they are not to be met with in a single subject; political progress is

[2] An archaic expression used to describe an open-air school, especially in Ireland.

confused here with moral progress; men must be made. Politics and morals are only static.

[On Paul Janet's book, *The Philosophy of Happiness:*]

Great joy brings great sorrow with it. Who wants the kind of happiness which involves being happy and feeling as little as possible? All theories on happiness tend to exclude passion, which is the source of trouble and pleasure, and consequently tend also to abolish sensitivity. A happiness which is determined by the balance of the faculties and by the proportionate use of all the powers is a regime which leads directly to boredom. Let us add that this very happiness is jeopardized by constant worrying about this balance; it can only be maintained at the cost of continual sacrifice. It is true that a naturally well-balanced organization is naturally happy; but what does it matter to me! If my own organization is passionate, your recipe cannot be of use to me unless I make myself unhappy in its very application; you have observed the conditions of happiness, but if they do not exist, can one create them? To balance one's soul correctly means being virtuous, but it does not mean bringing happiness to oneself; on the contrary, virtue is the sister of unhappiness. There is a kind of happiness for every man and it quite simply consists of the complete satisfaction of all his leanings; from which it can be seen how much happiness differs from virtue.

A book about happiness can only be good if it makes those who read it feel happy; for if they remain unhappy, obviously the recipe is worthless; it cannot be supposed that one tries it out unwillingly; the reader risks nothing more than his interest and his egoism.

Virtue is essentially unhappiness: try to turn it into joy, and what is left of it? What is a virtue which costs nothing? I would not even expect it to promise happiness, because I would be afraid of some kind of speculation. When one aims at happiness one is satisfied with not being guilty, but one cannot declare oneself to be virtuous; in fact, one is not very interesting.

Poetry.—A terrain full of brambles and nettles. A man clears it, the grass grows and it is a meadow.—Man cultivates the meadow, corn grows and it is a field.—Man crops the field and plows it up. The winds of Asia scatter flower seeds, and now the field becomes an immense balmy meadow. Man breathes the delicious air and says: "This land is beautiful. I shall never mow it again."

Humanity has been a horde of barbarians; God mowed it with the arm of death. It became a nation; he mowed it down again. It will become a pure and loving family. Then God will say: "Humanity is beautiful, I will never mow it down again."

Lord, that will be an act worthy of thy greatness, worthier than the insatiable voraciousness of the grave and we, the ephemerals, we will suffer and work with more courage for the last of our sons who will be the immortals.

Another subject for a poem.

I was nothing, I shall come to an end; and yet the land remains, it came before me and it will survive me. So I am really only a passer-by, and yet I love you. I am a passer-by who plucks a flower and brings it back to his own country to show it to his family and his friends, and says to them: "In the world which I have come from, there are flowers like this one."

1865 [*no further details*]. For a woman, one more crime exists than for a man: coquettishness. Coquettishness in a man is merely ridiculous and fatuous.

A woman of this kind only shows benevolence when she wishes to charm. A coquette likes to turn joy into pain and even pain into joy, because what matters to her is to dispense both one and the other as it suits her.

A coquette will not venture anything she cannot retract; with one word she can ruin an apparently well-established situation; she authorizes audacity and suddenly appears to condemn it with even greater audacity. A woman who is completely indifferent disconcerts and paralyzes gallantry; therefore, a coquette never appears indifferent. But what kind of feeling does she call into play? A feeling which by its very nature must remain undefinable, because if it were love it would mean an admission; if it were friendship the bait would be insufficient; and if it were compassion, it would be wounding; moreover, it must attract indefinitely. One may say, that which she allows people to catch a glimpse of is only the possibility of love.

The art of the coquette consists of allowing nothing, while letting it be understood that everything is possible.

Coquettishness is both a homage and an insult to modesty; it is a game of hide-and-seek behind the veil of modesty, an infamous trick, a toying with the fig leaf.

A coquette thinks little of compliments, she can only see the cleverness in them; but a word straight from the heart interests her, because then she can find a way of causing suffering.

Every woman knows full well her ability to please; she knows how to display to the world every effect of which she is capable, the effect of beauty, charm, wit, indulgence and even simplicity. But the masterpiece of the coquette consists in producing a powerful effect of simplicity.

The stupidity of a man is shown by his words, that of a woman by her silence. A dumb woman is a fool, but a man who never speaks can be considered clever. One way of exasperating a coquette is to always be gallant with her, never tender; this is a way of teasing her which I can recommend.

There is this difference between the coquette and the sensual woman, that the first bears a grudge against the heart, the second against the lips.

7th September. My thoughts sometimes receive sudden illuminations which all at once throw light on some question, and then it is night again. The pen is not quick enough to record these luminous shafts: I derive little benefit from them, because I feel them escaping from me as soon as I start to think them over in order to preserve them . . .

1868

Sunday 14th June. So I am going to make notes on my principal impressions every day. It is a task I undertook some time ago but which I did not have the steadfastness to pursue. I have an instinctive terror of the pen. Moreover, I do not benefit in any way from these impressions, because I cannot reread them. Is it not enough to have lived through those days? Does one have to torture oneself by going through all that suffering again, or by recalling dead pleasures one is powerless to resuscitate? Memories have a smell of the grave; yes, there is in them a smell of the past, a vague and insipid smell of old dust that plunges me into a heavy stupor, full of tears that cannot quite flow. Ah! at least with recent sorrows one can weep and groan over them; but old ones are in some way impossible to digest, they cannot be dispersed or assimilated.

The only advantage of these daily memoirs is to allow the pen complete sincerity, or rather complete spontaneity.

Sincerity is the first requirement of all products of the mind, in my view at any rate. To be insincere is to spoil the pleasure of following the fortunes of one's thoughts abroad, which is the only real joy of a writer worthy of the name. In the same way that one is only interested in the successes which one's children make of their careers in life, so also can one only really enjoy the fate of a work that is the fruit of one's loins. Furthermore, artistic creation has the immediate effect of relieving the soul, of lifting from it all the weight of the troubles which one has described, or of relaxing the tension of enthusiasm, ecstasy and happiness; finally, it also transforms passion into contemplation, because it separates the heart from its objective, not in order to remove the objective altogether but simply to disengage the heart and allow it to see the objective illuminated by the mind. How could all these benefits be felt without sincerity?

As for spontaneity, that is quite another matter. One does not write spontaneously for the public; one would have to be completely deprived of all modesty to allow the reactions of one's soul to be disclosed. Good taste in style is the modesty of sincerity. In poetic matters it is not a question of soliciting the reader's indiscreet curiosity, but his sympathy, that is to say the feeling which he may have in common with the poet: in other words, poetry must not be purely individualistic or biographical, it must be human. In scientific works spontaneity, which in this case is intuition and the immediate understanding of truth, is even more out of place than in works of imagination. One is supposed to have reflected before writing; reflection is the sincerity of the scientist and the philosopher, because it alone guarantees the writer's adherence to truth.

Writing for the public is therefore a harsh task, when one's attention is always on the alert to choose and criticize all the material provided by spontaneity; to write for oneself is not to work, it is to breathe.

Then let us breathe, let us pen these lines according to the whims of emotion and thought, without seeing them being born or ended, and in particular without rereading them; let the pen mechanically transcribe in shorthand the inner poem, whether it be sad or gay.

It is sad, tonight. Today I did some philosophy, but it was not analytical. Just as a painter from time to time steps back from the easel to judge the effect (which is the synthesis of his brush strokes), so also the philosopher must often suddenly abandon the skeleton of his thoughts in order to see from a distance whether it makes a picture, a whole. Each bone judged separately is defined exactly, but is the arrangement of all the bones true, natural and possible? It is only seen from a distance. The wonder is that a superior faculty seems to preside over the divided work of the organs of understanding and that, through supreme judgment and without resort to other things, this faculty can break up all the minute separate judgments which form the pieces of the system. With me, the faculty is disdainful and haughty, and it delivers sharp lessons to its little work girls on the lower floor. It leaves them to cope with the absurdities, the overrefinements, and all the paraphernalia of dissection and analysis, and it takes the throne in the midst of a frightening void. When its subalterns have thoroughly masticated, crumbled and turned the matter inside out, this faculty calls them idiots, laughs at their work and proves the futility of this infinitesimal fiddling through its haughty consciousness of an infinite overall picture, in which the ends of the interweaving threads all disappear from human sight. It makes me feel really sad.

Upon which, some shattering letters

arrive for me and a feeling of unspeakable loneliness completes my misery. It is late, let us go to bed. I have written for too long, but it gave me pleasure. Until tomorrow.

Monday 5th. I have thought of a new way of describing the moral sense. It is the art of actions, an aesthetic form of which everyday life is the material, and it consists in giving *beautiful forms* to its life. I think this is the way in which the ancients looked at it; to them honesty is more than the accomplishment of duty, it is nobility of conduct which implies a high sense of duty and a certain art in action. This is the only way in which to teach the moral sense effectively to young people. Do not tell them to "Do something well," that is servitude; but tell them to "Do something beautifully," that is art, that is liberty. Address yourself only to the creative spirit which devours them. This is what I would say to a friend who is a mother. Only a mother can really understand this method, which has the great advantage of allowing the teacher to dispense with all precise definition, since it connects goodness with beauty, which cannot be defined.

Does one not say to a child: "It's ugly, it's horrid, it's not pretty to tell lies," because to a child lying and putting its fingers in its nose are all the same thing. Later, one tries to substitute the conception of good for that of beauty in the child's mind, but one only succeeds in defining *justice* which does not imply the whole of good, for there is more good in charity than in justice. One should always revert to the heart's interest in the question. It is an error to believe that understanding suffices for the definition of good.

The identity of both beauty and good is instinctively preserved in the word "honor." Honor is beauty in the use of the will, but especially in our relations with other people; with regard to ourselves, good means moderation, and as moderation tends towards balance and harmony, it too is beauty. So when I envisage the moral sense I find the aesthetic on all sides. But, it will be objected, is the moral sense then only relative, like art? Is there not an absolute good, any more than there is absolute beauty?

This objection is based on a confusion which must be removed.

Doing good has two meanings: it means on the one hand using one's *will* to do that which one *judges to be good,* and on the other, accomplishing that which is good. We can always tend to accomplish that which we judge to be the right thing; as responsibility depends entirely on our *energy* and our *opinion,* we are always responsible unless we are in a state of idiocy. But, for lack of sufficient education and intelligence, we cannot always succeed in knowing what is really right, therefore we are only responsible within the limits of our knowledge. Thus, in one way, good is the intention of doing good, combined with the effort of achieving it; in another way, good is the absolute law of human nature, of which we have imperfect knowledge. Supposing there were perfect knowledge of human nature, the relationships between men and the rules of conduct would immediately and freely follow on, in order to fulfill nature's wishes regarding social relationships in the best possible way.

These two meanings of the word *good* are so different that, although we might have a thorough knowledge of human nature and the conditions of social life most consistent with this nature, *to do good* would still have two meanings. The good in our will would, in fact, remain very distinct from the conformity of our actions to the laws of nature which constitute absolute good. One can achieve this good without goodness, through luck or even through selfishness, and then one has *done good* in the sense of the achievement of absolute good, but one can have *acted wrongly* or at least have *acted indifferently,* in the sense of the goodness of intention. Let us then carefully separate the synonymous good of *merit* from the synonymous good of *accomplishing the absolute laws of nature.* It is obviously desirable that merit should be born from the achievement of absolute good, but it can exist even in opposition to good, if the intention of achieving it exists. Our deduction is not culpable, even though it may not be perfect.

From this point of view the analogy between the arts and the moral sense is complete. When one asks "Is there an absolute good and an absolute beauty?" it is as though one had asked whether nature were ruled by eternal laws, and scientific experience authorizes the answer: yes. What is relative is the knowledge of these laws, which varies from one man to another and from one century to the next.

A *meritorious* action and a work of *merit* are such through the degree of activity expended by their author and his degree of initiative with regard to the intellectual state of his time. Merit and talent are not measured by the conformity of the work to the absolute ideal, without which there would not be a good action in the life of a savage nor a beautiful picture by the primitives; they are measured by the goodness of the intention in the first case, and by the power of the inventive conception and the effort made by knowledge of form in the second, together with the delicacy of the sensory organs. But if, to take a different attitude, one compares the work or the action with absolute beauty and absolute good, irrespective of the amount of genius or goodness which they have called forth from their authors, one could pronounce a very different judgment to the first one, and say that the action is absurd and barbarous and the work incorrect and ugly.

As soon as man knows that his moral responsibility is subordinated to his knowledge of the laws of nature, he becomes responsible for his own ignorance, within the limits of being able to apply a remedy. The first duty, the one which comes before all others, is therefore to study the laws of human nature, the source of all other duties. That is why we assign the age of reason to children to put an end to their responsibility, and when they want to be excused from some wrong act and say "I did not know," we answer "You ought to know," because it is considered that the matter was within reach of their intelligence. Then one punishes them, not for having committed the act but for having ignored, either through negligence, frivolity or laziness, that it was contrary to the laws of human nature.

An artist who nowadays makes a mistake in anatomy is responsible for his ignorance because anatomy is a well-studied subject: one would not think of blaming a primitive, and the primitive may be considered superior to an academically correct dauber, even though from the point of view of absolute truth one ought to prefer the exact style of a present-day draughtsman to the imperfect style of a primitive.

In a given case one has always got to make a moral resolution, and responsibility is always involved, because one always has a more or less complete idea of human nature, even though it may only be the following one: As men are all of the same species it is not logical, in conformity with nature's wishes, that one should do something to someone which one does not want to have done to oneself. The moral sense is therefore founded on the knowledge of human nature and has always existed, because man has never been entirely ignorant of his own nature; but his nature has always been imperfect because he has never applied himself to its study.

The moral sense is thus *independent* in the same capacity and for the same reasons as science, of which it is but an application. Like science, it derives only from experience and reflection. An authority that imposes duties for which there is no apparent reason, has no more credit in the eyes of conscience than an unproved dogma has in the eyes of the scientific spirit.

The differences of opinion among men as to what is the best thing to do are no reason for not doing what one believes to be right; it is not the skepticism of others which can absolve us from our responsibility, but our own feeling of doubt. Therefore, before daring to break with the usual moral principles, everyone ought to ask himself if *his doubts are sincere,* no matter how great may be the skepticism of others. It is a question of fact, which one can only decide for oneself. I notice that instead of fixing my impressions, I am writing dissertations; so much the worse, because I want to put down on paper everything which goes through my mind, long or short, intelligible or not. Am I not speaking to myself?

16th June. It is eleven o'clock. I have been spending the evening in the house where I had dinner. A woman who is old, if you compare her to her portrait as a young woman. Beauty does not all disappear with the years; what is left of it? That which came from the soul, the smile, the look, and that basic construction of the head which shows intelligence and character, when the luxuriant plumpness of earlier years is no longer there to alter the expression. The fundamental quality of beauty remains, and it is still beauty, but the mask has been dropped and with it some of its charm; certain lines, of which the formidable portent was hidden by stoutness or was not yet accentuated, now declare themselves and betray the soul. There is in these shapes something which I call *tendencies.* I am alarmed to see what the child's face has become. The first thing to do when in the presence of a woman whom one wishes to love is to study and discover these tendencies; one must concentrate on the profile and scrutinize the sinuosities which seem inoffensive but which can eventually alter someone's character.

Today I read Helmholtz's treatise on acoustics, the physiological theory of music. How simple nature's proceedings are! She uses the simplest means to achieve the greatest results. But then how is it that there is not a unique being? how to explain multiplicity and variety? it would be very much simpler to reduce everything to an indivisible unity. There is incompatibility between the prodigality of creative nature and the economy of organizing nature. Seeds in abundance, few laws, perhaps only one. That does not explain my thoughts at all well, but I am not worrying much about explaining them, I just note them down.

I cannot manage to put my preface to *Lucrece* into any sort of order. Ideas have been manipulated to such an extent that one no longer knows how to present them under a new aspect; they still show us their old faces.

17th June. Someone asked me the other day why I do not write novels or plays. I did not dare say why not. The study of philosophy has minimized all human affairs in my eyes. I am quite indifferent to the *variable;* to create a setting, make some individual come alive, make him take up his walking-stick, dress him, sit him down, I consider all that to be pitiful and miserable. I would much rather take the essence of a passion or a grief, independently of all adventure, and search for the cadence and rhythm which are its eternal and necessary accompaniments. The *contingent* is odious to me. It has become impossible for me to read a novel, and I do not go to the theater because nowadays intrigue has been substituted for character. *Deeds* do not interest me, they are only the flowering of causes, which are the only essentials.

Go and tell that to some gentleman you meet for the first time!

I notice with regret that I have lost all my comic sense. I laugh with much more difficulty than before, and I am quite surprised when I see my friends laughing at certain things.

For the last two or three years I have been studying the essence of laughter and the causes which provoke it; I shall return to this study.

It seems to me, at first sight, that there are no laughable abstractions, and that some form is always involved in the motive for laughter. Perhaps form alone is ridiculous, perhaps it is so because of some discrepancy with idea . . . This must be gone into.

Midnight: I dined with some young men, an hour at the café, wasted time, stupidities and boredom. Is it not just another of life's evenings? I did practically nothing except mentally to calculate the passing of the hours.

Thursday 18th. A very dull day: no work. Time flies, and I am getting behindhand. I can only occupy myself in sponging myself, taking refreshment, and dozing: the heat exhausts me.

I have read *The Earthly Epic* by Lefèvre. His materialism proves nothing. The facts which he announces are hardly in question. It is absolutely true that there is an intimate relationship between the soul and the body and that one does not think without a brain, and so on. Nobody would think of denying this relationship, but the difficulty exists in explaining one by one two such distinct orders of phenomena as thought and movement. It is no solution to state that movement alone produces everything, if one does not also throw light on the mysterious transformation of material forces into mental faculties. It is to leave the problem unsolved and pose a pure hypothesis.

The Positivists are wiser and more consistent, they refrain from pronouncing any judgment on Substance and primary Cause.

Finally, Lefèvre tries to constitute happiness with the elements of earthly life, but in this he is completely unsuccessful. He ought to be sincere enough and courageous enough to admit that life is a misery without divine hope, and that there is no divine hope. Byron, Alfred de Musset and Leopardi have all put their finger in the gaping wound of the materialist. According to them, happiness is reduced to a party of pleasure which misfires. That which is threatened with an ending remains far from the idea of happiness.

This mediocrity of desire of the materialists disgusts me. I believe as they do that death results in a void, but I am not comforted by this and all the inventions of science seem to me puerile distractions in the face of the abyss.

His book is full of fine poems, solid, knotty, concise, which land on their twelve feet like three well-built horses, rather heavy but powerful.

Friday 19th. An overwhelming day . . . no energy, no work, lazy and shapeless ideas.

I have read the philosophical work of Funck-Brentano. Badly written, but seriously thought out. Yes, philosophy must concentrate entirely on the examination of the function of thinking. But even in this what a lot of vagueness, uncertainty and error there is!

What is reflection? How can the mind consider itself as the object? And is it not equally wonderful that a human being can think about anything except himself?

What can one know, if one does not even know what it is to know?

And yet we enjoy certainty, we are struck by evidence; all our actions reveal our faith in thought.

All these contradictions are irritating and aggravating. One does not know when to apply one's own intelligence. What a tangled skein! and how loose and brittle is the thread!

Intellectual facts which are apparently the most simple are astonishingly complex. A whole crowd of incomprehensible and yet perceptible elements enter into the smallest sensation, such as duration, extent, existence and qualities.

When one is weary of writing a novel one puts down the pen, but when one is tired of philosophizing one must go on philosophizing, even if it is only to doubt. As we only live thanks to thought, as men we can no more rest voluntarily from doubt than stop living by means of the will alone.

It is most fortunate that love is not conditioned by science.

And yet, does it too not depend on certainty? It has its doubt; it has its faith . . . Curiosity turns into jealousy with love. To ignore, to know; without, there is no more passion, no more man.

I believed for a long time that doubt was only a thought process; I am beginning to think that it is a disease. This evil, which is at first imaginative and poetic, takes on a positive reality when one has thoroughly examined one's thoughts. Until then, one had merely been ignorant, doors could open . . . but suddenly one realizes that one has been groping one's way along a wall and has returned to the point of departure without finding a single outlet. So then one no longer laughs with the mockers, one no longer sheds the golden tears of the poets, one's heart is heavy and oppressed, and one is well and truly in the dungeon.

Today I could not feel happy; I got no letters and did no work.

Life without a woman becomes daily more intolerable. No aim, no resting place, no heaven—neither shade nor sunshine, the mists of boredom, the abyss of disgust, thoughts of death, and the terrible "What is the use of it all?"

A youth which is eating itself up, useless. A few scraps of trifling notoriety here and there, the miserable charity which great Glory distributes to her beggars. The flattery of fools which is the scourge of ambition, and the absolute disdain of those who make the bread we eat and without which we would die like dogs . . . Dependence and pride; vanity which knows itself for what it is through vanity, and remains what it is. I know myself. One must not distress kindhearted people by despising their praise, one must thank them and smile; but this is when one must tighten a notch round the hidden hair shirt of modesty, and not forget in a moment of madness that one is nothing and that one knows nothing. We readily believe those whom we love, and we imagine that to please them is to succeed though, in fact, this is to please oneself. One takes pleasure in oneself and one's friends; this counts for nothing in the balance of criticism. Success should not be confused with the *conquest of affections;* we should know how to derive consolation for our mediocrity through affection. By mediocrity I mean what is called *talent*. What more can one say in all honesty to people who have no genius?

Saturday 20th. I have formed the bad habit of getting up late. It is not that my bed is agreeable when I am awake, but I am riveted to it by an indescribable lassitude. Getting up is hard work for me. But I regret the lost mornings, the only hours of the day when the temperature is cool and the mind is alert, clear and winged.

I have found it impossible to write a single line of verse. I can only read philosophy. I seem to be very near grasping the end of the thread, but illusions are frequent and I am on my guard.

I imagine for a moment that I have got to create or compose an intelligence, and I wonder how I would set about it and what elements would be necessary to its formation. And first of all, what is an intelligence and what would be my object in creating it? I would doubtless propose that I should give a kind of new existence to the phenomena of the universe, which would be like an echo or repercussion of their real existence in a human being. Thus, the universe must so to speak exist in something other than itself; it must be double, both reality and image. Then in what way will this new universe differ from the real universe? If it resembled it in everything, there would merely be a second universe, and not an intelligence of the universe. The intelligent being has his own reality, distinct from the exterior reality which he must contain; in a word, there are two different beings of whom one must nevertheless be contained in the other in a certain way. It cannot be substantially, because if so the beings would be confused, identified. How then does intelligence *contain* the world? As the substance, the *being* of the world cannot in any way be contained by the intelligent *being* and as these two beings must remain distinct, the intimate nature or substance of the world remains of necessity external to the spirit, and cannot be contained by it.

I am therefore obliged to give up the idea of creating a completely intelligent being, if I do not place intelligence in the world itself but in a being which is exterior to it. I would try in vain to substitute in the spirit an image of the substance of the world for the substance of the world itself; but there cannot be an image of the substance, because form in itself can be reproduced independently of substance in the spirit, in the image state; an image can only be a form, and there is no form which represents substance itself.

It is therefore only the forms of the world and its phenomena which can be contained by my intelligent creature. Here I notice several essential conditions imposed on this creature. If its substance is absolutely and in every way different to that of the world, then these two substances can have no common form; none of the world's form can be represented in the spirit. It is indeed clear that form is not independent of the nature of substance; due to the mere fact that it is allied to it, it participates in it and has some attribute in common with it: one cannot conceive the union of two *completely* different things, because they can never sustain a relationship between themselves. If therefore the spirit can contain the forms of the world in order to understand them, and if consequently these same forms exist both in the world and in the spirit, this means that some common attribute between the world and the spirit exists, and that the substance of one resembles the substance of the other, to a certain extent. The only part of the world which is comprehensible to the spirit is the attribute which they have in common in the forms which contain this attribute as a link with the world. The forms of any other attribute belonging to the substance of the world will not be understood by the spirit.

Thus, when I try to constitute an intelligent being I cannot extend his intelligence beyond his capacity of representation, which is restricted to the attributes which he may have in common with the world.

If this is true, I can confirm that any intelligent being can only know as much of the world as he has in common with it; in other words, the knowledge he may have of the nature of the world will never exceed the knowledge he may have of his own nature.

With a couple, there is always one tyrant. Why is this so? In the first place it is because, more often than not, love is not the same on both sides; the one who is most loved takes pleasure in exercising power and is the least afraid of losing it, because this power is only really valuable if it is combined with passion. It is the commonest case, but the same condition still holds good when love is the same on both sides. Everyone interprets love in their own fashion: for one person it consists of possessing, for another of being possessed; character determines it and allocates the roles. As soon as one loves, one instinctively tries to prove one's love and to know whether one is loved; each one makes his experiments and tests, according to his character, some as despots, others as slaves. This does not in any way result in a state of hostility, the despot is dear to the slave, and the slave to the despot. In fact the test is conclusive for both one and the other: when the tyrant ceases to tyrannize it means he no longer loves, and when the slave ceases to bend the knee, he also no longer loves. The first ceases to love by abdicating the domination which no longer interests him, the second by freeing himself from a servitude which is no longer sweet.

When the characters are alike, analogous and more remarkable situations arise: if the two beings are equally loving, tyranny reveals itself in jealous obsequiousness; the tenderest is the most obsessive, but it is a delicious obsession; slavery is then a sacrifice of the pleasure of fondling, one offers no resistance, through a delicate sense of the happiness which one provides in this way, a happiness which is unquestionable. Whenever there is a possible devotion there is emulation, combat and, admirably enough, it is the tyrant who shows the devotion and the slave is the one who accepts it, depriving himself of it to give to the other. When the characters are both dominating, the struggle for possession is passionate, often brutal, and love frequently has all the appearance of hatred: each one can only judge of the other's affection by the dominion which he can exert over the other.

Therefore, in every case love is an opposition of feelings which shows itself in each act of everyday life, because it means that one person always has to allow either domination or idolization when it is he himself who wants one or the other. One may detect, through these observations, the unmistakable signs of the state of an alliance . . .

Sunday 21st. I know only too well that I shall not write any more poetry today than yesterday. I have got several days of sterility ahead of me, I cannot do anything about it, I must just wait . . .

My preface is not going fast; it is not that I lack ideas, but I cannot put them forward in an intelligible way without developing them, and my preface is turning into a book. A very great art is needed immediately to enter into communication with the mind of the reader; one must guess the general state of mind, and the point of view of the time and relate one's own point of view to it, otherwise it becomes a complete exposition of doctrine. If everything is tackled by the roots, it is a work of a different kind.

The mass: the whole village has gone to mass, and I remain alone in the house. What are they going to do in church? Listen to the Latin chanting, watch the sacred gestures of the priest? No, some of them understand none of it, the others no longer pay any attention; the mass has no definite meaning for anyone. They all go there together, with very different kinds of intelligence, to humiliate man before God. What God? The necessary, absolute principle of all things, the cause of everything. Some people imagine him with a beard and a long robe, others imagine a sort of spirit, a universal breath; each one pictures him as best he can, but they all have the same conception.

They conceive of him as *one* and distinct from the world, because our understanding is made in such a way that it distinguishes cause from effect, rather than seizing the substantial link which unites and combines them. All these good people are within their rights, they are even following the way of nature, because by acting thus they are obeying the demands of their reason and their heart. Because after all it is an incontestable fact that man is horribly isolated from the cause of the world, whatever it may be; this isolation weighs on him and it would be lovely for him to feel supported and accompanied . . . It is quite natural that he should seek to relate himself to the necessary principle which resolves and explains everything, and that he should credit this principle with considerable force. The mass does not mean any more than this, all cults are equal in their intention. When I think of the organizing cause of the world (whether I place it in him or elsewhere), I prostrate myself, I feel dependent, I feel that the solution of all that concerns me is elsewhere than in myself; I am at the mass. Without the priest, the temple would be equal in nobility to the very idea of the divine.

Tonight, a party at Sceaux, a half-open-air ball in the park.

Monday 22nd. What is the use of setting down the languors and the sorrows of this day? . . .

Yesterday a letter helped me to live . . . Then the reaction came, solitude never allows itself to be jilted for long . . .

Really, this philosophy of Funck-Brentano is very remarkable. It is certain that a similar book written by Renan or Taine would be quite outstanding. I do not believe that anybody has penetrated the mind so deeply since Maine de Biron. But what a jumble! What language! In this forest one is obliged to find one's own way, and reading this work is more like discovery than learning. I shall not benefit from reading it except by making a written resume from memory, as I do with all important works. Unfortunately time is short: it is always short, and for everything. Life lets us know its price, and flees from us.

Today I felt a brilliance of mind which is not usual with me. I clearly see into my distant thoughts and could taste the *inexpressible* without obscurity, which is among the supreme delights of philosophy . . .

This pleasure was spoiled by returning to real, immediate life . . . The infinite variety of positive things leaves me more alone than the simple unity of the primary cause vaguely glimpsed.

Shall I never be able to enjoy a month of complete seclusion? To see nobody, to visit nobody!

A formal call on Madame X. She talked about love, I cannot remember on what pretext. It seems to me, that once I am old I shall never mention this word again; it belongs to lips which hold kisses. I shall keep the memory because it is internal, invisible, and buried; but I shall suppress the word.

The worst kind of despair is indifference in a warm heart.

The greatest flattery one can give to certain people is to show one's respect for them.

To please any woman one must begin by respecting her; all women like to be taken seriously. Gallantry implies disdain for a woman; it revolts sensitive natures, and it displeases coquettes because it does not provide them with a means of torturing. This sort of woman has to be offered a heart which can still suffer a little, be it ever so little.

At the age of five one rides astride a stick as though it were a horse; at eighteen one embraces a girl as though it were love; at the age of thirty one marries, as though it were happiness; at forty one looks for a good position, as if that were an honor; then one dies, as though one had lived.

Thursday 25th. An invitation to a large party in carriages (brake, bric or brac, I don't know what they call it, four horses, bells, and so on) . . . to leave Versailles on Sunday morning and drive to Chevreuse . . . I refused. Why? I do not know why at all. I do not like parties, all organization displeases me.

To amuse oneself, that is a word with a deep meaning, and all the unhappiness of man is in it. In a really happy world the idea of pleasure would not even be born, happiness would be life itself, it would be a brake, bric, brac . . . perpetual and unconscious. But a brake, bric, brac just once by chance, like that, with a lot of other people, my word no.

If people suspected to what extent all invitations are odious to me, how indifferent and ungrateful I am, and how little importance I attach to that which is not *the whole* in all matters, they would leave me well alone.

Oh for a friend! a good talk with Léon, with some old scientist, a philosopher or my little nephew—I can listen as long as you like to that kind of thing.

I am not saying anything about love, it is a little too vital to be pure pleasure; but I reserve for the last the ideal happiness, friendship combined with love, which is the most delicious thing that I have ever felt in the whole world.

Friday 26th. Wrote a few lines of verse, not too successful, to be resumed later.

Poetry of feeling is either passionate or thoughtful. Perhaps it is easier in the first case than in the second. I have rarely written expansive verse, perhaps I never have. I like to give emotion a movement which is contained; compression seems to me more lofty and more worthy than expansion. To repress the impulses of the heart is a better way to register the heartbeats; pondered sorrow is nobler than shouted sorrow. I simply mean to say that I suppress the exclamation to turn it into a sigh, I dry tears in order to make them flow back into the heart; it is my manner, or rather it is my ideal.

A piece of poetry is not written to initiate everybody into a particular sorrow, but to make it felt by those who are capable and worthy of it; this communication must therefore be *ad hominem,* discreet, mysterious, and it must pass from one soul to the other, communicating its meaning by hints. Those who do not understand in this way would not have understood a more developed thought either, and those who are touched feel more deeply, more intimately, and are grateful to the poet for having only addressed himself to them, and for having neither betrayed nor prostituted their grief.

It is hard to believe how difficult it is to keep within this limit, to observe this relative clarity, this half-light which only shines for those who are interested but which must nevertheless please everyone, at any rate from the artistic point of view.

To write dramatic and passionate poetry one is perhaps less bound by tact, philosophy or art, and it suffices to be a natural actor and to understand the part; but one is not obliged to consider the part in its external relations with this or that witness. I am not referring to dramatic verse, but to lyric poetry. Another thing is to suffer naturally, to reflect on one's suffering and to calculate the effect on people's sympathy.

One serious obstacle to the simplification of form is that poetry loses its effect when read; simplicity, which is communicated by means of delivery, becomes colorless and cold and absorbed in itself. And yet, in the midst of all these difficulties, it is always possible to hit the right note, one can foretell it; but the neighboring notes sound falser the nearer one gets to the right one. In spite of one's feelings, it is preferable to write something quite different to what one intended, rather than to register a near miss. An opposite may be the truth, but a near miss is always an untruth.

Saturday 27th. What were my feelings today? Nothing, except for the languor of odious idleness. Relative idleness however, because I did at least note the principal passages of Brentano's book and transcribe them. But no composition, nothing effective or creative.

Time which was neither wasted nor well employed.

On *duty*.—Duty helps one to live, because it divides time and it orders work. Perhaps what I lack is the absolute necessity to take action. Composition is, through its very nature, capricious not to say changeable; hence all the hundreds of sophisms which laziness invents to defer and put off the task. One can hardly consider it a duty to create beauty but it is one to try to do so each day, and not to give in too soon to the resistances and inertias of the spirit.

Most of all, I miss a helper, a support, living and actual encouragement. Alone, alone, alone!

I went to the country to examine the flowers at close quarters, like I used to do in the *Jardin des Plantes*. I am ashamed of not knowing their names. The genius of Nature (why not say God?) is not only powerful, it is witty and, like children, it amuses itself by cutting out shapes and paper boats! It is incomprehensible, admirable, ridiculous, sublime, foolish, charming—in a word, it bears no relation to the human genius, and yet we obstinately try to prove that it does. Perhaps the poetry which interprets these things is an absurd piece of vanity; but if, perchance, to feel these things were to know them, then the poetry would be profoundly revealing . . .

Poor *Jardin des Plantes!*

THE LIFE AND WORKS OF RENÉ SULLY-PRUDHOMME

By GABRIEL D'AUBARÈDE

ONE EVENING in February 1863, Sully-Prudhomme recorded in his *Journal* an amusing conversation with an old schoolfellow. He was then twenty-four years old. The two friends met each other on the Boulevard des Italiens in Paris. Having lost track of each other since leaving school, they started asking the usual questions. Each was curious to know what line of work the other had taken up. "I'm working in a dry goods store," said his friend. "What about you?" Sully-Prudhomme was equal to the occasion. With the straight face of a practiced wag, the poet replied:

"My dear fellow, I'm working on a definition of man."

His friend was taken aback.

"He stood there aghast," Sully-Prudhomme wrote, "his cigar dangling between his fingers, his mouth agape; then with a smile: 'You're lucky, you have plenty of spare time.'—'Spare time! This work leaves me none at all.'—'You must be rich then!'—'About as rich as Job.'—'Well, I'm surprised at you. Assuming you find the definition, what will you do with it?'—'I'll versify it!' That was the last straw. He would have to walk on to get over his amazement. So he made off as soon as he could, a little dazzled, *but, I must say, feeling for me.*"

The ultimate ambition of Sully-Prudhomme was to draw from philosophical speculation the stimulus and the subject matter of his poetry. The difficulties of writing this kind of poetry are such that success is almost necessarily partial or momentary—an ominous and cruel condition for a writer with a mania for perfection. Very few, even among his most discerning readers, would ever appreciate the scope and daring of his efforts. Sully-Prudhomme, author of the philosophical poems *Les Destins* (*The Destinies,* 1872), *Justice* (1878), and *Le Bonheur* (*Happiness,* 1888) is scarcely remembered for these greater works. Rather, he is famous as the crystalline poet of *"Le Vase brisé"* (The Broken Vase) and a few other drawing-room pieces. On these his fame rests. No wonder posterity has sometimes questioned his credentials.

René-François-Armand Prudhomme, to give him his right name, was born in Paris in 1839. He was only two years old when his father died of brain fever. He himself was of a delicate constitution, and grew up under the watchful eyes of his widowed mother and an elder sister. As a student, he had as strong an aptitude for mathematics as for the humanities. (The *Sully* was a surname borrowed from his father, which he added later on). He graduated at the head of his class in higher mathematics and set to work preparing for the entrance examinations for the École Polytechnique where he intended to study engineering. He studied so hard, however, and so much at night, that eye strain brought on an attack of ophthalmia, forcing him to interrupt his studies and ending his dream of a scientific career. He entered a notary's office in Paris, where for a time he applied himself diligently to deeds and affidavits. At night, with the single-minded concentration which he brought to bear on everything he undertook, he wrote poetry.

He also passed through a religious crisis while still trying to fix on a definite career. It came to a head when he was studying for his examinations and had gone to Lyon to visit his mother's relatives who were fervent Catholics. Living with them, in an atmosphere of overheated piety tinged with mysticism to which his introspective nature quickly responded, Sully-Prudhomme became an ardent believer, and thought momentarily of becoming a Dominican. But once he had left Lyon, the spark of faith passed. However, nothing could root out his deep-seated need for faith, and he always felt a gnawing curiosity about the supernatural which no philosophy could satisfy.

One of the important events of his early youth was an ill-starred love that left a lasting mark on his sensitive nature. While still a child he had become closely attached to one of his cousins, a girl two years his junior who was his constant companion and playmate. He made up his mind then that he would marry her in due course, taking it for granted that she shared his unexpressed feelings. But his pretty cousin came to him one day, and pretending ignorance of his real feelings, told him point-blank of her engagement to another man. He remained a bachelor to the end of his days.

Sully-Prudhomme's first book of verse, *Stances et Poèmes* (*Stanzas and Poems*) was published in 1865. The book not only attracted attention, it sold. And reading it over today, one is not surprised. There is hardly any sign in it of the gaucherie one would expect from a novice. On the contrary, it shows a mellow inspiration and unfailing artistry. Already we find some of the anthology pieces by which he is best known: *"Ici-bas tous les lilacs meurent"* (All the lilacs die on earth), *"Je ne vais plus la voir jamais"* (I shall never see her again), *"Le vase où meurt cette verveine"* (The vase where that verbena dies).

The next four years were the most productive of all. Between 1866 and 1870, in rapid succession, he wrote *Les Ecuries d'Augias* (The Augean Stables, 1866), a slightly paraphrased translation of the ancient Greek poem; *Croquis italiens* (Italian Notebook, 1866–1868), poems more carefully phrased than one would expect from a "notebook" and perhaps best described as album leaves for cultivated young honeymooners; and *Les Epreuves* (Trials, published posthumously in 1908), a collection of sonnets, some of them numbering among the most beautiful and most revealing of all his poems, notably those inspired by baffled religious yearnings. In 1869, he published *Solitudes,* whose low-pitched melancholy is often more poignant than the pompous outpourings of the Romantics, thanks to the simplicity of a diction which sometimes verges on the prosaic.

Through all the variety of the themes, it is clear that the works of this period are a poetic projection of the inner conflicts experienced by the young Sully-Prudhomme. His unrequited love for his cousin finds expression in them. So do his philosophical anxieties and, even more insistently, the painful aftermath of his shortlived religious enthusiasm in Lyon. Metaphysical doubt is the keynote of his poetry.

By the second half of the nineteenth century, Romantic poetry had lost its hold over the cultivated public in France. This change of taste accounts for the sudden popularity of Sully-Prudhomme, which may seem surprising to a present-day reader. His inspirations were compounded of compelling emotions, always fastidiously communicated; a wealth of symbolic invention, sometimes oversubtle, but usually quite explicit; the intensity of an inner life whose anxieties were obviously genuine.

But what especially appealed to the post-Romantic generation of his day was the fact that the delicate iridescences of this verse owed their coloring to personal experience lucidly sifted and ordered. Here at last was a thinking poet, one for whom reflection, deliberately oriented toward the things of the spirit, prevailed over the unreasoning imagination.

The crucial year in Sully-Prudhomme's life was 1870. The outbreak of the Franco-Prussian War must have been a cruel blow for a sensitive poet steeped in pacifist illusions. Sully-Prudhomme's patriotism, stirred to sudden life, found expression in two small volumes of verse, *Impressions de la guerre* (Impressions of War, 1870) and *France* (1874). Ultimately the strain and hardships of the Prussian siege of Paris, followed by an ill-advised course of treatment, shattered his health. The whole lower part of his body was paralyzed, and he never regained his full strength.

In January 1870, within the space of a few days, his uncle, aunt, and mother died in the Paris apartment he shared with them. Understandably, his impressionable mind was shaken by this sudden loss. His only sister was married. He experienced now that "solitude" whose intellectual forms he had described in so many poems.

The writings of his maturity reflect his genuine despair. The strain of his effort to overcome his true feelings makes itself felt. Again and again in his poetry one is made aware of the conflict of heart and head—summed up by Pascal in a pregnant phrase re-echoed in a line by Sully-Prudhomme: "The heart has reasons to which reason bows."

Sully-Prudhomme, in his middle years, took up a definite position, foreshadowed in many early poems, of frank determinism inspired by Lucretius, unquestionably one of the earliest and strongest formative influences on him. He repeatedly acknowledged his debt to the Roman poet, whom he cheerlessly emulated. But though he embraced Lucretius' confident belief that the world is not governed by the caprice of imaginary gods but by intangible laws, that belief failed to reconcile him to nature. On the contrary, he felt more estranged from nature than ever. Sully-Prudhomme's solution to his estrangement sent him looking to the human heart as the sanctuary for justice. Emotionally he convinced himself that moral progress would go hand in hand with the advance of science, that is, material progress. As an artist he saw it as his duty in his own work to promote the collective advance of mankind toward fulfillment through progress.

In the worldly sense, Sully-Prudhomme's success was complete. What was denied him, however—and he felt it keenly—was due recognition as a philosopher-poet. It vexed him to hear it said repeatedly that his masterpiece was "The Broken Vase," a mere lyric, when his more ambitious works were either passed over or criticized for their inevitable weak points.

But, whatever his private vexations, he enjoyed the full measure of official recognition. He was loaded with honors, beginning in 1881 (his fortieth year) with his election to the Académie Française. He soon became one of the most conspicuous and sought-after academicians of the day; one who was always called upon to preside over ceremonies requiring a writer who represented the scientific aspirations of the late nineteenth century. He became a grand officer of the Légion d'Honneur and a member of the grand council administering the order. Then, in 1901, came the honor of the first Nobel Prize for Literature; with the money he received, he founded a prize for poetry intended to encourage beginners, and this prize is still awarded today under his name—sometimes to young poets to whom the art of French verse, as he conceived it, has become altogether alien.

A painful illness, the aftermath of a breakdown in 1871, told more and more on Sully-Prudhomme's strength and nerves as the years passed, but his mind was as clear as ever to brood over the old misgivings. He suffered continually from insomnia. Yet he must have experienced rapt moments of inner peace under that night sky, so often and inquiringly gazed at, which inspired some of his most limpid stanzas:

O venerable night whose deepest urns,
In boundless space, so quietly pour
Long rivers of pearl and millions of worlds,
And, into the soul, divinest balm.

Toward the turn of the century he gave up his Paris apartment near the Palais de l'Elysée, where every Monday he had held open house to a group of younger poets and writers, and withdrew to a small country house at Châtenay, a few miles south of Paris.

There he lived in seclusion, his failing health permitting him to see only a few intimate friends. But the implacable spirit of analysis was still at work within him, attacking and undermining every philosophical or moral support to which the old poet tried to cling. His yearning for certitude was as keen in his sixties as it had been in his youth, at the time of his religious crisis in Lyon. He had honestly believed himself to have settled the issue in favor of science as against religion. Yet, faced by the riddle of the universe, he continued to waver between belief and disbelief to the very end. In the prose study that occupied his last years, *La Vraie Religion selon Pascal* (True Religion According to Pascal, 1905), he recorded his final views on the matter.

Needless to say, he never became one of the happy multitude ignorant of the conflict of "heart and mind," perfectly satisfied to enjoy what the world has to offer without asking awkward questions. In one of his last writings, a sort of intellectual audit entitled *Que sais-je?* (*What Do I Know?*) published in 1896, Sully-Prudhomme showed that he had no illusions about the power of human thought and saw its limitations pretty clearly: "However important the discoveries of Western man, the torch only lights up a single surface, and only within the limits prescribed by its radiance. I know that Being is inscrutable. . . . The origin of the things that strike the senses is unknowable."

It is to the credit of this noble spirit athirst for the absolute—an absolute undiscoverable on the plane of tangible reality where an exacting reason enjoined him to seek it—that in spite of everything he pursued a quest that was bound to be inconclusive and doomed him to the most painful ordeal of a sensitive mind: uncertainty.

Gabriel d'Aubarède, French novelist, won the Grand Prix du Roman of the Académie Française in 1959.

Translated by James Emmons.

THE 1901 PRIZE

By GUNNAR AHLSTRÖM

AFTER much hesitation, controversy, suspense, and some unavowed misgivings, the Swedish Academy in 1901 awarded its first Nobel Prize for Literature to Sully-Prudhomme, pen name of René-François-Armand Prudhomme, a member of the Académie Française. The decision was commented on by a leading Swedish daily as follows: "So the choice has fallen neither on Tolstoy, nor Ibsen, nor Björnson, nor Mommsen, nor Swinburne, nor Zola, nor Anatole France, nor Carducci, nor Mistral, nor Hauptmann, nor even Echegaray—it has fallen on Sully-Prudhomme. It is some satisfaction, however, to find that François Coppée is not the winner: in view of his innocuous sentimentality, he might well have been considered the best of all the present Swedish Academy."

Behind this waspish comment lay a long series of discussions. The suggestions and recommendations that had gradually piled up on the work tables of the Academy offered a broad picture of the state of literature in early twentieth-century Europe. Great Britain, insular and reserved, submitted no proposals. Poland put forward with eloquent conviction the name of Henryk Sienkiewicz, whose candidacy was also supported by two distinguished Swedish historians. Germany made its voice heard in a petition full of resounding phrases. A professor from Dresden solemnly urged that a little-known song writer should be taken into consideration on account of "his immense lyrical talent." One group of German scholars singled out an eminent historian of literature, a man of profound learning whose name lives today only on the faded backs of once standard editions. A group of other Germans nominated the Provençal poet Frédéric Mistral.

For France, Marcelin Berthelot, a leading scientist elected to the Académie Française in 1900, took advantage of his membership to propose Emile Zola, a writer inspired by the natural sciences and democratic liberalism. The name of Edmond Rostand, author of *Cyrano de Bergerac,* was put forward by Paul Hervieu.

Some arguments favored René Vallery-Radot, the author of a biography of his father-in-law, *Life of Pasteur,* a candidate who was all but unknown in Sweden and everywhere else outside France. As a grand-nephew of both Eugène Sue and Emile Legouvé, and the first co-editor with Buloz of the *Revue des Deux Mondes,* Vallery-Radot had long been knowledgeable about the mysteries of literary fame. Obviously, his presence among the Nobel Prize candidates was the result of some energetic string-pulling. He was first proposed by the author and academician Melchior de Vogüé; then, within a few days, a flood of wildly enthusiastic testimonials poured down on Stockholm, from Frenchmen of letters.

An interlude of this kind might have unsettled the grave deliberations of the Nobel Committee. But its effect was offset by the dignified intervention of the Académie Française which, over the signatures of many important literary men, submitted a lengthy statement in favor of an outstanding academician, Sully-Prudhomme, who thus made his appearance among the Nobel candidates.

Such a massive, semiofficial recommendation overshadowed the more modest proposals from Italy, Greece, Norway, and Sweden itself, where Gaston Paris had been recommended by an admiring colleague at the University of Uppsala. So in spite of these long, drawn-out preliminaries, there was not much room for choice, and after the final decision taken by the Academy in full session on November 14, 1901, Sully-Prudhomme was privately informed that the Nobel Prize had been awarded to him, "In special recognition of his poetic composition, which gives evidence of lofty idealism, artistic perfection, and a rare combination of the qualities of both heart and intellect."

On November 19, the Prizewinner wrote a graceful acknowledgment which he sent from his country retreat at Châtenay, near Paris: "I feel a proud joy and I rejoice at the thought that the honor of so high a distinction, contended for by writers whom I ranked above myself, will be reflected on my country, to which I owe everything in my work that this honor is meant to reward." And since it was not only a question of honor and one's country, but also of money, the laureate very sensibly added the address of his Paris bank.

The public had as yet no idea who the Prizewinner was, and the strictest secrecy had been enjoined on Sully-Prudhomme, pending the official Prize-giving ceremony on December 10, the anniversary of Alfred Nobel's death. The mystery deepened as the day drew near, and the newspapers found themselves unable to report the arrival in Stockholm of any literary notability.

It was known that Professor Roentgen had arrived at the Grand Hotel, but of course he had come to receive the Prize for Physics. Only the initiated knew that the literary seat would remain unoccupied. From the outset Sully-Prudhomme had made it clear that failing health would prevent him from making the journey to Stockholm. This rather upset the Academy's plans; his presence in full academic uniform would have lent a special luster to the first ceremony.

The Prize was received on behalf of Sully-Prudhomme and on behalf of his country by the French minister, Monsieur Marchand, whose "plain democratic dress, without so much as a star or ribbon on his black coat" (reported a Stockholm paper) contrasted strangely with the glittering audience of prominent Swedes.

A few days later Sully-Prudhomme himself was interviewed in his peaceful retreat in France. He told with a smile how surprised he had been to receive the Prize, which brought him at one stroke four times as much money as his poetry had earned him in thirty-five years. "I think of my young colleagues who cannot afford to have their maiden efforts printed. I intend to set aside a sum of money for them, to enable them to print their first books of poetry. I have already received a host of requests which, if all were met, would swallow up the whole of my Prize."

Translated by James Emmons.